Core Connections Algebra
Second Edition*, Version 5.0, Volume 1

Managing Editors / Authors

Leslie Dietiker, Ph.D., Director of Curriculum (Both Editions)
Boston University
Boston, MA

Evra Baldinger (First Edition)
University of California, Berkeley
Berkeley, CA

Michael Kassarjian (2nd Edition)
CPM Educational Program
Kensington, CA

Contributing Authors

Karen Arth
Central High School East

Mark Atkinson
North Salem High School

Carlos Cabana
San Lorenzo High School

John Cooper
Del Oro High School

Mark Coté
Beaver Lake Middle School

Elizabeth Coyner
Christian Brothers High School

Scott Coyner
Christian Brothers High School

Joanne da Luz
The Life Learning Academy

Dolores Dean
Holy Family High School

Ernest Derrera
Roosevelt High School

Leslie Dietiker
Boston University

David Gulick
Phillips Exeter Academy

Patricia King
Holmes Junior High School

Lara Lomac
Phillip and Sala Burton Academic HS

Chris Mikles
Post Falls Middle School

Misty Nikula
CPM Educational Program

Bob Petersen
Rosemont High School

Norm Prokup
The College Preparatory School

Ward Quincey
Gideon Hausner Jewish Day School

Barbara Shreve
San Lorenzo High School

Warren Takaya
La Cumbre Junior High School

Michael Titelbaum
University of California, Berkeley

Estelle Woodbury
San Lorenzo High School

Karen Wootton
CPM Educational Program

Technical Managers

Bethany Armstrong

Sarah Maile

Aubrie Maze

Program Directors

Elizabeth Coyner
CPM Educational Program
Sacramento, CA

Leslie Dietiker, Ph.D.
Boston University
Boston, MA

Lori Hamada
CPM Educational Program
Fresno, CA

Brian Hoey
CPM Educational Program
Sacramento, CA

Michael Kassarjian
CPM Educational Program
Kensington, CA

Judy Kysh, Ph.D.
Departments of Education and
Mathematics San Francisco
State University, CA

Tom Sallee, Ph.D.
Department of Mathematics
University of California, Davis

Karen Wootton
CPM Educational Program
Odenton, MD

*Based on *Algebra Connections*

e-book Manager
Carol Cho
Director of Technology
Martinez, CA

e-book Programmers
Rakesh Khanna
Daniel Kleinsinger
Kevin Stein

e-book Assistants
Debbie Dodd
Shirley Paulsen
Wendy Papciak
Anna Poehlmann
Jordan Wight

Assessment Manager
Karen Wootton
Director of Assessment
Odenton, MD

Assessment Assistants
Evra Baldinger
Marc Coté
Laura Evans

Carlos Cabana
Leslie Dietiker, Ph.D.
Judy Kysh, Ph.D.

Assessment Website
Elizabeth Fong
Michael Huang
Daniel Kleinsinger

Illustration
Kevin Coffey
San Francisco, CA

Homework Help Manager
Bob Petersen
CPM Educational Program

Homework Help Website
Carol Cho
Director of Technology

Parent Guide with Extra Practice
Bob Petersen (Managing Editor)
CPM Educational Program
Sacramento, CA

Bev Brockhoff
Glen Edwards Middle School
Lincoln, CA

Elizabeth Coyner
Christian Brothers High School
Sacramento, CA

Brian Hoey
Christian Brothers High School
Sacramento, CA

Patricia King
Holmes Junior High School
Davis, CA

Technical Manager
Rebecca Harlow

Technical Assistants
Stephanie Achondo	Robert Ainsworth	Erica Andrews
Eric Baxter	Rebecca Bobell	Delenn Breedlove
Diego Breedlove	Duncan Breedlove	Elizabeth Burke
Carrie Cai	Alex Contreras	Hannah Coyner
Mary Coyner	Carmen de la Cruz	Matthew Donahue
Bethany Firch	Elizabeth Fong	Miguel Francisco
Rebecca Harlow	Dana Kimball	Madeline Kimball
Leslie Lai	Keith Lee	Michael Leong
Michael Li	Jerry Luo	Eli Marable
James McCardle	Nyssa Muheim	Alexandra Murphy
Wendy Papciak	Atlanta Parrott	Ryan Peabody
Iris Perez	Steven Pham	Anna Poehlmann
Eduardo Ramirez	John Ramos	Ali Rivera
Andrea Smith	Rachel Smith	Claire Taylor
Christy Van Beek	Megan Walters	Sarah Wong
Alex Yu		

4 5 6   18 17 16 15 14   Version 5.0

Printed in the United States of America   ISBN: 978-1-60328-099-0

A Note to Students:

Welcome to a new year of math! In this course, you will learn to use new models and methods to think about problems as well as solve them. You will be developing powerful mathematical tools and learning new ways of thinking about and investigating situations. You will be making connections, discovering relationships, figuring out what strategies can be used to solve problems, and explaining your thinking. Learning to think in these ways and communicate about your thinking is useful in mathematical contexts, other subjects in school, and situations outside the classroom. The mathematics you have learned in the past will be valuable for learning in this course. That work, and what you learn in this course, will prepare you for future courses.

In meeting the challenges of this course, you will not be learning alone. You will cooperate with other students as a member of a study team. Being a part of a team means speaking up and interacting with other people. You will explain your ideas, listen to what others have to say, and ask questions if there is something you do not understand. In this course, a single problem can often be solved several ways. You will see problems in different ways than your teammates do. Each of you has something to contribute while you work on the lessons in this course.

Together, your team will complete problems and activities that will help you discover mathematical ideas and develop solution methods. Your teacher will support you as you work, but will not take away your opportunity to think and investigate for yourself. Each topic will be revisited many times and will connect to other topics. If something is not clear to you the first time you work on it, you will have more chances to build your understanding as the course continues.

Learning math this way has an advantage: as long as you actively participate, make sure everyone in your study team is involved, and ask good questions, you will find yourself understanding mathematics at a deeper level than ever before. By the end of this course, you will have a powerful set of mathematical tools to use to solve new problems. With your teammates you will meet mathematical challenges you would not have known how to approach before.

In addition to the support provided by your teacher and your study team, CPM has also created online resources to help you, including help with homework, and a parent guide with extra practice. You will find these resources and more at www.cpm.org.

We wish you well and are confident that you will enjoy this next year of learning!

Sincerely,

The CPM Team

Core Connections Algebra
Student Edition

Volume 1

Chapter 3 Simplifying and Solving

Chapter 4 Systems of Equations

Volume 2

FUNCTIONS

Chapter 1

Welcome to algebra! In previous courses, you may have learned about relationships between two quantities that could be graphed with a straight line. In this chapter, you will explore nonlinear functions and learn how to describe a function completely. You will see the shapes and behaviors of several different nonlinear functions. This chapter also introduces you to sharing your mathematical knowledge with a study team as you work together to solve problems.

Guiding Question

Mathematically proficient students model with mathematics.

As you work through this chapter, ask yourself:

Can I identify important quantities in situations and describe their relationships using graphs?

Chapter Outline

Section 1.1 This section starts with some function puzzles that you will solve with your team. Then you will encounter some real-life situations in which you will investigate the growth patterns, some of which are not linear. You will also investigate the family of quadratic functions to look at characteristics of their graphs.

Section 1.2 This section clarifies the description of non-linear graphs. You will make graphs of a variety of nonlinear functions. You will investigate what it means for a relationship to be a function, learn how to use function notation, and determine the domain and range of functions.

1.1.1 How can I work with my team to figure it out?

Solving Puzzles in Teams

In previous courses, you have looked at patterns in tables, graphs, equations, and situations. In this course, you will not only continue your study of linear functions (which you have previously called "linear equations"), but will extend these patterns to new kinds of functions. Working with patterns will be the key to many of these functions. Note that we will define a function formally in Section 2 of this chapter. In today's lesson, you and your team will use clues in order to find patterns and solve puzzles.

1-1. **TEAM SORT**

Your teacher will give you a card with a representation of a line (a table, graph, equation, or situation). Consider what you know about the line represented on your card. Then find the other students in your class who have a representation of the same line. These students will be your teammates, so you should sit together as instructed by your teacher. Be prepared to justify how you know your representation matches those of your teammates.

1-2. In this problem you will work with "function machines" like those pictured at right.

a. To help you work together in your new teams today, each member of your team has a specific job. Read the following Team Roles information on the next page.

b. When a value for x is put into the machine, a value for y comes out. That output then becomes the input for another machine. An example is shown at right.

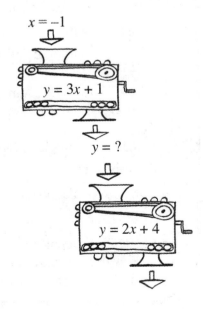

What is the output from the second function machine? Explain.

Team Roles for Problem 1-2

If you had the "graph" card in problem 1-1, you are the:

Resource Manager:

- Get supplies for your team and make sure that your team cleans up.
  Return the linear functions cards from problem 1-1 to the teacher.

- Make sure that everyone has shared all of their ideas and help the team decide when it needs outside help.
  "Does anyone have another idea? Are we ready to ask a question?"
  Don't call the teacher over unless the <u>entire</u> team is stuck and out of ideas.

- Call the teacher over for team questions.
  "Are we ready to ask a question?"

If you had the "table" card in problem 1-1, you are the:

Facilitator:

- Get your team started by having someone read the task out loud.

- Check that everyone understands what to work on.

- Make sure that everyone understands your team's answer before you move on.
  "Does everyone understand how we got our answer?"

If you had the "equation" card in problem 1-1, you are the:

Recorder/Reporter:

- Make sure that each team member can see the work the team is discussing.
  Place the resource page in the center of the table.

- Make sure that your team agrees about how to explain your ideas and each person has time to write their answer.
  "Does anyone need more time to write down our explanation?"

- Make sure that each member of your team is able to share ideas.
  "Is everybody ready to explain to the class how we got our answer?"

If you had the "situation" card in problem 1-1, you are the:

Task Manager:

- Make sure that no one talks outside your team.

- Help keep your team on task and talking about math.

- Listen for statements and reasons.
  "Why did you start that way?"
  "Will you say more about how you got that answer?"

1-3.   Obtain the Lesson 1.1.1C Resource Page, which is a set of four function machines. Copies of the resource pages for this course can be downloaded at www.cpm.org/students/resources.htm. Your team's job is to use a specified input to get a particular output by putting those machines in order so that one machine's output becomes the next machine's input.

As you work, discuss what you know about the kind of output each machine produces to help you arrange the machines in an appropriate order.

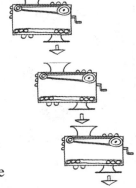

The four functions are reprinted below:

$$y = -2x + 34 \qquad y = \frac{-x}{3} - 10$$

$$y = -|3x| \qquad y = (x-2)^2$$

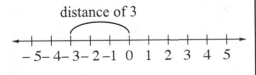

a.   In what order should you stack the machines so that when 15 is dropped into the first machine, and all four machines have had their effect, the last machine's output is –6?

b.   What order will result in a final output of 2 when the first input is 8?

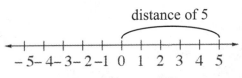

MᴇᴛHODS AND Mᴇᴀɴɪɴɢs

Definition of Absolute Value

Absolute value represents the numerical value of a number without regard to its sign. The symbol for absolute value is two vertical bars, | |. Absolute value can represent the distance on a number line between a number and zero. Since a distance is always positive, the absolute value is *always* either a positive value or zero. The absolute value of a number is *never* negative.

For example, the number –3 is 3 units away from 0, as shown on the number line at right. Therefore, the absolute value of –3 is 3. This is written $|-3| = 3$.

distance of 3

$$-5\ -4\ -3\ -2\ -1\ \ 0\ \ 1\ \ 2\ \ 3\ \ 4\ \ 5$$

Likewise, the number 5 is 5 units away from 0. The absolute value of 5 is 5, written $|5| = 5$.

distance of 5

$$-5\ -4\ -3\ -2\ -1\ \ 0\ \ 1\ \ 2\ \ 3\ \ 4\ \ 5$$

1-4.   Angelica is working with function machines. She has the two machines shown at right. She wants to put them in order so that the output of the first machine becomes the input of the second. She wants to use a beginning input of 6.

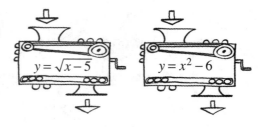

$y = \sqrt{x - 5}$ $y = x^2 - 6$

a.   In what order must she put the machines to get a final output of 5?

b.   Is it possible for her to find an input that will get a final output of –5? If so, show how she could do that. If not, explain why not.

1-5.   Evaluate each absolute value expression. Review the Math Notes box in the lesson for the definition of absolute value.

a. $|54|$ b. $-\left|-7\tfrac{3}{5}\right|$ c. $\left|3\right| - \left|-1\right|$ d. $|2.2 - 5.13|$

1-6.   Examine the tile pattern at right.

a.   On your paper, sketch Figures 4 and 5.

b.   How does the pattern grow? Explain how you know.

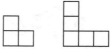

Figure 1   Figure 2   Figure 3

c.   How many tiles will there be in Figure 0 (the figure before Figure 1)? Explain how you know.

1-7.   Simplify each expression.

a. $-42 + (-17)$ b. $8 - (-9)$ c. $8(-9)$

d. $-42 \div (-7)$ e. $-2(-3)(-4)$ f. $-18 - 7$

g. $(-5)^2$ h. -5^2 i. $\sqrt{49}$

1-8.   For each equation below, find y if $x = 2$.

a. $y = 7 - |x|$ b. $y = x^2 - 1$ c. $y = \sqrt{x + 14}$

Core Connections Algebra

1.1.2 How does it grow?

Investigating the Growth of Patterns

How a pattern grows is a major focus of this course. Understanding how something changes can help you make decisions and predict the future. For example, when the local health department needs to respond to an outbreak of an infectious disease, it makes a difference if the number of infected people increases by 1000 or by 10,000 people each day. And what if they learned that the number of infected people tripled each day? That might affect the way they respond to the disease.

Today you will work with your study team to analyze this and other situations that involve different types of functions. Your team will collect data about three different situations. After collecting the data, you will complete a table and make a graph for each situation. As you work together, ask each other the following questions to start and continue productive mathematical discussions.

What is the pattern? How is it changing? How can you describe it?

How does it grow (or get smaller)?

How can we organize the data?

1-9.   DATA LABS

Today your team will collect and analyze data from three labs, which are described below. With your team, read and follow the directions for each lab carefully.
Each description will tell you how much data to collect and how to collect it. Be sure to record your data in an organized way. Make sure that every team member understands what the data represents and how each pattern is changing.

Lab A: Hot Tub Design
Perry is designing a hot tub that he will locate behind his house. He has 36 square designer tiles that he will use to build a surface in his yard where he will place his hot tub. He wants to use all of the tiles, but he does not yet know how he will arrange them to form the base of the hot tub. If his hot tub will be rectangular, how many different rectangles with an area of 36 square tiles does he have to choose from?

Use the square tiles provided by your teacher to find as many rectangular configurations as you can. Remember to record the length and the width of each rectangle you find. Assume that Perry's yard is big enough to accommodate any rectangular design you create and that it matters which dimension is the width and which is the length.

Problem continues on next page. →

1-9.   *Problem continued from previous page.*

Lab B: Local Crisis

Health officials in Parsnipville are concerned about the recent outbreak of the flu. While scientists are working hard to find a vaccine, the town leaders are turning to you to predict how many people will be sick over time. They hope to find a vaccine in a week. Here are the facts: The epidemic started on Day 0 when Velma and Stanley returned from their exotic jungle vacation with symptoms of the flu. Each day, a sick person infects two additional people. The town of Parsnipville has 3800 citizens.

Use the beans (or other material) provided by your teacher to represent the people infected with the flu. Start with two beans to represent Velma and Stanley. Then carefully add two beans to each existing bean to represent the growth of the disease. Collect (and record) data for how many people will be sick each day for a few days.

Lab C: Sign On the Dotted Line

Certain legal documents, such as those used when buying property, sometimes require up to 50 signatures! How long do you think that might take? To find out, collect data as one person of your team signs his or her first name. Have another team member use a stop watch to time

how long, in seconds, it takes to neatly sign his or her first name 2, 3, 5, 7, and 10 times. Be sure to record the time it takes for each number of signatures. In order to collect good data, be sure to have your team member practice signing his or her first name a few times before you start. This is not a speed competition, but rather a way to collect typical data for one person's signature.

1-10.   When you are working with your team to solve problems in this course, it will be important to work effectively with other people. Effective math conversations are a valuable part of the learning process throughout this course. Choose a member of your team to read these Collaborative Learning Expectations out loud.

COLLABORATIVE LEARNING EXPECTATIONS

Working with other students allows you to develop new ways of thinking about mathematics, helps you learn to communicate about math, and helps you understand ideas better by having to explain your thinking to others. The following expectations will help you get the most out of working together.

T   Together, work to answer questions.

E   Explain and give reasons.

A   Ask questions and share ideas.

M   Members of your team
        are your first resource.

S   Smarter together than apart.

1-11.   REPRESENTING DATA

In problem 1-9, you collected data for three different situations. Now your team will work together to find ways of representing the data. Obtain a Lesson 1.1.2D Resource Page from your teacher.

a.   For each lab, complete the corresponding table on the resource page. Use patterns to complete your table for any values in the top row not already included in your data from problem 1-9. Some entries are started for you.

Lab A: Hot Tub Design

Width of Hot Tub (tiles)	1	2	3	4	6	9	12	18	36
Length of Hot Tub (tiles)	36								

Lab B: Local Crisis

Day	0	1	2	3	4	5	6	7
# of Infected People	2							

Lab C: Sign on the Dotted Line

# of Signatures	0	1	2	3	4	5	6	7	8	9	10
Time (seconds)											

Problem continues on next page. →

1-11.   *Problem continued from previous page.*

   b.   Now plot your data from each lab on the set of axes provided on the
         resource page. Note that some data points may not fit on the given axes.
         Then describe each graph. What does each graph look like? Should the
         points be connected? Be prepared to share your observations with the
         class.

   c.   For each graph, find the point where $x = 4$ and label it with its coordinate.
         Then explain what that point represents in each situation.

1-12.   ANALYSIS

         Graphs and tables not only represent data, but they also allow you to answer
         questions about the data. Use your tables and graphs on the resource page from
         problem 1-11 to answer the questions below.

   a.   Which data appears to be linear? That is, when graphed, which data forms
         a line? Explain why it makes sense for this situation to have a linear
         graph.

   b.   The town of Parsnipville will have a flu vaccine available on Day 7. Only
         people who have not yet gotten the flu will need to be vaccinated. Since
         the town has 3800 citizens, how many people will need the vaccine on that
         day? Is it easier to answer this question with your graph or with your
         table? Explain.

   c.   Now that Perry knows his options for the design of his hot tub, he wants to
         pick the hot tub that has the smallest perimeter. What do you recommend?

   d.   Why isn't there a point when $x = 0$ on your graph for Lab A? Could there
         be? Explain.

METHODS AND MEANINGS

Families of Functions

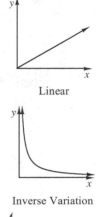

There are several "families" of special functions that you will study in this course. One of these is called **direct variation** (also called **direct proportion**) which is a **linear** function. The data you gathered in the "Sign on the Dotted Line" lab (in problem 1-9) is an example of a linear function.

Linear

Another function is **inverse variation** (also called **inverse proportion**). The data collected in the "Hot Tub Design" lab (in problem 1-9) is an example of inverse variation.

Inverse Variation

You also observed an **exponential** function. The growth of infected people in the "Local Crisis" (in problem 1-9) was exponential.

Exponential

Note that we will define and develop these and other functions later in the course, and formally introduce functions in Section 2 of this chapter.

Review & Preview

1-13.   Consider the situation described below.

a.   Meredith lives 24 blocks from her friend's house. If she travels 1 block every minute, how many minutes will it take her to reach her friend's house? What if she travels 2 blocks every minute? Show how you calculated each answer.

b.   Copy and complete the table below to represent the amount of time it would take Meredith to get to her friend's house if she traveled at different rates.

Speed (in blocks per minute)	1	2	3	4	6	8	10	12	24
Time to Get to Friend's House (in minutes)									

c.   What happens to the time it takes to get to her friend's house as Meredith's speed increases? Explain.

1-14.   Evaluate each expression if $r = -3$, $s = 4$, and $t = 7$.

   a. $r^2 + \sqrt{s}$ b. $\frac{t-r}{s}$ c. $2s^2 + r - t$ d. $3(s-t)^2$

1-15.   Finding and using a pattern is an important problem-solving skill you will use in algebra. The patterns in Diamond Problems will be used later in the course to solve other types of algebraic problems.

   Look for a pattern in the first three diamonds below. For the fourth diamond, explain how you could find the missing numbers (?) if you know the two numbers (#).

   Copy the Diamond Problems below onto your paper. Then use the pattern you discovered to complete each one.

   a.   b.   c.   d.   e.

1-16.   What value(s) of x will make each equation below true?

   a. $x + 5 = 5$ b. $2x - 6 = 3x + 1 - x - 7$

   c. $3x + 1 = 43$ d. $4x - 1 = 4x + 7$

1-17.   Simplify each expression.

   a. $\frac{2}{9} + \left(-\frac{1}{2}\right)$ b. $-\frac{6}{7} - \frac{3}{5}$ c. $\frac{9}{10}\left(-\frac{2}{3}\right)$ d. $\frac{1}{4} \div \frac{2}{7}$

1-18.   In December of 2003, the average price for a gallon of regular gas in the United States was $1.50.

   a.   At that time, what did it cost to buy 12 gallons of gas?

   b.   Gerald paid $12.60 for a tank of gas. How many gallons did he buy?

   c.   At right is a graph of this situation. Predict how the line would change to represent the average cost of gas in December of 2005, when gas cost $2.20 per gallon on average.

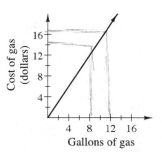

1-19.   Solve each linear equation. Check your solutions.

   a. $-2x - 3 = 3$ b. $7 + 2x = 4x - 3$ c. $6x - 10 = -8 + 3x$

1-20.   Evaluate the expressions below for the given values.

   a. $-2x^2 - 3x + 1$ for $x = -3$ b. $8 - (3x - 2)^2$ for $x = -2$

   c. $\frac{-3}{k+2}$ for $k = -3$ d. $\frac{15m}{n+1} - m^2 + n$ for $m = 1$ and $n = 2$

1-21.   Copy and complete each of the Diamond Problems below. The pattern used in the Diamond Problems is shown at right.

   a.   b.   c.   d.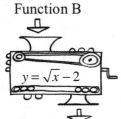

1-22.   Function Machines   Function A   Function B

   a.   If an input of –9 is put into each of the machines at right, what is each output?

   b.   Eric wants to get an ouput of 0. Can he do this with each machine' If so, how? If not, why not?

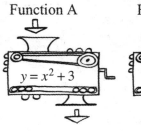

1.1.3   What do I know about a parabola?

Investigating the Graphs of Quadratic Functions

In the previous lesson, you observed linear, inverse variation, and exponential functions. In this lesson, you will study equations that create a family of functions called **quadratics**. The graph of a quadratic function has the shape of a **parabola**. You will learn all you can about their shape.

1-23.   FUNCTIONS OF AMERICA

Congratulations! You have just been hired to work at a national corporation called Functions of America. Recently your company has had some growing pains, and your new boss has turned to your team for help. See her memo below.

MEMO

To: *Your study team*
From: *Ms. Freda Function, CEO*
Re: *New product line*

I have heard that while lines are very popular, there is a new craze in Europe to have non-linear designs. I recently visited Paris and Milan and discovered that we are behind the times!

Please investigate a new function called a quadratic function. A quadratic function can be written in the form $y = ax^2 + bx + c$*. Quadratic functions have the shape of a parabola.*

I'd like a full report at the end of today with any information your team can give me about its shape and equation. Spare no detail! I'd like to know everything you can tell me about how the equation for a quadratic function affects its shape. I'd also like to know about any special points on a parabola or any patterns that exist in its table.

Remember, the company is only as good as its employees! I need you to uncover the secrets that our competitors do not know.

Sincerely,
Ms. Function, CEO

Problem continues on next page. →

1-23.   *Problem continued from previous page.*

Your Task: Your team will be assigned its own quadratic function to study. Investigate your team's function and be ready to describe everything you can about it by using its graph (which is in the shape of a parabola), equation, and table. Answer the questions below to get your investigation started. You may answer them in any order; however, do not limit yourselves to these questions!

- How would you describe the shape of your parabola? For example, would you describe your parabola as opening up or down? Do the sides of the parabola ever go straight up or down (vertically)? Why or why not? Is there anything else special about its shape?

- Does your parabola have any **lines of symmetry**? That is, can you fold the graph of your parabola so that each side of the fold exactly matches the other? If so, where would the fold be? Do you think this works for all parabolas? Why or why not? For more information on lines of symmetry, see the Math Notes box at the end of this lesson.

- Are there any special points on your parabola? Which points do you think are important to know?

- Are there *x*- and *y*-intercepts? What are they? Are there any intercepts that you expected but do not exist for your parabola?

- Is there a highest (maximum) or lowest (minimum) point on the graph of your parabola? If so, where is it? This point is called a **vertex**.

List of Quadratic Functions:

$$y = x^2 - 2x - 8 \qquad\qquad y = -x^2 + 4$$

$$y = x^2 - 4x + 5 \qquad\qquad y = x^2 - 2x + 1$$

$$y = x^2 - 6x + 5 \qquad\qquad y = -x^2 + 3x + 4$$

$$y = -x^2 + 2x - 1 \qquad\qquad y = x^2 + 5x + 1$$

1-24.   Prepare a poster for the CEO detailing
your findings from your quadratic
function investigation. Include any
insights you and your teammates
found. Explain your conclusions and
justify your statements. Remember to
include both a table and a complete
graph of your parabola with all special
points carefully labeled. Be thorough
and complete.

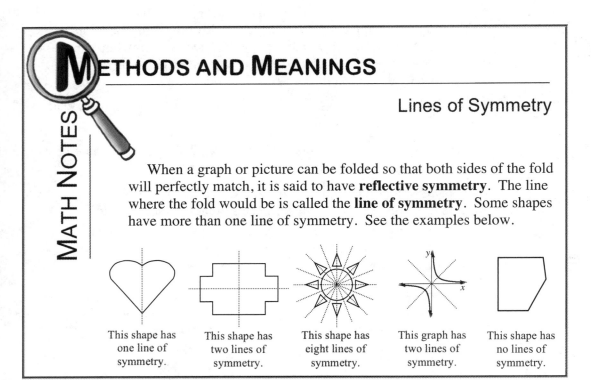

MATH NOTES

METHODS AND MEANINGS

Lines of Symmetry

When a graph or picture can be folded so that both sides of the fold
will perfectly match, it is said to have **reflective symmetry**. The line
where the fold would be is called the **line of symmetry**. Some shapes
have more than one line of symmetry. See the examples below.

| This shape has one line of symmetry. | This shape has two lines of symmetry. | This shape has eight lines of symmetry. | This graph has two lines of symmetry. | This shape has no lines of symmetry. |

1-25.   Freda Function has another quadratic function for you to investigate! Graph the
equation $y = x^2 + 3$ and then answer the questions from problem 1-23.

1-26. Copy these Diamond Problems and use the pattern you discovered earlier, shown at right, to complete each of them. Some of these may be challenging!

a.   b.   c.   d.

1-27. Copy the figure at right onto your paper. Then draw any lines of symmetry.

1-28. Solve the equations below for x and check your solutions.

a. $-3+2x=-x+6$ b. $5-3x=x+1$

c. $-2x=4x+9$ d. $4x+3=x$

1-29. Mr. Guo is thinking of a number. When he takes the absolute value of his number, he gets 15. What could his number be? Is there more than one possible answer?

1.2.1 How can I describe a graph?

Describing a Graph

What does it mean to describe the graph of a function completely? Today you will graph and investigate a new function: $y = \sqrt{x}$.

1-30. **DESCRIBING A GRAPH**

Your teacher will assign your team one of the functions below. On graph paper, graph your function for x-values between –4 and 10.

When your team is convinced that your graph is correct, discuss all the ways you can describe this graph. Obtain one or two "seed" questions from your teacher (on the Lesson 1.2.1A Resource Page) to get you started with describing the graph. Then write as many summary statements about the graph as you can.

$$y = \sqrt{x} \qquad\qquad y = \sqrt{x-1} + 3$$

$$y = \sqrt{x} + 1 \qquad\qquad y = -\sqrt{x}$$

$$y = \sqrt{x+2} - 1 \qquad\qquad y = -\sqrt{x} - 2$$

1-31. **PRESENT YOUR FINDINGS**

With your team, prepare to present your findings to the rest of the class. Your presentation should contain not only the graph of your function but also all of your observations and summary statements from problem 1-30. Be thorough and complete. Remember that a main goal of this activity is to determine what items a "complete description" of a graph must contain, so be sure to include everything you can. Remember to give reasons for all statements that you make.

1-32.   LEARNING LOG

Throughout this course, you will be asked to reflect about
your understanding of mathematical concepts in a Learning
Log. Writing about your understanding will help you
consolidate ideas, develop new ways to describe mathematical ideas, and
recognize gaps in your understanding. It is important to write each entry of the
Learning Log in your own words so that later you can use your Learning Log as
a resource to refresh your memory. Your teacher will tell you where to write
your Learning Log entries. Remember to label each entry with a title and a date
so that it can be referred to later.

In this first Learning Log entry, as a class, create a list of all the ways to
describe a graph from the presentations given by each team. Then, next to each
description, create a question that will prompt you to look for this quality in the
graphs of other functions you encounter.

Once your class's list is complete, copy the questions into your first entry in
your Learning Log. Title this entry "Graph Investigation Questions" and
include today's date.

1-33.   Copy these Diamond Problems and use the pattern you
discovered earlier, shown at right, to complete each of them.
Some of these may be challenging!

a.   b.   c.   d.

1-34.   Evaluate the following absolute value expressions.

a. $|-100|-98$

b. $5|2-8|$

c. $|-13|+|0|$

d. $14-|-10+3|$

1-35.   The solution to the equation $x^3 = 64$ is called the **cube root** of 64. The idea is similar to the idea of a square root, except that the value must be cubed (multiplied by itself three times) to become 64. One way to write the cube root of 64 is using the notation $\sqrt[3]{64}$. Use this information to evaluate each of the following expressions.

    a. $\sqrt[3]{64}$ b. $\sqrt[4]{16}$ c. $\sqrt[3]{-8}$ d. $\sqrt[3]{125}$

1-36.   Solve the following linear equations.

    a. $8x + 1 = -x - 1$ b. $-4x - 3 = 3x - 4 - 7x$

    c. $4 - 5x = 1 + 6x$ d. $7 - x + 3 = 9x + 10$

1-37.   Examine the tile pattern shown at right.

    a.   On graph paper, draw Figure 0 and Figure 4.

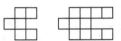

Figure 1   Figure 2   Figure 3

    b.   How many tiles will Figure 10 have? How do you know?

1-38.   Chari performed a series of jumps on a trampoline. Her coach measured the height of each jump. The coach's data was recorded in the table at right.

Jump Number	Height (feet)
1	0.5
2	0.9
3	1.6
4	2.9
5	5.2

    a.   Make a graph of the data.

    b.   Fully describe the graph.

    c.   If this pattern continues, what are a reasonable maximum and minimum for the graph?

    d.   Which family of functions could model this data? Review the Lesson 1.1.2 Math Note if you need help.

1-39.   Use the idea of cube root from problem 1-35 to evaluate the following expressions.

    a. $\sqrt[3]{1}$ b. $\sqrt[3]{0}$ c. $\sqrt[3]{2^3}$ d. $\sqrt[3]{7^3}$

1-40.   Solve the equations below for x and check your solutions.

    a. $-6+10x = x+12$

    b. $10+5x = 2x-11$

    c. $-9x = -3x+18$

    d. $2x-9 = -7x$

1-41.   Find y in each equation if $x = 16$.

    a. $y = 3+\sqrt[3]{x-8}$

    b. $y = \sqrt{x}-7$

    c. $y = 4+|9-x|$

1-42.   Use your graph investigation questions from problem 1-32 to describe the graph of the quadratic equation $y = x^2 + 8x + 7$, shown at right.

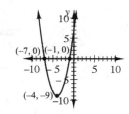

1.2.2 What is the difference?

Cube Root and Absolute Value Functions

You have drawn graphs of different families of functions: lines, quadratic functions, and square roots. As a class you saw an inverse proportional graph (in the hot tub design problem) and an exponential graph (in the flu outbreak problem). Today you will explore the graphs of two additional functions, cube root and absolute value.

1-43. CUBE ROOTS

The solution of the equation $b^3 = 8$ is called the **cube root** of 8. The idea of a cube root is similar to the idea of a square root, except that the cube root of 8 must be cubed (multiplied by itself three times) to become 8. One way to write the cube root of 8 is using the notation $\sqrt[3]{8}$.

a. How can this notation be used to write the solution of $t^3 = 30$?

b. What is the $(\sqrt{64})^2$? What is $(\sqrt{19})^2$?

c. Can you extend this logic to find $(\sqrt[3]{30})^3$?

d. Use your calculator to obtain a decimal estimate for the solution in part (a).

1-44. Lydia wants to know what the graph of the cube root function, $y = \sqrt[3]{x}$, looks like.

a. Help Lydia by making an $x \to y$ table. What values of x could you choose (between -150 and 150) to make all of the y-values in your table integers? Everyone should take a few moments on his or her own to think about how to create some values for the table.

Then, with your team put as many integer x-values between -150 and 150 in your table as you can.

b. Create a graph of $y = \sqrt[3]{x}$. Scale the x-axis from -150 to 150. Refer to your list of graph investigation questions from Lesson 1.2.1 to help you completely describe the graph. Be as detailed as you can.

1-45.   Riley is impressed with Lydia's graph of a cube root function. He wants to impress her in return by describing an absolute value graph.

   a.   Graph $y = |x|$. Describe for Riley what the graph looks like. Refer to your list of graph investigation questions from Lesson 1.2.1 to help you completely describe the graph. Be as detailed as you can.

   b.   Are there any values of x that you cannot use in the equation above? If so, what are they? Are there any values for y that you will never get when you evaluate the equation above? If so, what are they?

1-46.   Fully describe and graph the function $y = |2x - 1|$.

1-47.   Use your list of graph investigation questions from your Learning Log to answer questions about the graph shown at right.

$y = |x + 2| - 1$

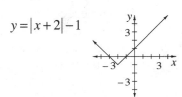

1-48.   Calculate the value of each expression below.

   a. $|-4| - 3$ b. $|6 - 11 + 3|$ c. $-9 - |-2|$ d. $5|6| - 2$

1-49. Throughout this book, key problems have been selected as "checkpoints." Each checkpoint problem is marked with an icon like the one at left. These checkpoint problems are provided so that you can check to be sure you are building skills at the expected level. When you have trouble with checkpoint problems, refer to the review materials and practice problems that are available in the "Checkpoint Materials" section at the back of your book.

This problem is a checkpoint for solving linear equations without parentheses. It will be referred to as Checkpoint 1.

Solve each equation.

a. $3x + 7 = -x - 1$

b. $1 - 2x + 5 = 4x - 3$

c. $4x - 2 + x = -2 + 2x$

d. $3x - 4 + 1 = -2x - 5 + 5x$

Check your answers by referring to the Checkpoint 1 materials located at the back of your book.

If you needed help solving these problems correctly, then you need more practice. Review the Checkpoint 1 materials and try the practice problems. Also consider getting help outside of class time. From this point on, you will be expected to do problems like this one quickly and easily.

1-50. Graph the points $(-3, 4)$ and $(1, 1)$. If you drew a line through the points, name 3 other points that would be on the line. How did you find them?

1-51. Copy and complete each of the Diamond Problems below. The pattern used in the Diamond Problems is shown at right.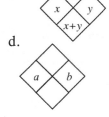

a.

b.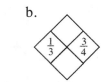

c.

d.

1.2.3 What is the function?

Function Machines

In the next few lessons you will add to your list of what you can ask about a graph of a function. Throughout this chapter, you have used functions between two variables (like $y = -x^2 + 3x + 4$) to make graphs and find information. Today you will look more closely at how equations that relate two variables help establish a function between the variables. You will also learn a new notation to help represent these functions.

1-52.   ARE WE RELATED?

Examine the table of input (x) and output (y) values below. Is there a relationship between the input and output values? If so, write an equation for this relationship. In what family is this function?

x	−3	−2	−1	0	1	2	3
y	8	3	0	−1	0	3	8

1-53.   FUNCTION MACHINES

A function works like a machine, as shown in the diagram below. A function is given a name that can be a letter, such as f or g. The notation $f(x)$ represents the output when x is processed by the machine. (Note: $f(x)$ is read, "f of x.") When x is put into the machine, $f(x)$, the value of a function for a specific x-value, comes out. In this notation, $f(x)$ replaces y.

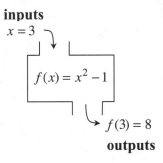

Numbers are put into the function machine (in this case, $f(x) = x^2 - 1$) one at a time, and then the function performs the operation(s) on each input to determine each output. For example, when $x = 3$ is put into the function $f(x) = x^2 - 1$, the function squares it and then subtracts 1 to get the output, which is 8. The notation $f(3) = 8$ shows that the function named f connects the input (3) with the output (8).

inputs
$x = 3$

$f(x) = x^2 - 1$

$f(3) = 8$
outputs

Problem continues on next page. →

1-53.   *Problem continued from previous page.*

a.   Find the output for $f(x) = x^2 - 1$ when the input is $x = 4$; that is, find $f(4)$.

b.   Now find $f(-1)$ and $f(10)$.

c.   If the output of this function is 24, what was the input? That is, if $f(x) = 24$, then what is x? Is there more than one possible input?

1-54.   Find the relationship between x and $f(x)$ in the table below and write the equation.

x	9	1	100	4	49		0	25	20
$f(x)$		1			7	4		5	

$$f(x) = \underline{\hspace{3cm}}$$

1-55.   Find the corresponding outputs or inputs for the following functions. If there is no possible output for the given input, explain why not.

a.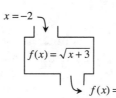

b.

c.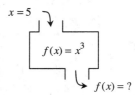

d.

e.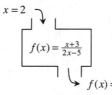

f.

g.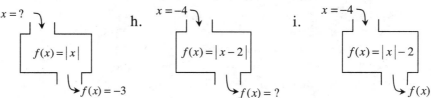

h.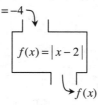

i.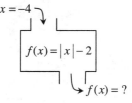

1-56. Examine the function defined at right. Notice that $g(1) = -1$; that is, when x is 1, the output (y or $g(1)$) is -1.

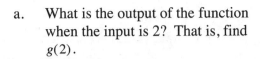
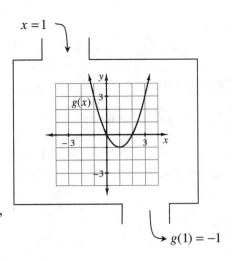

a. What is the output of the function when the input is 2? That is, find $g(2)$.

b. Likewise, what are $g(-1)$ and $g(0)$?

c. What is the input of this function when the output is 1? In other words, find x when $g(x) = 1$. Is there more than one possible solution?

1-57. If $f(x) = x^2$, then $f(4) = 4^2 = 16$. Find:

a. $f(1)$ b. $f(-3)$ c. $f(t)$

1-58. Evaluate each expression.

a. $\sqrt[3]{27}$ b. $\sqrt{144}$ c. $\sqrt{3^2}$ d. $\sqrt[4]{2^4}$

1-59. Graph and fully describe the function $y = \sqrt[3]{x} - 2$.

1-60. A line passes through the points A(–3, –2) and B(2, 1). Does it also pass through the point C(5, 3)? Justify your conclusion.

1-61. Find the following absolute values.

a. $|0.75|$ b. $|-99|$

c. $|4 - 2 \cdot 3|$ d. $|\pi|$

1.2.4 Can I predict the output?

Functions

You have studied relationships between input and output values. But what happens when your relationship gives you unpredictable results? That is, what happens when you cannot predict the output for a given input? Today you will study this situation and will be introduced to the quality that makes a relationship a *function*.

1-62.   THE COLA MACHINE

The cola machine at your school offers several types of soda. There are two buttons for your favorite drink, *Blast*, while the other drinks (*Slurp, Lemon Twister,* and *Diet Slurp*) each have one button.

a. Describe the input and output of this soda machine.

b. While buying a soda, Ms. Whitney pushed the button for *Lemon Twister* and got a can of *Lemon Twister*. Later she went back to the same machine, but this time pushing the *Lemon Twister* button got her a can of *Blast*. Is the machine functioning consistently? Why or why not?

c. When Brandi pushed the top button for *Blast* she received a can of *Blast*. Her friend, Miguel, decided to be different and pushed the second button for *Blast*. He, too, received a can of *Blast*. Is the machine functioning consistently? Why or why not?

d. When Loutfi pushed a button for *Slurp*, he received a can of *Lemon Twister*! Later, Tayeisha also pushed the *Slurp* button and received a can of *Lemon Twister*. Still later, Tayeisha noticed that everyone else who pushed the *Slurp* button received a *Lemon Twister*. Is the machine functioning consistently? Explain why or why not.

1-63.   FUNCTIONS

a.   In a relationship like the soda machine, we want the outcome to be consistent and predictable. When it is, we say that the machine is functioning properly.

Examine each of the tables and graphs below that show different inputs and their outputs. Decide if the graph or table could be describing a soda machine that is "functioning properly." Explain your reasoning.

i.

Button Number	1	1	2	4	2	3
Type of Candy	Stix	Stix	M&Ns	M&Ns	Duds	Duds

ii.

x	7	–2	0	4	9	–3	6
$f(x)$	6	–3	4	2	10	–3	0

iii.

x	3	–1	2	0	1	2	9
y	4	–5	9	7	4	–8	2

b.   A relationship between inputs and outputs is called a **function** if the inputs and outputs behave like a soda machine that is functioning properly. Discuss with your team what it means for a relationship between inputs and outputs to be a **function**.

c.   Examine each of the tables and graphs below. Compare the inputs and outputs and decide if the graph or table could be a **function**. Explain your reasoning.

iv.
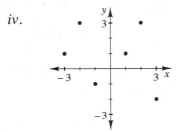

v.
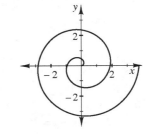

vi.

x	$h(x)$
–8	11
4	3
11	–8
6	3
–8	11

vii.
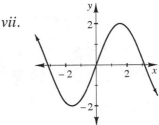

1-64.   Jade noticed that the line graphed at right is a function. "Hey – I think *all* lines are functions!" she exclaimed. Is she correct? Support your claim with a diagram.

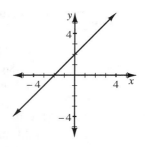

1-65.   LEARNING LOGS

Throughout this course, you will be asked to reflect about your understanding of mathematical concepts in a Learning Log. Writing about your understanding will help you consolidate ideas, develop new ways to describe mathematical ideas, and recognize gaps in your understanding. It is important to write each entry of the Learning Log in your own words so that later you can use your Learning Log as a resource to refresh your memory. Your teacher will tell you where to write your Learning Log entries. Remember to label each entry with a title and a date so that it can be referred to later.

In this Learning Log entry, describe what it means for a relationship to be a function. Think of a type of machine that you use on a regular basis and describe how it also operates as a function. Title this entry "Functions" and include today's date.

1-66.   If $g(x) = \sqrt{x-7}$, find $g(8)$, $g(32)$, and $g(80)$.

1-67.   Solve each equation below. Check each solution.

   a. $6 - x - 3 = 10$ b. $100x + 300 = 200$

   c. $\frac{1}{3}x + 4 = x - 2$ d. $36 - 2x = -x + 2$

1-68.   Find $f(-4)$ for each function below.

   a. $f(x) = |x - 3|$ b. $f(x) = -5|x|$

   c. $f(x) = |x + 1|$ d. $f(x) = |x + 3| - 6$

1-69.   Graph and fully describe the function $f(x) = -x^2 + 3$. Graph values of x from -3 to 3.

1-70.   Find the corresponding inputs or outputs for the following functions. If there is no solution, explain why not. Be careful: In some cases, there may be no solution or more than one possible solution.

a. $x = 8$

$f(x) = |x|$

$f(8) = ?$

b. $x = ?$

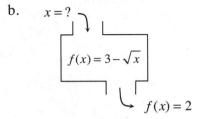

$f(x) = 3 - \sqrt{x}$

$f(x) = 2$

c. $k = -6$

$f(k) = \frac{k}{2} + 1$

$f(-6) = ?$

d. $x = 3$

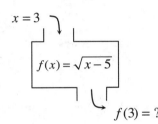

$f(x) = \sqrt{x - 5}$

$f(3) = ?$

1.2.5 What can go in? What can come out?

Domain and Range

You have many characteristics that you can describe about graphs and functions using the questions that you began developing in Lesson 1.2.1. You also have learned how to tell if a relationship is a function. Today you will complete your focus on functions by describing the inputs and outputs of functions.

1-71. Examine the graph of the relationship at right. Use it to estimate:

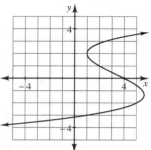

    a. y when $x = -4$

    b. y when $x = 1$

    c. y when $x = 4$

    d. Is this relationship a function? Why or why not?

1-72. Examine the function shown at right.

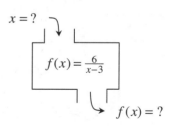

    a. Find $f(-3)$, $f(0)$, and $f(2)$.

    b. Find $f(3)$. What happened?

    c. Are there any other inputs that cannot be evaluated by this function? In other words, are there any other values that x cannot be? Explain how you know.

    d. The set (collection) of numbers that can be used for x in a function and still get an output is called the **domain** of the function. The domain is a description or list of all the possible x-values for the function. Describe the domain of $f(x) = \frac{6}{x-3}$.

    e. What other types of functions have you looked at thus far in this course or in previous courses that have limited domains? How were they limited?

Core Connections Algebra

1-73.   Now examine $g(x)$ graphed at right.

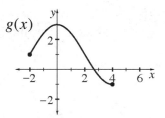

   a.   Is $g(x)$ a function? How can you tell?

   b.   Which x-values have points on the graph?
         That is, what is the domain of $g(x)$?

   c.   What are the possible outputs for $g(x)$? This is called the **range** of the
         function.

   d.   Ricky thinks the range of $g(x)$ is: $-1, 0, 1, 2,$ and 3. Is he correct? Why
         or why not?

   e.   What other functions have you worked with previously in this course or
         previous courses that have limited ranges? How were they limited?

1-74.   FINDING DOMAIN AND RANGE

   The domain and range are good descriptors of a function because they help you
   know what numbers can go into and come out of a function. The domain and
   range can also help you set up useful axes when graphing and help you describe
   special points on a graph (such as a missing point or the lowest point).

   Work with your team to describe in words the domain and range of each
   relationship below. Then state whether or not the relationship is also a function.

   a.   b.   c.

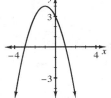   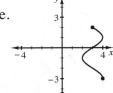   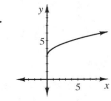

   d.   e.   f.

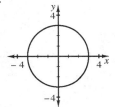   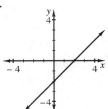   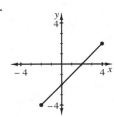

1-75.   Chiu loves tables! He has decided to make the table below for a function $f(x)$ to help him find its domain and range.

x	−3	−2	−1	0	1	2	3
$f(x)$	5	0	−3	−4	−3	0	5

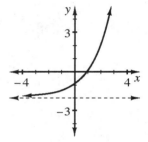

a.   From his table, can you tell what the domain of $f(x)$ is? Why or why not?

b.   From the table, can you tell the range of $f(x)$? Why or why not?

c.   Is using a table an effective way to determine the domain and range of a function?

1-76.   Daniel is thinking about the function shown at right.

a.   He noticed that the curve continues to the left and to the right. What is the domain of this function?

b.   He found out that the dotted line is a line that the graph gets closer and closer to as x gets very, very large. (Another name for this dotted line is **asymptote**.) How should Daniel describe the range?

1-77.   TEAM CHALLENGE

Sketch the graph of a function that has a domain of all numbers greater than or equal to −2 and a range of all numbers less than or equal to 3. Is there more than one possible answer?

Core Connections Algebra

METHODS AND MEANINGS

Functions

A relationship between inputs and outputs is a **function** if there is no more than one output for each input. We often write a function as y = some expression involving x, where x is the input and y is the output. The following is an example of a function.

$$y = (x-2)^2$$

x	−2	−1	0	1	2	3	4	5
y	16	9	4	1	0	1	4	9

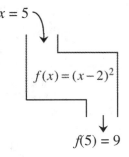

In the example above the value of y depends on x, so y is also called the **dependent variable** and x is called the **independent variable**.

Another way to write a function is with the notation "$f(x)$ =" instead of "y =". The function named "f" has output $f(x)$. The input is x.

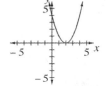

In the example at right, $f(5) = 9$. The input is 5 and the output is 9. You read this as, "f of 5 equals 9."

The set of all inputs for which there is an output is called the **domain**. The set of all possible outputs is called the **range**. In the example above, notice that you can input any x-value into the equation and get an output. The domain of this function is "all real numbers" because any number can be an input. But the outputs are all greater than or equal to zero. The range is $y \geq 0$.

$x^2 + y^2 = 1$ is not a function because there are two y-values (outputs) for some x-values, as shown below.

$$x^2 + y^2 = 1$$

x	−1	0	0	1
y	0	−1	1	0

1-78.   Which of the relationships below are functions? If a relationship is not a function, give a reason to support your conclusion.

a.

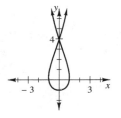

b.

x	y
−3	19
5	19
19	0
0	−3

c.

x	7	−2	0	7	4
y	10	0	10	3	0

d.

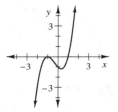

1-79.   Find the *x*- and *y*-intercepts for the graphs of the relationships in problem 1-78.

1-80.   Find the inputs for the following functions with the given outputs. If there is no possible input for the given output, explain why not.

a.   x = ?

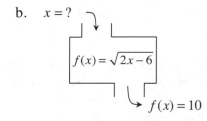

$f(x) = 3x - 7$

$f(x) = -1$

b.   x = ?

$f(x) = \sqrt{2x - 6}$

$f(x) = 10$

1-81.   Use the relationship graphed at right to answer the questions below.

a.   Is the relationship a function?

b.   What is the domain?

c.   What is the range?

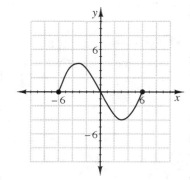

1-82.   What value(s) of *x* will make each equation true?

a. $\sqrt[3]{x} = -2$

b. $\sqrt{x} = 12$

c. $|x + 1| = 4$

Chapter 1 Closure   What have I learned?

Reflection and Synthesis

The activities below offer you a chance to
reflect about what you have learned during this
chapter. As you work, look for concepts that
you feel very comfortable with, ideas that you
would like to learn more about, and topics you
need more help with. Look for connections
between ideas as well as connections with
material you learned previously.

①   TEAM BRAINSTORM

What have you studied in this chapter? What ideas were important in what you
learned? With your team, brainstorm a list. Be as detailed as you can. To help
get you started, a list of Learning Log entries and Math Notes boxes are below.

What topics, ideas, and words that you learned *before* this chapter are connected
to the new ideas in this chapter? Again, be as detailed as you can.

How long can you make your list? Challenge yourselves. Be prepared to share
your team's ideas with the class.

Learning Log Entries
- Lesson 1.2.1 – Graph Investigation Questions
- Lesson 1.2.4 – Functions

Math Notes
- Lesson 1.1.1 – Definition of Absolute Value
- Lesson 1.1.2 – Families of Functions
- Lesson 1.1.3 – Lines of Symmetry
- Lesson 1.2.5 – Functions

The following is a list of the vocabulary used in this chapter. Make sure that you are familiar with all of these words and know what they mean. Refer to the glossary or index for any words that you do not yet understand.

domain	function	graph
input	maximum	output
range	minimum	equation
parabola	x-intercept	$x \rightarrow y$ table
y-intercept function	line of symmetry	quadratic
absolute value		

Make a concept map showing all of the connections you can find among the key words and ideas listed above. To show a connection between two words, draw a line between them and explain the connection, as shown in the model below. A word can be connected to any other word as long as you can justify the connection. For each key word or idea, provide an example or sketch that shows the idea.

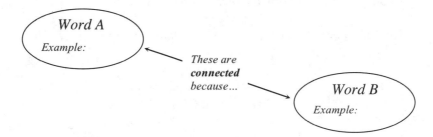

Your teacher may provide you with vocabulary cards to help you get started. If you use the cards to plan your concept map, be sure either to re-draw your concept map on your paper or to glue the vocabulary cards to a poster with all of the connections explained for others to see and understand.

While you are making your map, your team may think of related words or ideas that are not listed above. Be sure to include these ideas on your concept map.

③　　PORTFOLIO: EVIDENCE OF MATHEMATICAL PROFICIENCY

Your teacher may have instructed you to take a photograph of the poster you made for Lesson 1.1.3 as evidence of your early understanding about describing functions. If so, include the photograph in your portfolio.

Your teacher will give you instructions for how to showcase your current understanding of describing a function. Part of this showcase will be to choose a function or two and make a graph and table of it. Make a list of the questions you will ask to fully investigate the function. Your teacher may give you the Chapter 1 Closure Resource Page: Function Investigations Graphic Organizer to help you organize your work. The purpose of the portfolio is to give you an opportunity to show what you know about fully investigating a function. Make sure you do your best work, and include as much detail as you can.

④　　WHAT HAVE I LEARNED?

Most of the problems in this section represent typical problems found in this chapter. They serve as a gauge for you. You can use them to determine which types of problems you can do well and which types of problems require further study and practice. Even if your teacher does not assign this section, it is a good idea to try these problems and find out for yourself what you know and what you still need to work on.

Solve each problem as completely as you can. The table at the end of the closure section has answers to these problems. It also tells you where you can find additional help and practice with problems like these.

CL 1-83. Use the Order of Operations to simplify the following expressions.

a.　$5 - 2 \cdot 3^2$　　　　　　　　　　b.　$(-2)^2$

c.　$18 \div 3 \cdot 6$　　　　　　　　　d.　-2^2

e.　$(5 - 3)(5 + 3)$　　　　　　　f.　$24 \cdot \frac{1}{4} \div -2$

g.　Why are your answers for parts (b) and (d) different?

CL 1-84. Copy the pattern below onto graph paper. Draw the 1st and 5th figures on your paper.

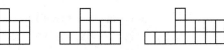

Figure 2   Figure 3   Figure 4

    a.   How many tiles are in each figure?

    b.   Describe how the pattern is changing.

    c.   How many tiles would the 6th figure have? The 10th figure?

CL 1-85. Copy and complete each of the Diamond Problems below. The pattern used in the Diamond Problems is shown at right.

    a.   b.   c.   d.

CL 1-86. Graph and fully describe the function $y = 2\sqrt{x-1} + 3$.

CL 1-87. Solve each equation. Check your solution.

    a. $3x - 1 = 4x + 8 - x$ b. $-10 + 5x = 7x - 4$

    c. $28 - 6x + 4 = 30 - 3x$ d. $4x - 1 = 9x - 1 - 5x$

CL 1-88. Find $f(4)$ for each function below.

    a. $f(x) = -|x - 7| + 3$ b. $f(x) = \frac{\sqrt{x+12}}{4}$ c. $f(x) = 2 - \sqrt[3]{x + 23}$

CL 1-89. Evaluate each expression.

    a. $2 \div |3 - 4|$ b. $11|-6| + 15$ c. $-19 + \sqrt[3]{-8}$ d. $-11 - \sqrt{16}$

CL 1-90. Use the function machine shown at right to answer the following questions.

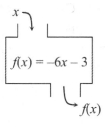

$f(x) = -6x - 3$

a.   If the input is –8, what is the output?

b.   If the output was 21, what was the input?

CL 1-91. Check your answers using the table at the end of the closure section. Which problems do you feel confident about? Which problems were hard? Use the table to make a list of topics you need help with and a list of topics you need to practice more.

Answers and Support for Closure Activity #4
What Have I Learned?

MN = Math Note, LL = Learning Log

Problem	Solution		Need Help?	More Practice
CL 1-83.	a. –13	b. 4	Problems 1-7 and 1-14	Problems 1-20 and 1-28
	c. 36	d. –4		
	e. 16	f. –3		
	g. They are different because $(-2)^2 = (-2)(-2) = 4$, while $-2^2 = -(2 \cdot 2) = -4$.			
CL 1-84.			Lesson 1.1.2	Problems 1-6 and 1-37

Figure 1   Figure 5

a.   5, 8, 11, 14, 17

b.   Each figure has three more tiles than the one before it.

c.   The 6th figure would have 20 tiles. The 10th figure would have 32 tiles.

Problem	Solution	Need Help?	More Practice

CL 1-85.

a. Diamond: top −81, left 9, right −9, bottom 0

b. Diamond: top −36, left −6, right 6, bottom 0

c. Diamond: top −20, left 4, right −5, bottom −1

d. Diamond: top $-\frac{6}{25}$, left $-\frac{3}{10}$, right $\frac{4}{5}$, bottom $\frac{1}{2}$

Need Help? Problem 1-15

More Practice: Problems 1-21, 1-26, 1-33, and 1-51

CL 1-86. The graph is half of a parabola on its side. As x increases, y increases. The starting point is $(1, 3)$.

Domain: $x \geq 1$ Range: $y \geq 3$

Need Help? Lessons 1.1.3, 1.2.1, and 1.2.2

LL: 1.2.1

More Practice: Problems 1-25, 1-30, 1-42, 1-47, 1-59, and 1-69

CL 1-87.

a. no solution

b. $x = -3$

c. $x = \frac{2}{3}$

d. all real numbers

Need Help? Checkpoint 1

More Practice: Problems 1-16, 1-19, 1-36, 1-40, 1-49, and 1-67

CL 1-88.

a. 0

b. 1

c. −1

Need Help? Lesson 1.2.3

More Practice: Problems 1-57, 1-66, and 1-67

CL 1-89.

a. 2   b. 81

c. −21   d. −15

Need Help? Lesson 1.2.2

MN: 1.1.1

More Practice: Problems 1-5, 1-34, 1-35, 1-39, 1-48, 1-58, and 1-60

CL 1-90.

a. 45

b. −4

Need Help? Lesson 1.2.3

MN: 1.2.5

More Practice: Problems 1-71 and 1-81

Chapter 2   Linear Relationships

Chapter 2 will focus on the starting value and growth of linear functions. You will look for connections between the multiple representations of linear functions: table, graph, equation, and situation. In this chapter, you will come to a deeper understanding of slope than you may have had in previous courses, and you will explore the idea of slope as a rate of change.

Guiding Question

Mathematically proficient students reason abstractly and quantitatively.

As you work through this chapter, ask yourself:

Can I create a representation of a problem, consider the units involved, and understand the meaning of the quantities using tables, graphs and equations?

Chapter Outline

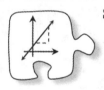

Section 2.1 In this section, you will connect the starting value and growth in geometric tile patterns with the slope and *y*-intercept on a graph. You will learn how to measure the steepness of a line on a graph. You will also study the difference between lines that point upward, lines that point downward, and lines that are horizontal or vertical.

Section 2.2 In this section, you will investigate situations where slope represents the speed in a real-life situation, culminating in an activity called "The Big Race." You will also look at how slope represents rate of change in situations that do not involve motion.

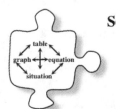

Section 2.3 In Section 2.3, you will complete the multiple representations web, so that you can find the growth and starting value in various representations, and can convert readily between them. In particular, you will develop an algebraic method for finding the equation of a line when given only two points on the line.

2.1.1 How does it grow?

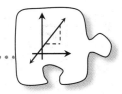

....

Seeing Growth in Linear Representations

Throughout this chapter you will explore the multiple representations of a linear relationship. You will use the growth and starting value of linear relationships to find specific connections between situations, tables, graphs, and equations.

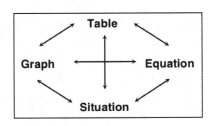

The specific situation you will work with today is the growth of tile patterns.

As you work today, keep these questions in mind:

> How can you see growth in the tile pattern?

> What is the starting value for the tile pattern?

> What is the connection to the equation? To the table?

2-1.   TILE PATTERN INVESTIGATION

Find Pattern A on the Lesson 2.1.1B Resource Page, shown below. Complete the following tasks for Pattern A, recording your work on the resource page or on your paper as appropriate.

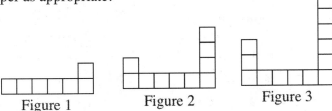

Figure 1   Figure 2   Figure 3

a.   What do you notice about the pattern? After everyone has had a moment on his or her own to examine the figures, discuss what you see with your team.

b.   Sketch the next figure in the sequence (Figure 4) for Pattern A on your resource page. Figure 0 is the name of the figure that comes before Figure 1. Sketch Figure 0.

c.   By how much is tile Pattern A growing? Where are the tiles being added with each new figure? Color in the new tiles in each figure with a marker or colored pencil on your resource page for each pattern.

Problem continues on next page. →

2-1.   *Problem continued from previous page.*

   d.   What would Figure 100 look like for Pattern A? Describe it in words.
        How many tiles would be in the 100th figure? Find as many ways as you
        can to justify your conclusion. Be prepared to report back to the class with
        your team's findings and methods.

   e.   Write an equation that relates the figure number, x, to the number of tiles,
        y.

2-2.   Complete parts (a) through (e) from problem 2-1 for Pattern B, shown below
        and on the Lesson 2.1.1B Resource Page.

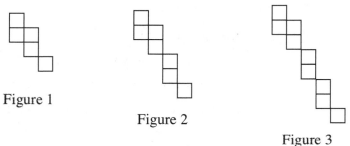

Figure 1

Figure 2

Figure 3

2-3.   The growth of a tile Pattern C is represented by the equation $y = 3x + 1$.

   a.   Copy and fill in the table for Pattern C.

Figure # x	0	1	2	3	4
# of tiles y					

   b.   By how many tiles is Pattern C growing? What is the starting value?

   c.   Where do you look in the table to see the growth and starting value?

   d.   Where do you look in the equation to see the growth and starting value?

2-4.   Look back at the growth of Patterns A, B, and C. Imagine that the team next to
        you created a brand new tile pattern, but they refused to show the pattern to
        you. What other information would you need in order to predict the number of
        tiles in Figure 100? Explain your reasoning.

Core Connections Algebra

2-5.   Now consider Tile Pattern D, shown below and on the Lesson 2.1.1B Resource Page.

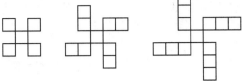

Figure 1   Figure 2   Figure 3

a.   Draw Figures 0 and 4 for this pattern on the resource page.

b.   Write an equation for the number of tiles in this pattern. Use color to show where the numbers in your equation appear in the tile pattern. Use x for the figure number, and y for the number of tiles in the figure.

c.   Make a table for the equation you wrote in part (b). Does the information in your table match the diagrams from part (a)?

d.   What is the same about this pattern and Pattern C? What is different? What would those similarities and differences look like in a tile pattern?

e.   What do the similarities and differences in part (d) look like in the equations?

f.   What do the similarities and differences look like in the table?

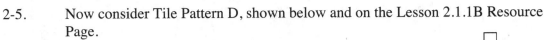

2-6.   A tile pattern has 5 tiles in Figure 0 and adds 7 tiles in each new figure. Write the equation of the line that represents the growth of this pattern.

2-7.   Evaluate each expression if $r = -3$, $s = 4$, and $t = -7$.

a. $\sqrt{s} + |r|$ b. $\frac{s-r}{t}$ c. $2s^3 + r - t$ d. $\sqrt[3]{2(t-r)}$

2-8.   Examine the relation $h(x)$ defined at right. Then estimate the values below.

a. $h(1)$

b. $h(3)$

c. x when $h(x) = 0$

d. $h(-1)$

e. $h(-4)$

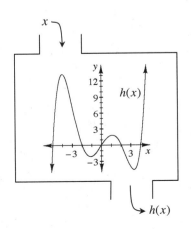

2-9.   Which of the relations below are functions? Justify your answer.

a.
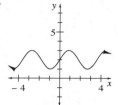

b.
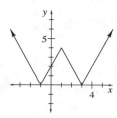

c.
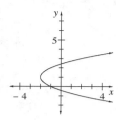

d.   For each graph above, state the domain and range.

2-10.   Examine the graphs in problem 2-9 again. Which, if any, have lines of
         symmetry? Copy each graph on your paper and show any lines of symmetry.

48

2.1.2 How can I measure steepness?

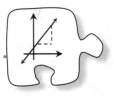

Slope

In the previous lesson, you determined the growth and starting value of geometric tile patterns, and made connections to the table and equation. In this lesson you will use your knowledge to determine an accurate value of growth from a graph.

During this lesson, ask your teammates the following focus questions:

What makes lines steeper? What makes lines less steep?

How is growth related to steepness?

Where is the starting value on a line?

2-11.   Write an equation that represents the tile pattern in the table below.

Figure #	0	1	2	3	4
# of tiles	2	7	12	17	22

2-12.   Does the relation in the table above appear to be a function? If so, write the equation in function notation. If not, explain why it is not a function.

2-13.   For each of the graphs below:

- Describe how the pattern grows and how many tiles are in Figure 0.
  x represents the figure number, and y represents the number of tiles in the figure.

- Write an equation that relates the figure number, x, to the number of tiles, y.

- Decide if the graph represents a function. If so, write the equation using function notation. If not, explain why the graph does not represent a function.

a.

b.

c.

2-14.   The graph at right shows a line for a tile pattern. How is the line growing? That is, how many tiles are added each time the figure number is increased by 1? Explain how you found your answer.

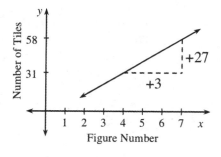

2-15. The triangles in problems 2-13 and 2-14 are called **slope triangles**. **Slope** is a measure of the steepness of a line. It is the ratio of the vertical distance to the horizontal distance of a slope triangle. The vertical part of the triangle is called **Δy** (read "change in y"), while the horizontal part of the triangle is called **Δx** (read "change in x"). Note that " Δ " is the Greek letter "delta" that is often used to represent a difference or a change.

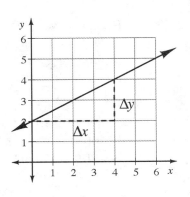

a. What is the vertical distance (Δy) for this slope triangle?

b. What is the horizontal distance (Δx) for this slope triangle?

c. Find this graph on the Lesson 2.1.2 Resource Page. Draw smaller slope triangles for this line that have a horizontal distance (Δx) of 1. Use one of these triangles to find the slope for this line.

d. How could you use Δy and Δx to find the slope of this line?

e. What is the equation of this line?

2-16. Find the line graphed at right with slope triangles A, B, and C on the Lesson 2.1.2 Resource Page.

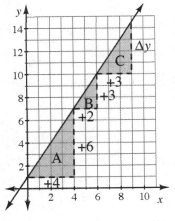

a. Find the slope using slope triangles A and B. What do you notice?

b. What is the vertical distance (Δy) of slope triangle C? Explain your reasoning.

c. Draw a slope triangle on the line with a horizontal distance (Δx) of 1 unit. Find the vertical distance (Δy) of this new triangle. What do you notice?

2-17. Draw a line with $\Delta y = 0$. How can you describe this line? Draw a line with $\Delta x = 0$. How can you describe this line?

2-18.   Michaela was trying to find the slope of the line shown at right, so she selected two **lattice points** (locations where the grid lines intersect) and then drew a slope triangle.

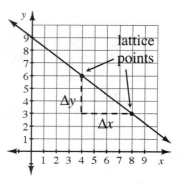

Her teammate, Cynthia, believes that $\Delta y = 3$ because the triangle is three units tall, while her other teammate, Essie, thinks that $\Delta y = -3$ because the triangle is three units tall and the line is pointing downward.

a.   With whom do you agree and why?

b.   When writing the slope of the line, Michaela noticed that Cynthia wrote $\frac{-3}{4}$ on her paper, while Essie wrote $-\frac{3}{4}$. She asked, "Are these ratios equal?" Discuss this with your team and answer her question.

c.   Find the equation of Michaela's line.

2-19.   What shape will the graph of $y = x^2 + 2$ be? How can you tell? Justify your prediction by making a table and graphing $y = x^2 + 2$ on graph paper.

2-20.   Evaluate each expression for $x = -2$ and $y = -5$.

a. $1 - 2x + 3y$

b. $-|x - y|$

c. $\sqrt{x^2} + \sqrt[3]{y^3}$

d. $\frac{1}{2}x + \frac{1}{3}y$

2-21.   Create a tile pattern that matches the table below. Be creative and make your pattern interesting!

Figure # x	0	1	2	3	4
# of tiles y	2	5	8	11	14

2-22.   Figure 2 of a tile pattern is shown at right. If the pattern grows linearly and if Figure 5 has 15 tiles, then find a rule for the pattern.

Figure 2

2-23.   Find the output for the relation with the
         given input. If there is no possible output
         for the given input, explain why not.

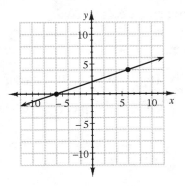

2-24.   Find the slope of the line
         shown on the graph at right.

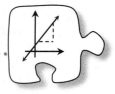

Comparing Δy and Δx

In Lesson 2.1.2, you used the dimensions of a slope triangle to measure the steepness of a line. Today you will use the idea of stairs to understand slope even better. You will review the difference between positive and negative slopes and will draw a line when given information about Δx and Δy.

During the lesson, ask your teammates the following focus questions:

How can you tell if the slope is positive or negative?

What makes a line steeper? What makes a line less steep?

What does a line with a slope of zero look like?

2-25.   One way to think about slope or growth triangles is as stair steps on a line.

a.   Picture yourself climbing (or descending) the stairs from left to right on each of the lines on the graph (shown below, at right). Of lines A, B, and C, which is the steepest? Which is the least steep?

b.   Examine line D. What direction is it traveling from left to right? What number should be used for Δy to represent this direction?

c.   Find this graph on the Lesson 2.1.3A Resource Page and label the sides of a slope triangle on each line. Then find the slope of each line.

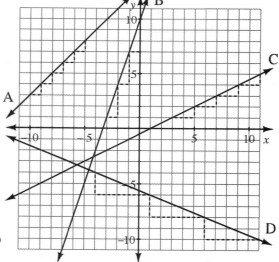

d.   How does the slope relate to the steepness of the graph?

e.   Cora answered part (d) with the statement, "The steeper the line, the greater the slope number." Do you agree? If so, use lines A through D to support her statement. If not, change her statement to make it correct.

2-26.   Find the graph shown at right on the
         Lesson 2.1.3A Resource Page.

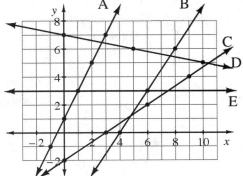

   a.   Which is the steepest line?
         Which is steeper, line B or line C?

   b.   Draw slope triangles for lines A,
         B, C, D, and E using the
         highlighted points on each line.
         Label Δx and Δy for each.

   c.   Match each line with its slope
         using the list below. Note: There
         are more slopes than lines.

$$m = 6 \qquad m = 2 \qquad m = -\tfrac{1}{5} \qquad m = \tfrac{3}{2}$$

$$m = 0 \qquad m = -\tfrac{2}{3} \qquad m = -5 \qquad m = \tfrac{2}{3}$$

   d.   Viewed left to right, in what direction would a line with slope $-\tfrac{3}{5}$ point?
         How do you know?

   e.   Viewed left to right, in what direction would a line with slope $-\tfrac{5}{3}$ point?
         How do you know? How would it be different from the line in part (d)?

2-27.   On graph paper, graph a line to match each description below.

   a. $y = \tfrac{3}{5}x - 1$

   b.   A line with $\Delta x = 4$ and $\Delta y = -6$.

   c. $f(x) = x - 7$

   d.   A line that has $\Delta y = 3$ and $\Delta x = 0$.

2-28.   Which of the lines that you graphed in problem 2-27 represent a function? If
         the line does not represent a function, why not?

2-29.   What happens to the slope when the slope
         triangles are different sizes? For example, the
         line at right has three different slope triangles
         drawn as shown.

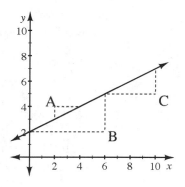

   a.   Find the slope using each of the slope
         triangles. What do you notice?

   b.   The triangle labeled A is drawn above the
         line. Does the fact that it is above the line
         instead of below it affect the slope of the
         line?

   c.   On the Lesson 2.1.3A Resource Page provided by your teacher, draw
         another slope triangle for this line so that $\Delta x = 1$. What is the height (Δy)
         of this new slope triangle?

2-30.   LEARNING LOG

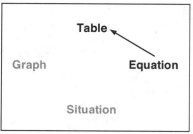

         For today's Learning Log, you will consider what
         connections between different representations of a linear
         relationship you can already use. Copy the web below,
         without any arrows, into your Learning Log. Discuss with your team the
         connections you have used so far in this chapter. For example, if you have a
         linear equation, such as $y = 3x + 1$, can you complete a table? If so, draw an
         arrow from "equation" to "table," as shown below.

         Draw arrows to show which representations you can connect already. Which
         connections have you not used yet but you are confident that you could? Which
         connections do you still need to explore?

         Can you think of examples from this chapter
         to support your conclusions? Write down the
         problem numbers next to your arrows.

         Title this entry "Multiple Representations
         Web for Linear Relationships" and label it
         with today's date. Be ready to share your
         findings with the rest of the class.

2-31. Does the table below appear to represent a function? If so, write an equation using function notation that represents the table. If not, explain why it cannot represent a function.

Figure # x	0	1	2	3	4
# of tiles y	4	8	12	16	20

2-32. When Yoshi graphed the lines $y = 2x + 3$ and $y = 2x - 2$, she got the graph shown at right.

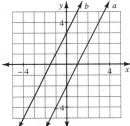

a. One of the lines at right matches the equation $y = 2x + 3$, and the other matches $y = 2x - 2$. Which line matches which equation?

b. Yoshi wants to add the line $y = 2x + 1$ to her graph. Predict where it would lie and sketch a graph to show its position. Justify your prediction.

c. Where would the line $y = -2x + 1$ lie? Again, justify your prediction and add the graph of this line to your graph from part (b).

2-33. On graph paper, graph a line with y-intercept $(0, -4)$ and x-intercept $(3, 0)$. Find the equation of the line.

2-34. Draw Figures 1, 2, and 3 for a tile pattern that could be described by $y = -3x + 10$.

2-35. What number is not part of the domain of $f(x) = \frac{3}{x+5}$? How can you tell?

2.1.4 What information determines a line?

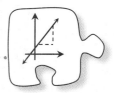

$y = mx + b$ and More on Slope

In previous lessons, you found the slope and starting values of linear relations. You connected growth and start to their representations in patterns, tables, equations, and graphs. Today you will complete your focus on finding slope as well as using slope and the y-intercept to find the equation of a line. During this lesson, keep the following questions in mind:

> How can you find the growth? How can you find the starting value?
>
> Is there enough information to graph the line?
>
> How can you find the slope of a line without graphing it?

2-36. Equations for linear patterns can all be written in the form $y = mx + b$.

a. x and y represent **variables**. When you wrote equations relating the figure number to the number of tiles, what did x represent? What did y represent?

b. m and b are **parameters** – they do not change within the situation of a given linear pattern. m is also called a **coefficient** since it multiplies the variable x. What do m and b represent in a linear pattern like the tile patterns?

c. What effect does m have on a graph of the line? What effect does b have?

2-37.   THE LINE FACTORY

You are an engineer at the city's premiere
Line Factory. Your job is to process
customers' orders for lines.

Analyze the recent orders below. If the
customer has provided enough information to
produce one (and only one) line, then pass it
on to your production department with an equation and a graph. However, if
you do not have enough information to draw one specific line, draw at least two
lines that fit the order and send it back to the customer.

The Line Factory standardizes its graphs by scaling the axes from –10 to 10 in
both directions.

a.   Line A goes through the point $(2, 5)$.

b.   Line B has a slope of –3 and goes through the origin.

c.   Line C goes through points $(-3, -2)$ and $(3, 10)$.

d.   Line D has the following table:

x	2	3	4	5
y	1	3.5	6	8.5

e.   Line E grows by 4.

f.   Line F goes through the point $(8, -1)$ and has a slope of $-\frac{3}{4}$.

g.   Customer G sent the following table:

x	–2	–1	0	1	2	3
y	$\frac{1}{9}$	$\frac{1}{3}$	1	3	9	27

2-38.   FINDING THE SLOPE OF A LINE WITHOUT GRAPHING

While finding the slope of a line that
goes through the points (6, 5) and (3, 7),
Gloria figured that $\Delta y = -2$ and $\Delta x = 3$
without graphing.

a.   Explain how Gloria could find the
horizontal and vertical distance of
the slope triangle without graphing.
Draw a sketch of the line and
validate her method.

b.   What is the slope of the line?

c.   Use Gloria's method (without graphing) to find the slope of the line that
goes through the points (4, 15) and (2, 11).

d.   Use Gloria's method to find the slope of the line that goes through the
points (28, 86) and (34, 83).

e.   Another student found
the slope from part (d)
to be 2. What error or
errors did that student
make?

Note: This stoplight icon will appear
periodically throughout the text.
Problems that display this icon
contain errors of some type.

When you explain why something is
a mistake, you are less likely to
make the same mistake yourself.

2-39.   SLOPE CHALLENGE

What is the steepest line possible? What is its slope? Be ready to justify your
statements.

2-40.   LEARNING LOG

Consider the equation for a line, $y = mx + b$. What does
the m represent? What does the b represent? Now
consider the four representations of a linear pattern:
situation, table, equation, and graph. Where in each of
these representations would you look if you wanted to determine the growth?
The starting value? Title this Learning Log entry, "$y = mx + b$" and include
today's date.

METHODS AND MEANINGS

The Slope of a Line

The **slope** of a line is the ratio of the vertical distance to the horizontal distance of a slope triangle formed by two points on a line. The vertical part of the triangle is called **Δy** (read "change in *y*"), while the horizontal part of the triangle is called **Δx** (read "change in *x*"). It indicates both how steep the line is and its direction, upward or downward, left to right.

$$\text{slope} = \frac{\text{vertical change}}{\text{horizontal change}} = \frac{\Delta y}{\Delta x}$$

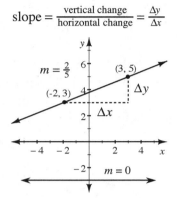

Note that " Δ " is the Greek letter "delta" that is often used to represent a difference or a change.

Note that lines pointing upward from left to right have positive slope, while lines pointing downward from left to right have negative slope. A horizontal line has zero slope, while a vertical line has undefined slope.

To calculate the slope of a line, pick two points on the line, draw a slope triangle (as shown in the example above), determine Δy and Δx, and then write the slope ratio. You can verify that your slope correctly resulted in a negative or positive value based on its direction. In the example above, $\Delta y = 2$ and $\Delta x = 5$, so the slope is $\frac{2}{5}$.

2-41.   If $y = \frac{1}{2}x - 4$:

a.   What is the slope of the line?

b.   What is the *y*-intercept of the line?

c.   Graph the line.

2-42.   Without graphing, find the slope of each line described below.

    a.   A line that goes through the points $(4, 1)$ and $(2, 5)$.

    b.   A line that goes through the origin and the point $(10, 5)$.

    c.   A vertical line (one that travels "up and down") that goes through the point $(6, -5)$.

    d.   A line that goes through the points $(1, 6)$ and $(10, 6)$.

2-43.   Ms. Cai's class is studying a tile pattern. The rule for the tile pattern is $y = 10x - 18$. Kalil thinks that Figure 12 of this pattern will have 108 tiles. Is he correct? Justify your answer.

2-44.   State the slope and y-intercept of each line.

    a. $y = \frac{5}{3}x - 4$
          b. $y = -\frac{4}{7}x + 3$
          c. $y = -5$

2-45.   Evaluate the expressions below for the given values.

    a. $-x^2 + 3x$ for $x = -3$
          b. $5 - (x - 2)^2$ for $x = -1$

    c. $\frac{-5}{k+1}$ for $k = -1$
          d. $\left|\frac{x}{x+y}\right| - x^2 + y$ for $x = 2$, $y = -3$

2.2.1 What is the equation of the line?

Slope as Motion

Today you will start to look at slope as a measurement of rate. Today's activity ties together the equation of a line and motion. Look for ways to connect what you know about m and b as you create motion graphs to match equations.

2-46.   SLOPE WALK

Congratulations! The president of the Line Factory has presented your class with a special challenge. She now wants a way to find the equation of a line generated when a customer walks in front of a motion detector. That way, a customer can simply "walk a line" to order it from the factory.

Your Task: Once a motion detector has been set up with the correct software, have a volunteer walk *away* from the motion detector at a *constant* rate. In other words, he or she should walk the same speed the entire time. Then, once a graph is generated, use the graphing technology provided by your teacher to find the equation of the line. Also find the equation of a line formed when a different volunteer walks *toward* the motion detector at a constant rate.

Discussion Points

What do you expect the first graph to look like? Why?

What will be different about the two graphs?

What would happen if the volunteer did not walk at a constant rate?

How does the volunteer's speed affect the graph?

2-47.   WALK THE WALK

To impress the president, you have decided to reverse the process: Write
instructions for a client about how to walk in front of the motion detector in
order to create a graph for a given equation.

Each team in the class will be assigned one or two equations from the list
below. Then, as a team, decide how to walk so that you will get the graph for
your equation. After the entire team understands how to walk, one member will
try to graph the line by walking in front of the motion detector. Pay close
attention to detail! Your team only has two tries!

a. $y = 3x + 2$ b. $y = -x + 10$

c. $y = 6$ d. $y = 2x + 4$

e. $y = -2x + 13$ f. $y = x + 5$

g. $y = -0.5x + 15$ h. $y = 1.5x + 3$

2-48.   The graph below represents the number of tiles in a tile pattern.

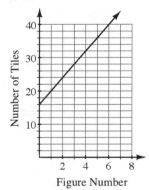

a.   Based on the information in the graph, how
      many tiles are being added each time (that
      is, what is the slope of the line)? Pay close
      attention to the scale of the axes.

b.   How many tiles are in Figure 0?

c.   Write the equation for the tile pattern.

d.   How would the line change if the pattern
      grew by 12 tiles each time instead?

2-49.   On graph paper, graph the line that goes through the points (–6, 3) and (–3, –1).

a.   What is the slope of the line?

b.   What is the y-intercept?

c.   Find the equation of the line.

2-50.   Solve each of the following equations.

   a. $2x + 8 = 3x - 4$ b. $1.5w + 3 = 3 + 2w$

   c. $48 + 8x + 23 = 7$ d. $6x - 21 = 5x + 17 + x$

2-51.   Write an equation for the line containing the points shown in the table below.

x	−2	−1	0	1
y	5	1	−3	−7

2-52.   Which graphs below have a domain of all numbers? Which have a range of all numbers? Which are functions?

a.
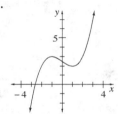

b.
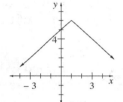

c.
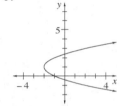

2.2.2 What can rate of change represent?

Rate of Change

Today you will focus on the meaning of "rate of change" in various situations. What does a rate of change represent? How can you use it? As you graph the results of a competitive tricycle race today, think about how the participants' rates of change compare to each other.

2-53.   THE BIG RACE – HEAT 1

Before a big race, participants often compete in heats, which are preliminary races that determine who competes in the final race. Later in this chapter, your class will compete in a tricycle race against the winners of these preliminary heats.

In the first heat, Leslie, Kristin, and Evie rode tricycles toward the finish line. Leslie began at the starting line and rode at a constant rate of 2 meters every second. Kristin got an 8-meter head start and rode 2 meters every 5 seconds. Evie rode 5 meters every 4 seconds and got a 6-meter head start.

a.   On neatly scaled axes, graph and then write an equation in terms of x and y for the distance Leslie travels. Let x represent time in seconds and y represent distance in meters. Then do the same for Kristin and Evie using the same set of axes.

b.   After how many seconds did Leslie catch up to Evie? How far were they from the starting line when Leslie caught up to Evie? Confirm your answer algebraically and explain how to use your graph to justify your answer.

c.   The winner of this heat will race in the final Big Race. If the race is 20 meters long, who won? Use both the graph and the equations to justify your answer.

d.   How long did it take each participant to finish the race?

e.   The school newspaper wants to report Kristin's speed. How fast was Kristin riding? Write your answer as a unit rate.

Core Connections Algebra

2-54.   THE BIG RACE – HEAT 2

In the second heat, Elizabeth, Kaye, and Hannah raced down the track. They knew the winner would compete against the other heat winners in the final race.

a.   When the line representing Kaye's race is graphed, the equation is $f(x) = \frac{2}{3}x + 1$. What was her speed (in meters per second)? Did she get a head start?

b.   Elizabeth's race is given by the equation $f(x) = \frac{12}{16}x + 4$. Who is riding faster, Elizabeth or Kaye? How do you know?

c.   Just as she started pedaling, Hannah's shoelace came untied! Being careful not to get her shoelace tangled in the pedal, she rode slowly. Hannah's race is represented by the table to the right. At what unit rate was she riding? Write your answer as a unit rate.

Hannah's Race	
Time (sec)	Distance (meters)
14	10
28	14
42	18

d.   To entertain the crowd, a clown rode a tricycle in the race described by the equation $f(x) = 20 - x$. Without graphing or making a table, fully describe the clown's ride.

2-55.   OTHER RATES OF CHANGE

The slope of a graph can represent many things. In this lesson you concentrated on situations where the rate of change of a line (the slope) represented speed. However, the rate of change can represent many other things besides speed, depending on the situation.

a.   For each graph below:

*   Explain what real-world quantities the slope and *y*-intercept represent.

*   Find the rate of change for each situation.

i.
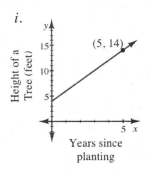

ii.
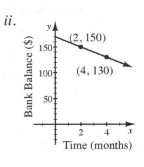

iii.
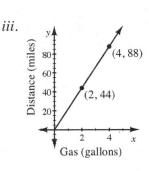

b.   In each of the situations, would it make sense to draw a different line with a negative *y*-intercept?

2-56.   TAKE A WALK

The president of the Line Factory is so impressed
with your work that you have been given a special
assignment: to analyze the graph below, which was
created when a customer walked in front of a
motion detector. The motion detector recorded the
distance between it and the customer.

Obtain the Lesson 2.2.2 Resource Page from your teacher. The graph is a
piecewise graph. A piecewise graph is a graph that has a different equation for
different intervals along the *x*-axis. Working with your team, explain the
motion that the graph describes.

Make sure you describe:

- If the customer was walking *toward* or
  away from the motion detector.

- Where the customer began walking when
  the motion detector started collecting data.

- Any time the customer changed direction
  or stopped.

- When the customer walked slowly and
  when he or she walked quickly by
  calculating the rate of change. Find the speed in feet per second.

- An equation representing each piece of the graph.

- The domain (the interval along the *x*-axis) for which each of the
  equations is valid.

2-57.   Write a memo to the president of the Line Factory explaining why you cannot
use a motion detector to collect the data plotted below. The *x*-axis represents
time in seconds, and the *y*-axis represents the distance from the motion detector
in feet.

a.

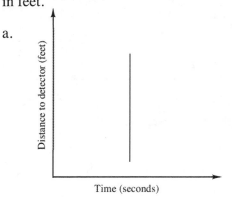

Time (seconds)

b.

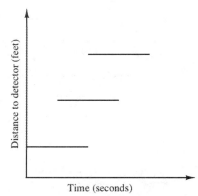

Time (seconds)

2-58.   LEARNING LOG

For today's Learning Log entry, create your own situation
with a rate of change, similar to problem 2-55. Make a
sketch of the graph and label the axes. Use the ideas you
have developed in class to answer the questions below in
your Learning Log. Title this entry "Rates of Change and
Slope" and label it with today's date.

In the situation you created:

What does it mean if the line is steeper? Less steep?

What does a positive slope mean? What about a negative slope?

What does a line with slope zero look like?
What does a zero slope mean in your situation?

Why does a vertical line have undefined slope?

(M)ETHODS AND MEANINGS

MATH NOTES

Writing the Equation of a Line from a Graph

One of the ways to write the equation of a line directly from a
graph is to find the slope of the line (m) and the y-intercept (b).
These values can then be substituted into the general slope-intercept
form of a line: $y = mx + b$.

For example, the slope of the line at right
is $m = \frac{1}{3}$, while the y-intercept is $(0, 2)$.
By substituting $m = \frac{1}{3}$ and $b = 2$ into
$y = mx + b$, the equation of the line is:

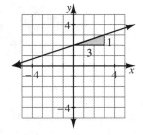

$$y = mx + b \; \rightarrow \; y = \tfrac{1}{3}x + 2$$

slope y-intercept

2-59.   Find the rule for the following tile pattern.

Figure 2   Figure 3   Figure 4

2-60.   Copy and complete each of the Diamond Problems below.
         The pattern used in the Diamond Problems is shown at right.

a.   b.   c.   d.

2-61.   THE BIG RACE – HEAT 3

Barbara, Mark, and Carlos participated in the
third heat of "The Big Race." Barbara thought
she could win with a 3 meter head start even
though she only pedaled 3 meters every 2
seconds. Mark began at the starting line and
finished the 20 meter race in 5 seconds.
Meanwhile, Carlos rode his tricycle so that his
distance (y) from the starting line in meters
could be represented by the equation $y = \frac{5}{2}x + 1$,
where x represents time in seconds.

a.   What is the dependent variable? What is the independent variable?

b.   Using the given information, graph lines for
      Barbara, Mark, and Carlos on the same set of axes.
      Who won the 20 meter race and will advance to the
      final race?

c.   Find equations that describe Barbara's and Mark's motion.

d.   How fast did Carlos pedal? Write your answer as a unit rate.

e.   When did Carlos pass Barbara? Confirm your answer algebraically.

2-62. Create a table and a graph for the line $y = 5x - 10$. Find the x-intercept and y-intercept in the table and on the graph.

2-63. Find the slope of the line containing the points in the table below.

IN (x)	2	4	6	8	10
OUT (y)	4	10	16	22	28

2-64. Use what you know about $y = mx + b$ to graph each of the following equations quickly on the same set of axes.

a. $y = 3x + 5$ b. $y = -2x + 10$ c. $y = 1.5x$

2-65. Review what you know about graphs by answering the following questions.

a. Find the equation of the line graphed at right.

b. What are its x- and y-intercepts?

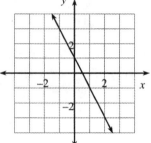

2-66. Use the idea of cube root from problem 1-35 to evaluate the following expressions.

a. $\sqrt[3]{1}$ b. $\sqrt[3]{0}$ c. $\sqrt[3]{2^3}$ d. $\sqrt[3]{7^3}$

2-67. Each part (a) through (d) below represents a different tile pattern. For each one, determine how the pattern is growing and the number of tiles in Figure 0.

a. 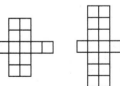 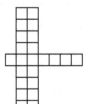   b.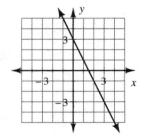

Figure 2   Figure 3   Figure 4

c. $y = 3x - 14$

d.

x	-3	-2	-1	0	1	2	3
y	18	13	8	3	-2	-7	-12

2.2.3   How can I use $y=mx+b$?

Equations of Lines in Situations

During this chapter you have found linear equations using several different strategies and starting from many different types of information. Today you are going to apply what you know about writing linear equations to solve a complicated puzzle: Who among you will win "The Big Race"?

2-68.   **THE BIG RACE – FINALS**

Today is the final event of "The Big Race"! Your teacher will give you each a card that describes how you travel in the race. You and your study team will compete against the heat 1 and 2 winners, Leslie and Elizabeth, at today's rally in the gym. Unfortunately, Mark, the winner of heat 3, is absent from school and will not be participating against you. (The clue cards are on the Lesson 2.2.3 Resource Page.)

Your Task: As a team, do the following:

- Draw a graph (on graph paper) showing all of the racers' progress over time. Identify the independent and dependent variables.

- Write an equation for each participant.

- Figure out who will win the race!

Rules:

- Your study team must work cooperatively to solve the problems. No team member has enough information to solve the puzzle alone!

- Each member of the team will select rider A, B, C, or D. You may not show your card to your team. You may only communicate the information contained on the card.

- Assume that each racer travels at a constant rate throughout the race.

- Elizabeth's and Leslie's cards will be shared by the entire team.

Core Connections Algebra

2-69.   Use your results from "The Big Race – Finals " to answer the following
questions. You may answer the questions in any order, but be sure to justify
each response.

a.   Who won the finals of The Big Race? Who came in last place?

b.   How fast was Rider D traveling? How fast was Elizabeth traveling?

c.   At one point in the race, four different participants were the same distance
from the starting line. Who were they and when did this happen?

METHODS AND MEANINGS

MATH NOTES

x- and y-Intercepts

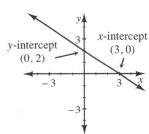

Recall that the **x-intercept** of a
line is the point where the graph
crosses the x-axis (where $y = 0$). To
find the x-intercept, substitute 0 for y
and solve for x. The coordinates of the
x-intercept are $(x, 0)$.

Similarly, the **y-intercept** of a line is the
point where the graph crosses the y-axis, which happens when $x = 0$.
To find the y-intercept, substitute 0 for x and solve for y.
The coordinates of the y-intercept are $(0, y)$.

Example: The graph of $2x + 3y = 6$ is a line, as shown above right.

To calculate the x-intercept,   To calculate the y-intercept,
let $y = 0$: $2x + 3(0) = 6$ let $x = 0$: $2(0) + 3y = 6$

$$2x = 6$$ $$3y = 6$$

$$x = 3$$ $$y = 2$$

x-intercept: $(3, 0)$ y-intercept: $(0, 2)$

2-70.   Sometimes the quickest and easiest two points to use to graph a line that is not in slope-intercept form are the *x*- and *y*-intercepts. Find the *x*- and *y*-intercepts for the two lines below and then use them to graph each line. Write the coordinates of the *x*- and *y*-intercepts on your graph.

   a. $x - 2y = 4$ b. $3x + 6y = 24$

2-71.   Find the slope of the line passing through each pair of points below.

   a. $(1, 2)$ and $(4, -1)$ b. $(7, 3)$ and $(5, 4)$

   c. $(-6, 8)$ and $(-8, 5)$ d. $(55, 67)$ and $(50, 68)$

   e.   Azizah got 1 for the slope of the line through points $(1, 2)$ and $(4, -1)$. Explain to her the mistake she made and how to find the slope correctly.

2-72.   Evaluate the following expressions.

   a. $8\frac{2}{5} \div 3\frac{1}{4}$ b. $5\frac{1}{2} \cdot \left(-6\frac{3}{4}\right)$ c. $-3\frac{5}{8} - 1\frac{1}{2}$ d. $-7 + \frac{2}{3}$

2-73.   Copy and complete the table below. Then write the corresponding equation.

IN (*x*)	2	4	6	7		10
OUT (*y*)	−7	−17			−37	

2-74.   MATCH-A-GRAPH

Match the following graphs with their equations. Pay special attention to the scaling of each set of axes. Explain how you found each match.

a. $y = \frac{1}{4}x + 4$

b. $y = \frac{1}{2}x + 4$

c. $y = 2x + 4$

d. $y = -\frac{2}{3}x + 4$

1.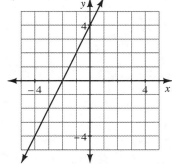

2.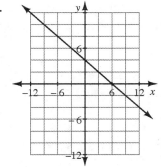

3.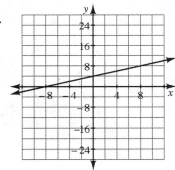

4.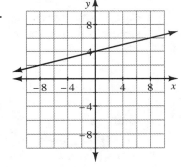

2.3.1 How can the solutions help find an equation?

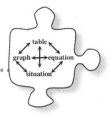

Finding an Equation Given the Slope and a Point

To do well in "The Big Race," you had to find the equation of a line with a given rate (slope) that passed through a given point. Your method probably involved estimating the *y*-intercept of the line visually or working backward on a graph. What if the given point is far away from the *y*-axis? What if an estimate is not good enough in a particular situation?

During this lesson, you will develop an algebraic method for finding the equation of a line when given its slope and a point on the line.

2-75.   DOWN ON THE FARM

Colleen recently purchased a farm that raises chickens. Since she has never raised chickens before, Colleen wants to learn as much about her baby chicks as possible. In particular, she wants to know how much a baby chick weighs when it is hatched.

To find out, Colleen decided to track the weight of one of the chicks that was born just before she purchased the farm. She found that her chick grew steadily by about 5.2 grams each day, and she assumes that it has been doing so since it hatched. Nine days after it hatched, the chick weighed 98.4 grams.

Your Task: Determine how much the chick weighed the day it was hatched using two different representations of the chick's growth: a graph and an *x*→*y* table. Then, assuming the chicken will continue to grow at the same rate, determine when the chick will weigh 140 grams.

Discussion Points

What are you looking for?

What information are you given?

What do you expect the graph to look like? Why?

Which representation (graph or table) will give more accurate results? Why?

Core Connections Algebra

2-76.   USING A GRAPH

Use the information in problem 2-75 to answer these questions.

a.   What is the baby chick's rate of growth? That is, how fast does the baby chick grow each day? How does this rate relate to the equation of the line?

b.   Before graphing, describe the line that represents the growth of the chick. Do you know any points on the line? Does the line point upward or downward? How steep is it?

c.   Draw a graph for this situation. Let the horizontal axis represent the number of days since the chick hatched, and let the vertical axis represent the chick's weight. Label and scale your axes appropriately and title your graph "Growth of a Baby Chick."

d.   What is the y-intercept of your graph? According to your graph, how much did Colleen's chick weigh the day it hatched?

e.   When will the chick weigh 140 grams?

f.   How is the minimum and the y-intercept related in this graph?

2-77.   USING A TABLE

Use the information in problem 2-75 to answer these questions.

a.   Now approach this problem using a table. Make a table with two columns, the first labeled "Days Since Birth" and the second labeled "Weight in Grams." In the first column, write the numbers 0 through 10.

b.   Use Colleen's measurements to fill one entry in the table.

c.   Use the chick's growth rate to complete the table.

d.   According to your table, how much did the chick weigh the day it was hatched? When will the chick weigh 140 grams? Do these answers match your answers from the graph? Which method do you think is more accurate? Why?

*Further Guidance
section ends here.*

2-78.   FINDING AN EQUATION WITHOUT A TABLE OR GRAPH

Now you will explore another way Colleen could find the weight of her chick when it hatched without using a table or a graph.

a.   Since Colleen is assuming that the chick grows linearly, the equation will be in the form $y = mx + b$. Without graphing, what do m and b represent? Do you know either of these values? If so, what are their units?

b.   You already know the chicken's rate of growth. Place this into the equation of the line. What information is still unknown?

c.   In Lesson 2.1.4, you discovered that knowing the slope and a point is enough information to determine a line. Therefore, using the point (9, 98.4) should help you find the y-intercept. How can you use this point in your equation? Discuss this with your team and be ready to share your ideas with the rest of the class.

d.   Work together as a class to solve for b (the weight of the chick when it was hatched). Write the equation of the line that represents the weight of the chick.

e.   Does the y-intercept you found algebraically match the one you found using the graph? Does it match the one you found using the table? How accurate do you think your algebraic answer is? What are the units for the y-intercept?

f.   Use your equation to determine when Colleen's chicken will weigh 140 grams.

2-79.   Use this new algebraic method to find equations for lines with the following properties:

a.   A slope of –3, passing through the point (15, –50).

b.   A slope of 0.5 with an x-intercept of (28, 0).

2-80.   MIGHTY MT. EVEREST

The Earth's surface is composed of gigantic
plates that are constantly moving.
Currently, India lies on a plate that is
slowly drifting northward. India's plate is
grinding into the rest of Asia. As it does
so, it pushes up the Himalayan Mountains,
which contain the world's highest peak, Mt.
Everest. In 1999, mountain climbers
measured Mt. Everest with satellite gear
and found it to be 8850 meters high.
Geologists estimate that Mt. Everest may
be growing by as much as 5 cm per year.

Your Task: Assuming a constant growth of 5 cm per year, determine how tall
Mt. Everest was in the year 0. (The year 0 is the year that came 2000 years
before the year 2000.) Write an equation for the height of Mt. Everest over
time, with x representing the year and y representing the height of the mountain.

What are the units for m and b in your equation? How many decimal places
should be in your answer? Explain why.

2-81.   LEARNING LOG

For today's Learning Log, you will consider what
connections between different representations of a linear
relationship you now know. Copy the web below,
without any arrows, into your Learning Log. Discuss
with your team the connections you have used so far in this chapter. Refer to
the web that you made in problem 2-30.

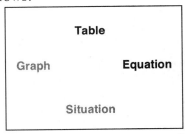

Draw arrows to show which representations you can connect already. Pay
special attention to arrows that you did not draw in problem 2-30. Are there
any connections (arrows) that you can complete better than you did before?
Can you think of examples from this chapter to support your new arrows?
Write down the problem numbers next to your arrows.

Title this entry "Multiple Representations Web
for Linear Relationships" and label it with
today's date. Be ready to share your findings
with the rest of the class.

	Table	
Graph		Equation
	Situation	

2-82.   The point $(21, 32)$ is on a line with slope 1.5.

    a.   Find the equation of the line.

    b.   Find the coordinates of another point on the line.

2-83.   Copy and complete each of the Diamond Problems below. The pattern used in the Diamond Problems is shown at right.

    a.   b.   c.   d.

2-84.   The graph of the equation $2x - 3y = 7$ is a line.

    a.   Find the x- and y-intercepts and graph the line using these two points.

    b.   If a point on this line has an x-coordinate of 10, what is its y-coordinate?

2-85.   Without graphing, identify the slope and y-intercept of each equation below.

    a. $y = 3x + 5$ b. $y = \frac{5}{-4}x$

    c. $y = 3$ d. $y = 7 + 4x$

2-86.   Graph the line $y = -\frac{2}{3}x + 3$.

2.3.2 What is the equation of the line?

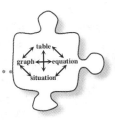

Finding the Equation of a Line Through Two Points

In past lessons, you learned facts about m and b by graphing lines from equations. In today's lesson, you will reverse the process used in Lesson 2.1.4 so that you can find the equation of a line when you know its graph.

2-87.   In this problem, you will find the equation of the line that goes through the points in the table below. Use the questions below to help you organize your work.

IN (x)	29	18	–8	14	–27
OUT (y)	97	64	–14	52	–71

   a.   What is the slope of the line?

   b.   Does it matter which points you used to find the slope of your line? Find the slope with two other points to verify your answer.

   c.   How can you use a point to find the equation? Find the equation of the line.

   d.   Once you have the slope, does it matter which point you use to find your equation? Why or why not?

   e.   How can you verify that your equation is correct?

2-88.   LINE FACTORY LOGO

The Line Factory needs a new logo for its pamphlet. After much work, the
stylish logos below were proposed. The design department knows the
coordinates of the special points in each logo. However, programmers need to
have the equations of the lines to program their pamphlet-production software.

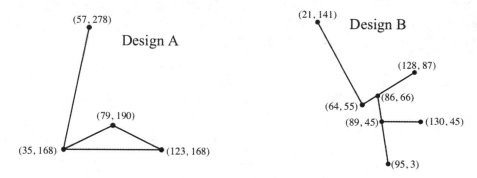

a.   Work in pairs today. Choose one logo for each pair in your team to work
      on. What are the equations of the four line segments that make up this
      logo?

b.   What are the domain and range of each of the line segments in the logo?

c.   Trade equations with the other pair of students in your team. Sketch each
      of their equations on graph paper. How did each sketch compare with the
      original logos? Discuss any equation modifications needed with your
      team.

2-89.   LEARNING LOG

In your Learning Log, describe the process you used to find
the equation of a line through two points. Include an
example. Title this entry "Finding the Equation of a Line
Through Two Points" and include today's date.

2-90.   Explain what the slope of each line below represents. Then find the slope and
         give its units.

a.

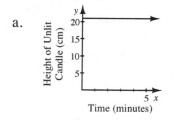

Time (minutes)

b.

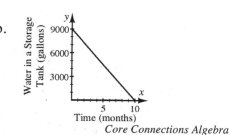

2-91.   Find the equation of the line that goes through the points $(-15, 70)$ and $(5, 10)$.

2-92.   This problem is the checkpoint for evaluating expressions and the Order of Operations. It will be referred to as Checkpoint 2.

Evaluate each expression if $x = -2$, $y = -3$, $z = 5$.

a. $2x + 3y + z$ b. $x - y$ c. $2\left(\frac{x+y}{z}\right)$

d. $3x^2 - 2x + 1$ e. $3y(x + x^2 - y)$ f. $\frac{-z^2(1-2x)}{y-x}$

Check your answers by referring to the Checkpoint 2 materials located at the back of your book.

If you needed help solving these problems correctly, then you need more practice. Review the Checkpoint 2 materials and try the practice problems. Also, consider getting help outside of class time. From this point on, you will be expected to do problems like these quickly and easily.

2-93.   Greta is opening a savings account. She starts with $100 and plans to add $50 each week. Write an equation she can use to calculate the amount of money she will have after any number of weeks. How much money will she have after 1 year?

2-94.   Paula found a partially completed table that her friend Donna was using to determine how fast water evaporated from a bucket during the summer. Every other day she measured the height of the water remaining in the bucket in centimeters.

Days (x)	0	2	4	6	8
Height cm (y)	30	27	24		

a.   Complete the table.

b.   For this table, what is the rate of change, including the units?

c.   Write an equation to represent the height of the water after any number of days.

Extension Activity What is the equation of the line?

Finding $y = mx + b$ from Graphs and Tables

In past lessons, you learned facts about m and b by graphing lines from equations. In today's lesson, you will reverse the process to find the equation of a line when you know its graph.

2-95. SAVE THE EARTH

The Earth Protection Service (EPS) has asked your team to defend our planet against dangerous meteors. Luckily, the EPS has developed a very advanced protection system, called the Linear Laser Cannon. This cannon must be programmed with an equation that dictates the path of a laser beam and destroys any meteors in its path. Unfortunately, the cannon uses a huge amount of energy, making it very expensive to fire.

Your Mission: Using the technology (or resource page) provided by your teacher, find equations of lines that will eliminate the meteors as efficiently as possible. The EPS offers big rewards for operators who use the fewest number of lasers possible to eliminate the meteors.

Game #1

X	Y
6	-5
2	8
-6	8
9	-9
4	-7
-4	4

Game #2

X	Y
9	-2
3	-7
-4	-5
-8	7
-6	2
-1	-1

Game #3

X	Y
-1	-5
-4	2
6	2
9	6
0	5
-2	-1

2-96.   Which equation below has *no* solution? Explain how you know.

   a. $4(x+1) = 2x + 4$ b. $9 - 5x + 2 = 4 - 5x$

2-97.   Rena says that if $x = -5$, the equation below is true. Her friend, Dean, says the answer is $x = 3$. Who is correct? Justify your conclusion.

$$9(x + 4) = 1 + 2x$$

2-98.   Sally currently weighs 120 pounds and is on a diet to lose five pounds every two months.

   a.   What is the rate of growth for this situation, including the units?

   b.   Write an equation that represents this situation.

2-99.   Graph the equation $y = -2x + 9$.

2-100.   Write the equation for the function in the table below.

x	−1	1	3	5
y	2	16	30	44

Chapter 2 Closure   What have I learned?

Reflection and Synthesis

The activities below offer you a chance to
reflect about what you have learned during this
chapter. As you work, look for concepts that
you feel very comfortable with, ideas that you
would like to learn more about, and topics you
need more help with. Look for connections
between ideas as well as connections with
material you learned previously.

①   TEAM BRAINSTORM

What have you studied in this chapter? What ideas were important in what you
learned? With your team, brainstorm a list. Be as detailed as you can. To help
get you started, a list of Learning Log entries and Math Notes boxes are below.

What topics, ideas, and words that you learned *before* this chapter are connected
to the new ideas in this chapter? Again, be as detailed as you can.

How long can you make your list? Challenge yourselves. Be prepared to share
your team's ideas with the class.

Learning Log Entries
- Lesson 2.1.3 – Multiple Representations Web for Linear
  Relationships
- Lesson 2.1.4 – $y = mx + b$
- Lesson 2.2.2 – Rates of Change and Slope
- Lesson 2.3.1 – Multiple Representations Web for Linear
  Relationships
- Lesson 2.3.2 – Finding the Equation of a Line Through
  Two Points

Math Notes
- Lesson 2.1.4 – The Slope of a Line
- Lesson 2.2.2 – Writing the Equation of a Line from a Graph
- Lesson 2.2.3 – x- and y-Intercepts

② **MAKING CONNECTIONS**

Below is a list of the vocabulary used in this chapter. Make sure that you are familiar with all of these words and know what they mean. Refer to the glossary or index for any words that you do not yet understand.

graph	zero slope	growth
linear equation	piecewise graph	Δy
starting value	rate of change	slope
Figure 0	situation	steepness
function	Δx	x-intercept
$y = mx + b$	parameter	coefficient
variable	slope triangle	table
y-intercept	unit rate	

Make a concept map showing all of the connections you can find among the key words and ideas listed above. To show a connection between two words, draw a line between them and explain the connection, as shown in the model below. A word can be connected to any other word as long as you can justify the connection. For each key word or idea, provide an example or sketch that shows the idea.

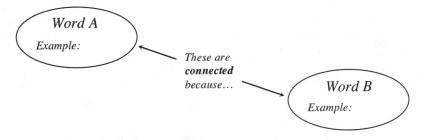

Your teacher may provide you with vocabulary cards to help you get started. If you use the cards to plan your concept map, be sure either to re-draw your concept map on your paper or to glue the vocabulary cards to a poster with all of the connections explained for others to see and understand.

While you are making your map, your team may think of related words or ideas that are not listed here. Be sure to include these ideas on your concept map.

Congratulations! You are now the owner of the city's premiere Line Factory. However, instead of raking in huge profits, you've noticed that you are only breaking even because many customers are ordering the incorrect line. After your company has produced the customer's line (at great expense!), they have refused to pay for it, saying it was not the line that they wanted!

Your Task: To prevent your customers from ordering the wrong lines, you need to produce a pamphlet to explain how to order a line. Carefully determine what information should be in the pamphlet so that customers will know how to write their equation in $y = mx + b$ form to get the line they want.

You can view some examples of pamphlets to help determine the layout of your pamphlet. A sample is shown at right. Your pamphlet can contain some advertisements, but remember that it needs to include *everything* you know about equations and graphs of lines so that your customers can order wisely. Remember to be specific and show examples!

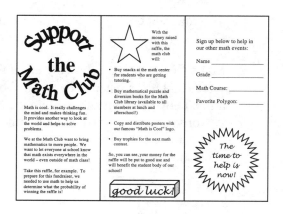

Discussion Points

How do m and b affect the equation of a line?

What information does a customer need to know to order a line correctly?

How could a customer figure out what line to order if he or she only knew two points on the line? One point and the slope?

④   WHAT HAVE I LEARNED?

Most of the problems in this section represent typical problems found in this chapter. They serve as a gauge for you. You can use them to determine which types of problems you can do well and which types of problems require further study and practice. Even if your teacher does not assign this section, it is a good idea to try these problems and find out for yourself what you know and what you still need to work on.

Solve each problem as completely as you can. The table at the end of the closure section has answers to these problems. It also tells you where you can find additional help and practice with problems like these.

CL 2-101.   For the line graphed at right:

a.   Find the slope.

b.   Find the y-intercept.

c.   Write the equation.

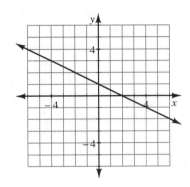

CL 2-102.   Find m and b in the following equations.
What do m and b represent?

a. $y = 2x + 1$

b. $y = \frac{2}{5}x - 4$

CL 2-103.   Graph each equation in problem CL 2-102.

CL 2-104.   Shirley starts with $85 in the bank and saves $15 every 2 months. Write an equation for the balance of Shirley's bank account.

CL 2-105.   Find the slope for each linear relation described in the tables below.

a.

x	−2	−1	0	1	2
y	19	14	9	4	−1

b.

x	2	3	4	5	6
y	22	31	40	49	58

CL 2-106.   Write a rule for the given tile pattern. How many tiles will be in figure 58?

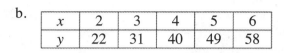

Figure 1   Figure 2   Figure 3

CL 2-107.   Solve for w: $6w - 5 + 8w - 2w - 3 = 9w - 24$.

CL 2-108.   Copy and complete the table below for the rule $y = x^2 - 6x + 5$. Then graph the rule on graph paper.

x	−1	0	1	2	3	4	5	6	7
y									

a.   Completely describe the graph.

b.   Is the relation a function?

c.   State the domain and range.

CL 2-109.   Find the slope of the line that passes through the points $(-5, 7)$ and $(10, 1)$.

CL 2-110. Evaluate the expressions below for the given values.

  a. $-3x^2 + 4x + 5$ for $x = -2$ b. $6 - (5x - 9)^2$ for $x = 1$

  c. $\frac{-4}{k+7}$ for $k = -8$ d. $\frac{2m}{n-1} - m^3 - n$ for $m = -2, n = 3$

  e. If (c) were $f(k) = \frac{-4}{k+7}$, what value of k would be excluded from the domain?

CL 2-111. Check your answers using the table at the end of the closure section. Which problems do you feel confident about? Which problems were hard? Use the table to make a list of topics you need help with and a list of topics you need to practice more.

Answers and Support for Closure Activity #4
What Have I Learned?

Note: MN = Math Note, LL = Learning Log

Problem	Solution	Need Help?	More Practice
CL 2-101.	a. The slope is $-\frac{1}{2}$. b. The y-intercept is $(0, 1)$. c. $y = -\frac{1}{2}x + 1$	Sections 2.1 and 2.2 MN: 2.1.4 and 2.2.2 LL: 2.1.3 and 2.1.4	Problems 2-18, 2-24, 2-33, 2-48, 2-49, 2-65, 2-74, and 2-94
CL 2-102.	m represents the slope and b represents the y-intercept. a. $m = 2$, $b = 1$ b. $m = \frac{2}{5}$, $b = -4$	Lesson 2.1.4 LL: 2.1.4 and 2.3.1	Problems 2-41, 2-44, and 2-85
CL 2-103.	a. b.	Lesson 2.1.4 LL: 2.1.4 and 2.3.1	Problems 2-41, 2-62, 2-64, 2-86, and 2-99
CL 2-104.	Let $x = $ # of months that have passed. Let $y = $ amount of money in the account. $y = \frac{15}{2}x + 85$	Lesson 2.2.3	Problems 2-61(c) and 2-93

Problem	Solution	Need Help?	More Practice
CL 2-105.	a. $m = -5$ b. $m = 9$	Section 2.1 MN: 2.1.4	Problems 2-31, 2-51, 2-63, 2-73, and 2-100
CL 2-106.	$y = 3x + 3$ Figure 58 will have 177 tiles.	Lesson 2.1.1 LL: 2.3.1	Problems 2-6, 2-22, and 2-59
CL 2-107.	$w = -\frac{16}{3}$	Checkpoint 2	Problems CL 1-87, 2-50, 2-96, and 2-97
CL 2-108.	y-values in table: $12, 5, 0, -3, -4,$ $-3, 0, 5, 12$ 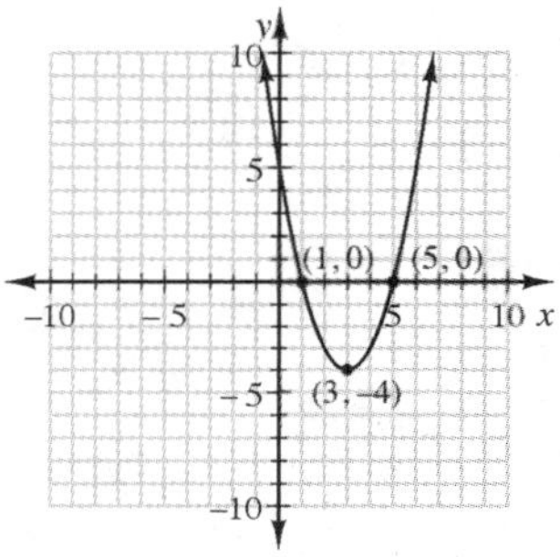 a. The graph is a parabola opening up. The vertex is at $(3, -4)$ and is a minimum. The x-intercepts are $(1, 0)$ and $(5, 0)$. The y-intercept is $(0, 5)$. There is a vertical line of symmetry through the vertex. b. Yes, it is a function. c. Domain: all numbers Range: $y \geq -4$	Lessons 1.1.3, 1.2.1, and 1.2.2 LL: 1.2.1	Problems CL 1-86, 2-9, and 2-43
CL 2-109.	$m = -\frac{2}{5}$	Lessons 2.1.2 and 2.1.3 MN: 2.1.4 LL: 2.2.2 and 2.3.2	Problems 2-42 and 2-71
CL 2-110.	a. -15 b. -10 c. 4 d. 3 e. $x \neq -7$	Checkpoint 2	Problems CL 1-83, 2-7, 2-20, 2-23, 2-35, and 2-45

CHAPTER 3

Simplifying and Solving

In this chapter you will focus on multiplying expressions. You will also solve equations that contain products. While these new ideas will be introduced using algebra tiles, you will also develop a method to multiply expressions without using tiles.

Guiding Question

Mathematically proficient students use appropriate tools strategically.

As you work through this chapter, ask yourself:

How can algebra tiles and area models help me better understand multiplication?

Chapter Outline

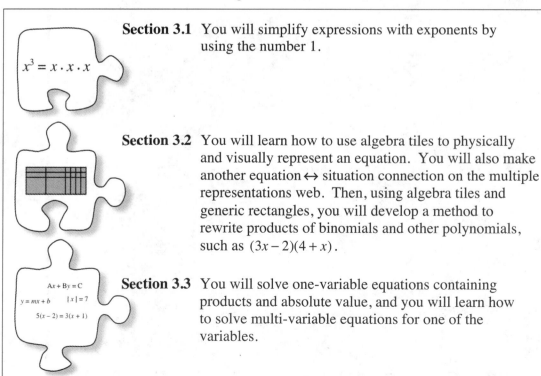

Section 3.1 You will simplify expressions with exponents by using the number 1.

$$x^3 = x \cdot x \cdot x$$

Section 3.2 You will learn how to use algebra tiles to physically and visually represent an equation. You will also make another equation ↔ situation connection on the multiple representations web. Then, using algebra tiles and generic rectangles, you will develop a method to rewrite products of binomials and other polynomials, such as $(3x - 2)(4 + x)$.

Section 3.3 You will solve one-variable equations containing products and absolute value, and you will learn how to solve multi-variable equations for one of the variables.

$Ax + By = C$

$y = mx + b$ $|x| = 7$

$5(x - 2) = 3(x + 1)$

3.1.1 How can I rewrite it?

Simplifying Exponential Expressions

$$x^3 = x \cdot x \cdot x$$

Today you will examine how to simplify expressions with exponents. Using patterns, you will develop strategies to simplify expressions when the exponents are too large to expand on paper.

3-1.   An **exponent** is shorthand for repeated multiplication. For example, $n^4 = n \cdot n \cdot n \cdot n$. In an exponential expression like b^a, b is called the **base** and a is called the **exponent**.

Expand each of the expressions below. For example, to expand x^3, you would write: $x \cdot x \cdot x$.

a. y^7 b. $5(2m)^3$ c. $(x^3)^2$ d. $4x^5y^2$

3-2.   Ms. Wang has just explained to her class how to simplify exponents by using the number 1. She wrote the following on the board:

$$\frac{xy^8}{y^2}$$
$$= \frac{x}{1} \cdot \frac{y^2}{y^2} \cdot \frac{y^6}{1}$$
$$= \frac{x}{1} \cdot 1 \cdot \frac{y^6}{1}$$
$$= \frac{xy^6}{1}$$
$$= xy^6$$

a.   Copy Ms. Wang's steps on to your paper. Explain each step.

b.   Simplify each of the expressions below using what you know about exponents and the number 1. Start by expanding the exponents, and then simplify your results.

i. $\frac{x \cdot x \cdot x}{x}$ ii. $\frac{x^5}{x^2}$ iii. $x^2 \cdot x^3$ iv. $k^3 \cdot k^5$

v. $\frac{16k^3}{8k^2}$ vi. $m^6 \cdot m$ vii. $x^4 \cdot x^5 \cdot x^3$ viii. $\frac{6x^3y}{2y}$

challenge: $\frac{5x^{50}}{10x^{15}}$

3-3.   Simplify each of the expressions below. Start by expanding the exponents, and then simplify your results. Look for patterns or possible shortcuts that will help you simplify more quickly. Be prepared to justify your patterns or shortcuts to the class.

a. $y^5 \cdot y^2$

b. $\frac{w^5}{w^2}$

c. $(x^2)^4$

d. $x^{10} \cdot x^{12}$

e. $\frac{13p^4q^5}{p^2q^2}$

f. $\left(\frac{x^2}{y}\right)^3$

g. $5h \cdot 2h^{24}$

h. $\frac{10m^{30}}{2m^8}$

i. $(3k^{20})^4$

j. $\frac{24hg^2}{3hg^9}$

k. $\left(\frac{m^3}{n^{10}}\right)^4$

l. $w^4 \cdot p \cdot w^3$

3-4.   Work with your team to write four exponent problems, each having a simplification of x^{12}. At least one problem must involve multiplication, one must involve grouping, and one must involve division. Be creative!

3-5.   Lacey and Haley are simplifying expressions.

a. Haley simplified $x^3 \cdot x^2$ and got x^5. Lacey simplified $x^3 + x^2$ and got the same result! However, their teacher told them that only one simplification is correct. Who simplified correctly and how do you know?

b. Haley simplifies $3^5 \cdot 4^5$ and gets the result 12^{10}, but Lacey is not sure. Is Haley correct? Be sure to justify your answer.

3-6.   Use what you have learned about exponents to rewrite each of the expressions below.

  a. $\dfrac{h^9}{h^{11}}$

  b. $x^3 \cdot x^4$

  c. $(3k^5)^2$

  d. $n^7 \cdot n$

  e. $\dfrac{16x^4 y^3}{2x^4}$

  f. $4xy^3 \cdot 7x^2 y^3$

3-7.   Gerardo is simplifying expressions with very large exponents. He arrives at each of the results below. For each result, decide if he is correct and justify your answer using the meaning of exponents.

  a. $\dfrac{x^{150}}{x^{50}} \Rightarrow x^3$

  b. $y^{20} \cdot y^{41} \Rightarrow y^{61}$

  c. $(2m^2 n^{15})^3 \Rightarrow 2m^6 n^{45}$

3-8.   Use what you know about slope and y-intercept to graph $y = -\frac{1}{2}x + 3$.

3-9.   Write an expression to represent the given situation. Be sure to define your variable.

Sam currently has \$150 in a savings account and is saving \$10 per week.

3-10.   Find $f(-3)$ for each function below.

  a. $f(x) = -2x + 3$

  b. $f(x) = -\left|1 - x\right|$

  c. $f(x) = \sqrt[3]{9x} + 2$

  d. $f(x) = \frac{1}{2}x + 2$

3-11.   Simplify each expression.

  a. $-\frac{1}{2} + \left(-\frac{1}{5}\right)$

  b. $-\frac{2}{3} - 2$

  c. $-1\frac{2}{3}(-2)$

  d. $-2 \div \frac{2}{3}$

3.1.2 How can I rewrite it?

Zero and Negative Exponents

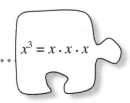

In Lesson 3.1.1, you used the meaning of an exponent to rewrite expressions such as $y^4 \cdot y^2$ and $(x^2 y)^3$. Today you will use the patterns you discovered to learn how to interpret expressions with exponents that are negative or zero.

3-12.   Review what you learned about exponents in Lesson 3.1.1 to rewrite each expression below as simply as possible. If you see a pattern or know of a shortcut, be sure to share it with your teammates.

a. $x^7 \cdot x^4$ b. $(x^3)^3$ c. $\dfrac{m^{14}}{m^2}$

d. $(x^2 y^2)^4$ e. $\dfrac{x^2 y^{11}}{x^5 y^3}$ f. $\dfrac{2x^{12}}{8x^2}$

3-13.   With your study team, summarize the patterns you found in problem 3-12. For each one, simplify the given expression and write an expression that represents its generalization. Then, in your own words, explain why the pattern works.

	Expression	Generalization	Why is this true?
a.	$x^{25} \cdot x^{40} = ?$	$x^m \cdot x^n = ?$	
b.	$\dfrac{x^{36}}{x^{13}} = ?$	$\dfrac{x^m}{x^n} = ?$	
c.	$(x^5)^{12} = ?$	$(x^m)^n = ?$	

3-14.   Describe everything you know about $\dfrac{x^m}{x^m}$. What is its value? How can you rewrite it using a single exponent? What new conclusions can you draw? Be prepared to explain your findings to the class.

3-15.   Problem 3-14 helped you recognize that $x^0 = 1$. Now you will similarly use division to explore the meaning of x^{-1}, x^{-2}, etc. Simplify each of the expressions below *twice*:

- Once by expanding the terms and simplifying.

- Again by using your new pattern for division with exponents.

Be ready to discuss the meaning of negative exponents with the class.

a. $\dfrac{x^4}{x^5}$ b. $\dfrac{x^2}{x^4}$ c. $\dfrac{x^7}{x^{10}}$

3-16.   Use your exponent patterns to rewrite each of the expressions below. For example, if the original expression has a negative exponent, then rewrite the expression so that it has no negative exponents, and vice versa. Also, if the expression contains multiplication or division, then use your exponent rules to simplify the expression.

a. k^{-5} b. m^0 c. $x^{-2} \cdot x^5$ d. $\dfrac{1}{p^2}$

e. $\dfrac{y^{-2}}{y^{-3}}$ f. $(x^{-2})^3$ g. $(a^2b)^{-1}$ h. $\dfrac{1}{x^{-1}}$

3-17.   EXPONENT CONCENTRATION

Split your team into two pairs and decide which is Team A and which is Team B. Your teacher will distribute a set of cards for a game described below.

- Arrange the cards face down in a rectangular grid.

- Team A selects and turns over two cards.

- If Team A thinks the values on the cards are equivalent for all values of x, they must justify this claim to Team B. If everyone in Team B agrees, Team A takes the pair. If the values are not equivalent, Team A returns both cards to their original position (face down). This is the end of the turn for Team A.

- Team B repeats the process.

- Teams alternate until no cards remain face down. The team with the most matches wins.

3-18. In your Learning Log, describe the meaning of zero and negative exponents. That is, explain how to interpret x^0 and x^{-1}. Title this entry "Zero and Negative Exponents" and include today's date.

METHODS AND MEANINGS

Laws of Exponents

In the expression x^3, x is the **base** and 3 is the **exponent**.

$$x^3 = x \cdot x \cdot x$$

The patterns that you have been using during this section of the book are called the **laws of exponents**. Here are the basic rules with examples:

Law	Examples	
$x^m x^n = x^{m+n}$ for all x	$x^3 x^4 = x^{3+4} = x^7$	$2^5 \cdot 2^{-1} = 2^4$
$\dfrac{x^m}{x^n} = x^{m-n}$ for $x \neq 0$	$x^{10} \div x^4 = x^{10-4} = x^6$	$\dfrac{5^4}{5^7} = 5^{-3}$
$(x^m)^n = x^{mn}$ for all x	$(x^4)^3 = x^{4 \cdot 3} = x^{12}$	$(10^5)^6 = 10^{30}$
$x^0 = 1$ for $x \neq 0$	$\dfrac{y^2}{y^2} = y^0 = 1$	$9^0 = 1$
$x^{-1} = \dfrac{1}{x}$ for $x \neq 0$	$\dfrac{1}{x^2} = (\dfrac{1}{x})^2 = (x^{-1})^2 = x^{-2}$	$3^{-1} = \dfrac{1}{3}$

Review & Preview

3-19. Which of the expressions below are equivalent to $16x^8$? Make sure you find *all* the correct answers!

a. $(16x^4)^2$

b. $8x^2 \cdot 2x^6$

c. $(2x^2)^4$

d. $(4x^4)^2$

e. $(2x^4)^4$

f. $(\frac{1}{16}x^{-8})^{-1}$

3-20. Rewrite each expression below without negative or zero exponents.

    a. 4^{-1} b. 7^0 c. 5^{-2} d. x^{-2}

3-21. With or without tiles, simplify, and solve each equation below for x. Record your work.

    a. $3x - 7 = 2$ b. $1 + 2x - x = x - 5 + x$

    c. $3 - 2x = 2x - 5$ d. $3 + 2x - (x + 1) = 3x - 6$

3-22. For the line graphed at right:

    a.   Determine the slope.

    b.   Find the equation of the line.

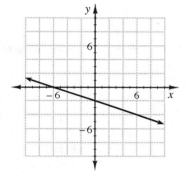

3-23. Write and solve an equation to represent the given situation. Be sure to define your variable.

Samantha currently has $1500 in the bank and is spending $35 per week. How many weeks will it take until her account is worth only $915?

3-24. Determine the equation of the line containing the points given in the table below.

x	−2	−1	2	3
y	−7	−4	5	8

3.2.1 How can I represent an equation?

Equations ↔ Algebra Tiles

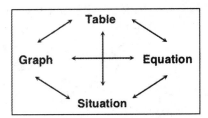

In Chapter 2, you learned about the multiple representations of a linear function, as shown in the web at right. Today you will look more at the equation ↔ situation connection. You will do this by using "algebra tiles" to model them. Algebra tiles are a way to represent an equation physically and visually.

3-25.   Your teacher will distribute a set of algebra tiles for your team to use during this course.

a.   The tiles have a positive side and a negative side. In this text the positive side will be the shaded side. Flip the tiles so that the positive side of each tile is facing up. Trace one of each of the six tiles provided by your teacher on your paper. Leave plenty of space between each tracing.

b.   The dimensions of some of the tiles are shown at right. Label the dimensions of all the tiles next to the tracings you made.

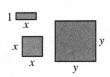

c.   The algebra tiles will be named according to each of their areas. Write the name of each tile in the center of your tracing with a colored pen or pencil. Make the name of the tile stand out.

d.   Below each tile write "P =" and then find the perimeter of each tile.

3-26.   JUMBLED PILES

a.   Your teacher will show you a jumbled pile of algebra tiles similar to the one below. Write the shortest description for the collection of tiles on your paper.

b.   Build each collection of tiles below. Then name the collection using the simplest algebraic expression you can.

   i. $3x + 5 + x^2 + y + 2x^2 + 2 + x$ *ii.* $3y + 2 + 2xy + 4x + y^2 + 4y + 1$

3-27.   For each of the shapes formed by algebra tiles below:

   • Use tiles to build the shape.

   • Sketch and label the shape on your paper.

   • Write a simplified expression that represents the perimeter.

   • Write a simplified expression that represents the area.

a. 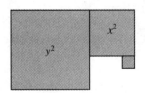   b.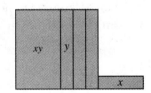

3-28.   NEGATIVES AND SUBTRACTION

Let's look at how you can use algebra tiles to represent "negative." Below are several tiles with their associated values. Note that the shaded tiles are positive and the un-shaded tiles are negative (as shown in the diagram at right, which will appear throughout the text as a reminder).

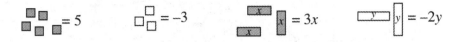

"Subtraction" can be represented with a tool called an **Equation Mat**. For example, the equation $-2x - 6 = x + 3 - (-x)$ can be represented by the Equation Mat below.

The double line represents the equal sign (=).

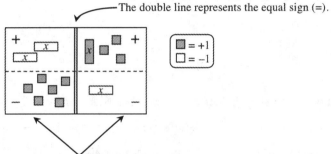

For each side of the equation, there is an addition and a subtraction region.

a.   What equation is represented by the Equation Mat at right? Do not simplify the equation; simply write down what you see.

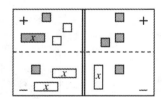

b.   What equation is represented by the Equation Mat at right? Do not simplify.

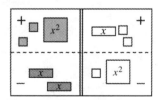

3-29.   SOLVING WITH AN EQUATION MAT

   a.   Obtain the Lesson 3.2.1B Resource Page ("Equation Mat") from your
        teacher. Build the equation from part (a) of problem 3-28 with tiles.

   b.   Read the Math Notes box at the end of this lesson to learn the "legal"
        moves you can make on an Equation Mat.

   c.   Solve the equation by making "legal" moves on your Equation Mat.
        Check your solution by evaluating the equation you wrote in part (a) of
        problem 3-28.

   d.   Build the equation from part (b) of problem 3-28. Solve the equation by
        using "legal" tile moves and check your solution.

3-30.   Using algebra tiles on an Equation Mat, create a physical representation of the
         equation $-x+(-3)-(1+(-x))=-x+2-(2x+(-x))$. Use "legal" moves to solve
         the equation and check your answer.

3-31.   Write an equation (without simplifying) for each representation below.
         Build each equation on an Equation Mat, solve for the variable by
         making "legal" moves, and check your solution.

         $\blacksquare = +1$
         $\square = -1$

   a.   b.   c.

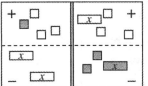   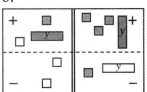   

3-32.   Build each equation below. Then use "legal" moves to simplify it, solve for x
         or y, and check your solution. Write down the algebraic result of each step and
         the legal tile move you made to get there.

   a. $-2x+2=-8$ b. $4x-2+x=2x+8+3x$

   c. $3y-9+y=6$ d. $9-(2+(-3y))=6+2y-(5+y)$

METHODS AND MEANINGS

Using Algebra Tiles to Solve Equations

Algebra tiles are a physical and visual representation of an equation. For example, the equation $2x + (-1) - (-x) - 3 = 6 - 2x$ can be represented by the Equation Mat below.

The double line represents the equal sign (=).

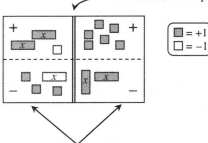

$\square = +1$
$\square = -1$

For each side of the equation, there is an addition and a subtraction region.

An Equation Mat can be used to represent the process of solving an equation. The "legal" moves on an Equation Mat correspond with the mathematical properties used to algebraically solve an equation.

"Legal" Tile Move	Corresponding Algebra
Group tiles that are alike together.	Combine like terms.
Flip all tiles from subtraction region to addition region.	Change subtraction to "adding the opposite."
Flip everything on both sides.	Multiply (or divide) both sides by −1.
Remove zero pairs (pairs of tiles that are opposites) within a region of the mat.	A number plus its opposite equals zero.
Place or remove the same tiles on or from both sides.	Add or subtract the same value from both sides.
Arrange tiles into equal-sized groups.	Divide both sides by the same value.

Core Connections Algebra

3-33. Copy and simplify the following expressions by combining like terms. Using or drawing sketches of algebra tiles may be helpful.

    a. $2x + 3x + 3 + 4x^2 + 10 + x$
    b. $4x + 4y^2 + y^2 + 9 + 10 + x + 3x$

    c. $2x^2 + 30 + 3x^2 + 4x^2 + 14 + x$
    d. $20 + 5xy + 4y^2 + 10 + y^2 + xy$

3-34. Solve each equation. Show the check to prove your answer is correct.

    a. $3x + 5 - x = x - 3$
    b. $5x - (x + 1) = 5 - 2x$

3-35. Fisher thinks that any two lines must have a point of intersection. Is he correct? If so, explain how you know. If not, produce a **counterexample**. That is, find two lines that do not have a point of intersection and explain how you know.

3-36. Write and solve an equation for the following problem.

In the last election, candidate C received 15,000 fewer votes than candidate B. If a total of 109,000 votes were cast, how many votes did candidate B receive?

3-37. Evaluate the following expressions.

    a. $10\frac{7}{9} + \left(-9\frac{2}{3}\right)$
    b. $-10\frac{7}{10} - 2\frac{3}{5}$

    c. $\left(4\frac{1}{2}\right)\left(-3\frac{3}{10}\right)$
    d. $-8\frac{3}{5} \div 1\frac{1}{5}$

3-38. Find the equation of the line based on the table.

x	2	4	6	8
y	2	3	4	5

3-39.   For each of the shapes formed by algebra tiles below:

- Sketch and label the shape on your paper and write an expression that represents the perimeter.

- Simplify your perimeter expression as much as possible.

a.

b.

c.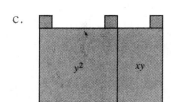

d.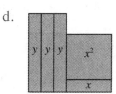

3-40.   Translate the Equation Mat at right into an equation. Do not simplify your equation. Remember that the double line represents "equals."

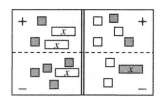

$\square = +1$
$\square = -1$

3-41.   Consider the rule $y = \frac{1}{2}x - 4$.

a.   Without graphing, find the x-intercept of $y = \frac{1}{2}x - 4$.

b.   Make a table and graph $y = \frac{1}{2}x - 4$ on graph paper.

c.   How could you find the x-intercept of $y = \frac{1}{2}x - 4$ with your graph from part (b)? How would you find it with the table? Explain.

3-42.   Evaluate each expression below for a when $a = \frac{2}{3}$, if possible.

a. $24a$ b. $3a$ c. $\frac{a}{0}$ d. $\frac{0}{a}$

3-43.   **Multiple Choice:** What is the slope of the line that goes through the points $(-7, 10)$ and $(1, 4)$?

a. $\frac{3}{4}$ b. $-\frac{3}{4}$ c. 1 d. -1

3-44.   Simplify each expression below, if possible.

a. $5x(3x)$ b. $5x + 3x$ c. $6x(x)$ d. $6x + x$

3.2.2 What can I do with rectangles?

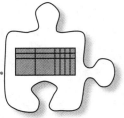

Exploring an Area Model

In the last lesson, you used tiles to represent algebraic equations. Today you will use algebra tiles again, but this time to represent expressions using multiplication.

3-45.   Your teacher will put this group of tiles on the overhead:

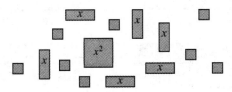

a.   Using your own tiles, arrange the same group of tiles into one large rectangle, with the x^2 tile in the lower left corner. On your paper, sketch what your rectangle looks like.

b.   What are the dimensions (length and width) of the rectangle you made? Label your sketch with its dimensions, then write the area of the rectangle as a *product*, that is, length · width.

c.   The area of a rectangle can also be written as the sum of the areas of all its parts. Write the area of the rectangle as the *sum* of its parts. Simplify your expression for the sum of the rectangle's parts.

d.   Write an equation that shows that the area written as a product is equivalent to the area written as a sum.

3-46.   Your teacher will assign several of the expressions below. For each expression, build a rectangle using all of the tiles, if possible. Sketch each rectangle, find its dimensions, and write an expression showing the equivalence of the area as a *sum* (like $x^2 + 5x + 6$) and as a *product* (like $(x+3)(x+2)$). If it is not possible to build a rectangle, explain why not.

a. $x^2 + 3x + 2$ b. $6x + 15$

c. $2x^2 + 7x + 6$ d. $xy + x + y + 1$

e. $2x^2 + 10x + 12$ f. $2y^2 + 6y$

g. $y^2 + xy + 2x + 2y$ h. $3x^2 + 4x + 1$

i. $x^2 + 2xy + y^2 + 3x + 3y + 2$ j. $2xy + 4y + x + 2$

3-47.   LEARNING LOG

Make a rectangle from any number of tiles. Your rectangle
must contain at least one of each of the following tiles: x^2,
y^2, xy, x, y, and 1. Sketch your rectangle in your
Learning Log and write its area as a product and as a sum.
Explain how you know that the product and sum are
equivalent. Title this entry "Area as a Product and as a
Sum" and label it with today's date.

METHODS AND **M**EANINGS

MATH NOTES

Multiplying Algebraic Expressions with Tiles

The area of a rectangle can be written two
different ways. It can be written as a *product* of
its width and length or as a *sum* of its parts. For example,
the area of the shaded rectangle at right can be written
two ways:

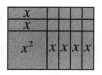

$$\underbrace{(x+4)(x+2)}_{\substack{length \quad width}} = \underbrace{x^2+6x+8}_{area}$$

area as a product = area as a sum

Review & Preview

3-48.   For the entire rectangle at right, find the area of each
part and then find the area of the whole.

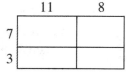

3-49.   Write the area of the rectangle at
right as a *product* and as a *sum*.

3-50.   When solving $\frac{x}{6} = \frac{5}{2}$ for x, Nathan noticed that x is divided by 6.

    a.   What can he do to both sides of the equation to get x alone?

    b.   Solve for x. Then check your solution in the original equation.

    c.   Use the same process to solve this equation for x: $\frac{x}{10} = \frac{2}{5}$.

3-51.   Jamila wants to play a game called "Guess My Line." She gives you the following hints: "Two points on my line are $(1, 1)$ and $(2, 4)$."

    a.   What is the slope of her line? A graph of the line may help.

    b.   What is the y-intercept of her line?

    c.   What is the equation of her line?

3-52.   A calculator manufacturer offers two different models for students. The company has sold 10,000 scientific calculators so far and continues to sell 1500 per month. It has also sold 18,000 graphical models and continues to sell 1300 of this model each month. When will the sales of scientific calculators equal the sales of graphical calculators?

3-53.   On graph paper, make an $x \rightarrow y$ table and graph $y = 2x^2 - x - 3$. Find its x- and y-intercepts.

3.2.3 How can I rewrite a product?

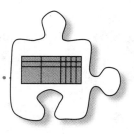

Multiplying Binomials and the Distributive Property

In Lesson 3.2.2, you made rectangles with algebra tiles and found the dimensions of the rectangles. Starting with the area of a rectangle as a sum, you wrote the area as a product. Today you will reverse the process, starting with the product and finding its area as a sum.

3-54. For each of the following rectangles, find the dimensions (length and width) and write the area as the *product* of the dimensions and as the *sum* of the tiles. Remember to combine like terms whenever possible.

a.

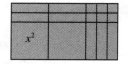

b.

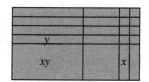

3-55. Your teacher will assign your team some of the expressions below. Use your algebra tiles to build rectangles with the given dimensions. Sketch each rectangle on your paper, label its dimensions, and write an equivalence statement for its area as a product and as a sum. Be prepared to share your solutions with the class.

a. $(x+3)(2x+1)$

b. $2x(x+5)$

c. $x(2x+y)$

d. $(2x+5)(x+y+2)$

e. $(2x+1)(2x+1)$

f. $(2x)(4x)$

g. $2(3x+5)$

h. $y(2x+y+3)$

3-56. With your team, examine the solutions you found for parts (b), (c), (g), and (h) of problem 3-55. This pattern is called the Distributive Property. Multiply the following expressions without using your tiles and simplify. Be ready to share your process with the class.

a. $2x(6x+5)$

b. $6(4x+1)$

c. $3y(4x+3)$

d. $7y(10x+11y)$

3-57.   CLOSED SETS

Whole numbers (positive integers and zero) are said to be a **closed set** under addition: if you add two whole numbers, you always get a whole number. Whole numbers are not a closed set under subtraction: if you subtract two whole numbers, you do not always get a whole number: $2 - 5 = -3$ (-3 is not a whole number).

a.   Investigate with your team whether the integers are a closed set under addition, and whether the integers are a closed set under subtraction. Give examples. If you find that integers are closed under either of the operations, can you explain how you know they are closed for *all* integers?

b.   Read the Math Notes box that follows. Are polynomials a closed set under addition? Are polynomials a closed set under subtraction? That is, if you add or subtract two polynomials, will you always get a polynomial as your answer? Give examples and explain how you know your answer is always true.

METHODS AND MEANINGS

Vocabulary for Expressions

MATH NOTES

A mathematical **expression** is a combination of numbers, variables, and operation symbols. Addition and subtraction separate expressions into parts called **terms**. For example, $4x^2 - 3x + 6$ is an expression. It has three terms: $4x^2$, $3x$, and 6. The **coefficients** are 4 and 3. 6 is called a **constant term**.

A one-variable **polynomial** is an expression which only has terms of the form:
$$(\text{any real number})x^{(\text{whole number})}$$

For example, $4x^2 - 3x^1 + 6x^0$ is a polynomial, so the simplified form, $4x^2 - 3x + 6$ is a polynomial.

The function $f(x) = 7x^5 + 2.5x^3 - \frac{1}{2}x + 7$ is a polynomial function.

The following are not polynomials: $2^x - 3$, $\frac{1}{x^2-2}$, and $\sqrt{x-2}$.

A **binomial** is a polynomial with only two terms, for example, $x^3 - 0.5x$ and $2x + 5$.

3-58.   Examine the rectangles formed with tiles below. For each figure, write its area as a product of the width and length and as a sum of its parts.

a.

b.

3-59.   Find the total area of each rectangle below. Each number inside the rectangle represents the area of that smaller rectangle, while each number along the side represents the length of that portion of the side.

a.

12	39

11

4

b.

3-60.   Solve each equation below for x. Then check your solutions.

a. $\frac{x}{8} = \frac{3}{4}$

b. $\frac{2}{5} = \frac{x}{40}$

c. $\frac{1}{8} = \frac{x}{12}$

d. $\frac{x}{10} = \frac{12}{15}$

3-61.   Mailboxes Plus sends packages overnight for $5 plus $0.25 per ounce. United Packages charges $2 plus $0.35 per ounce. Mr. Molinari noticed that his package would cost the same to mail using either service. How much does his package weigh?

3-62.   What is the equation of the line that has a y-intercept of $(0,-3)$ and passes through the point $(-9,-9)$?

3-63.   Evaluate each expression.

a. $-7\frac{5}{6} + \left(-7\frac{1}{4}\right)$ b. $-8\frac{1}{2} - \left(-3\frac{1}{4}\right)$ c. $\left(-2\frac{3}{7}\right)(-7)$ d. $-2\frac{1}{8} \div \frac{1}{5}$

$3.2.4$ How can I generalize the process?

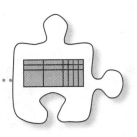

Using Generic Rectangles to Multiply

You have been using algebra tiles and the concept of area to multiply polynomial expressions. Today you will be introduced to a tool that will help you find the product of the dimensions of a rectangle. This will allow you to multiply expressions without tiles.

3-64.   Use the Distributive Property to find each product below.

    a. $6(-3x+2)$ b. $x^2(4x-2y)$

    c. $5t(10-3t)$ d. $-4w(8-6k^2+y)$

3-65.   Write the area as a *product* and as a *sum* for the rectangle shown at right.

3-66.   Now examine the following diagram. How is it similar to the set of tiles in problem 3-65? How is it different? Talk with your teammates and write down all of your observations.

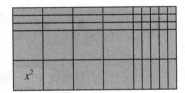

3-67.   Diagrams like the one in problem 3-66 are referred to as **generic rectangles**. Generic rectangles allow you to use an area model to multiply expressions without using the algebra tiles. Using this model, you can multiply with values that are difficult to represent with tiles.

Draw each of the following generic rectangles on your paper. Then find the area of each part and write the area of the whole rectangle as a *product* and as a *sum*.

a.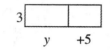

b.

c.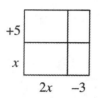

d.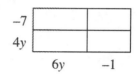

e.   How did you find the area of the individual parts of each generic rectangle?

3-68.   Multiply and simplify the following expressions using either a generic rectangle or the Distributive Property. For part (a), verify that your solution is correct by building a rectangle with algebra tiles.

a. $(x+5)(3x+2)$

b. $(2y-5)(5y+7)$

c. $3x(6x^2-11y)$

d. $(5w-2p)(3w+p-4)$

3-69.   THE GENERIC RECTANGLE CHALLENGE

Copy each of the generic rectangles below and fill in the missing dimensions and areas. Then write the entire area as a product and as a sum. Be prepared to share your reasoning with the class.

a.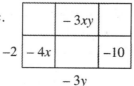

b.

c.

d.

MᴇᴛHODS AND MᴇANINGS

Properties of Real Numbers

MATH NOTES

The legal tiles moves have formal mathematical names, called the **properties of real numbers**.

The **Commutative Property** states that when *adding* or *multiplying* two or more numbers or terms, order is not important. That is:

$$a+b=b+a \quad \text{For example, } 2+7=7+2$$

$$a \cdot b = b \cdot a \quad \text{For example, } 3 \cdot 5 = 5 \cdot 3$$

However, *subtraction* and *division* are <u>not</u> commutative, as shown below.

$$7-2 \neq 2-7 \text{ since } 5 \neq -5$$

$$50 \div 10 \neq 10 \div 50 \text{ since } 5 \neq 0.2$$

The **Associative Property** states that when *adding* or *multiplying* three or more numbers or terms together, grouping is not important. That is:

$$(a+b)+c=a+(b+c) \quad \text{For example, } (5+2)+6=5+(2+6)$$

$$(a \cdot b) \cdot c = a \cdot (b \cdot c) \quad \text{For example, } (5 \cdot 2) \cdot 6 = 5 \cdot (2 \cdot 6)$$

However, *subtraction* and *division* are <u>not</u> associative, as shown below.

$$(5-2)-3 \neq 5-(2-3) \text{ since } 0 \neq 6 \qquad (20 \div 4) \div 2 \neq 20 \div (4 \div 2) \text{ since } 2.5 \neq 10$$

The **Identity Property of Addition** states that adding zero to any expression gives the same expression. That is:

$$a+0=a \qquad \text{For example, } 6+0=6$$

The **Identity Property of Multiplication** states that multiplying any expression by one gives the same expression. That is:

$$1 \cdot a = a \qquad \text{For example, } 1 \cdot 6 = 6$$

The **Additive Inverse Property** states that for every number a there is a number $-a$ such that $a+(-a)=0$. A common name used for the additive inverse is the **opposite**. That is, $-a$ is the opposite of a. For example, $3+(-3)=0$ and $-5+5=0$.

The **Multiplicative Inverse Property** states that for every nonzero number a there is a number $\frac{1}{a}$ such that $a \cdot \frac{1}{a} = 1$. A common name used for the multiplicative inverse is the **reciprocal**. That is, $\frac{1}{a}$ is the reciprocal of a. For example, $6 \cdot \frac{1}{6} = 1$.

3-70.   Use a generic rectangle to multiply the following expressions. Write each solution both as a sum and as a product.

   a. $(2x+5)(x+6)$

   b. $(m-3)(3m+5)$

   c. $(12x+1)(x^2-5)$

   d. $(3-5y)(2+y)$

3-71.   Find the rule for the pattern represented at right.

Figure 1

3-72.   Harry the Hungry Hippo is munching on the lily pads in his pond. When he arrived at the pond, there were 20 lily pads, but he is eating 4 lily pads an hour. Heinrick the Hungrier Hippo found a better pond with 29 lily pads! He eats 7 lily pads every hour.

   a.   If Harry and Heinrick start eating at the same time, when will their ponds have the same number of lily pads remaining?

   b.   How many lily pads will be left in each pond at that time?

3-73.   Graph each equation below on the same set of axes and label the point of intersection with its coordinates.

$$y = 2x + 3 \qquad y = x + 1$$

3-74.   Are the odd numbers a closed set under addition? Justify your conclusion.

3-75.   Simplify each of the expressions below. Your final simplification should not contain negative exponents.

   a. $(5x^3)(-3x^{-2})$

   b. $(4p^2q)^3$

   c. $\dfrac{3m^7}{m^{-1}}$

Core Connections Algebra

3.3.1 What if an equation has a product?

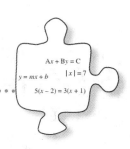

Solving Equations With Multiplication and Absolute Value

Now that you know how to multiply algebraic expressions, you can solve equations that involve multiplication. You will also solve equations that have an absolute value in them.

3-76. Review what you learned in Lesson 3.2.4 by multiplying each expression below. First decide if you will multiply each expression using the Distributive Property or using a generic rectangle. Remember to simplify your result.

a. $(6x-11)(2x+5)$

b. $-2x^2(15x^2-3t)$

c. $(6-y)(y+2)$

d. $16(3-m^2)$

3-77. Work with your team to solve each of these equations. Use the Distributive Property or draw generic rectangles to help you rewrite the products. Be sure to record your algebra work for each step.

a. $2(y-2)=-6$

b. $5x^2+43=(x-1)(5x+6)$

c. $(x+3)(x+4)=(x+1)(x+2)$

d. $2(x+1)+3=3(x-1)$

3-78. ABSOLUTE VALUE EQUATIONS

Find as many solutions to the following equations as you can.

a. $|x|=5$

b. $|x|=133$

c. $|x|=-2$

d. $|x-7|=10$

3-79. Solve $|3x-5|=16$. Work with your team to organize your work so that anyone could follow along to find both solutions.

3-80. Solve $|7-8x|=1$. Record your steps.

METHODS AND MEANINGS

The Distributive Property

The **Distributive Property** states that for any three terms a, b, and c:

$$a(b + c) = ab + ac$$

That is, when a multiplies a group of terms, such as $(b + c)$, then it multiplies *each* term of the group. For example, when multiplying $2x(3x + 4y)$, the $2x$ multiplies both the $3x$ and the $4y$. This can be shown with **algebra tiles** or in a **generic rectangle** (see below).

	x	x	x	y	y	y	y
x	x^2	x^2	x^2	xy	xy	xy	xy
x	x^2	x^2	x^2	xy	xy	xy	xy

$2x$	$2x \cdot 3x$	$2x \cdot 4y$
	$3x$	$4y$

$2x(3x + 4y)$
$2x(3x) + 2x(4y)$, simplifying results in

The $2x$ multiplies each term.

Review & Preview

3-81. Find each of the following products by drawing and labeling a generic rectangle or by using the Distributive Property.

a. $-4y(5x + 8y)$ b. $9x(-4 + 10y)$ c. $(x^2 - 2)(x^2 + 3x + 5)$

Core Connections Algebra

3-82. Is the set of even numbers closed under addition? That is, if you add two even numbers, do you *always* get an even number? Is the set of odd numbers closed under addition? Explain your answers.

3-83. Find the dimensions of the generic rectangle at right. Then write an equivalency statement (length · width = area) of the area as a product and as a sum.

x^2	$-5x$
$3x$	-15

3-84. Solve for x. Use any method. Check your solutions by testing them in the original equation.

a. $|x-3|=5$

b. $5|x|=35$

c. $|x+1|=2$

d. $|x+3|=-2$

3-85. Copy and complete each of the Diamond Problems below. The pattern used in the Diamond Problems is shown at right.

a.

b.

c.

d.

3-86. If $f(x)=7+|x|$ and $g(x)=x^3-5$, then find:

a. $f(-5)$

b. $g(4)$

c. $f(0)$

d. $f(2)$

e. $g(-2)$

f. $g(0)$

$3.3.2$ How can I change it to $y = mx + b$ form?

Working With Multi-Variable Equations

So far in this course you have solved several types of equations with one variable. Today you will apply your equation-solving skills to rewrite equations with two or more variables.

3-87.   You now have a lot of experience working with equations that compare two quantities. For example, while working on the Big Race, you found relationships of the form $y = mx + b$, which compared x (time in seconds) with y (distance in meters). If a participant's race can be modeled with the equation $y = 3x + 4$:

   a.   How much of a head start did the participant get? How can you tell from the equation?

   b.   What was participant's rate of speed? That is, how fast did they go? Justify your answer.

3-88.   CHANGING FORMS

You could find the slope and starting value for $y = 3x + 4$ quickly because the equation is in $y = mx + b$ form. But what if the equation is in a different form? Explore this situation below.

   a.   The line $-6x + 2y = 10$ is written in **standard form**. Can you easily tell what the slope of the line is? Its starting value? Predict these values.

   b.   The equation $-6x + 2y = 10$ is shown on the Equation Mat at right. Set up this equation on your Equation Mat using tiles. Using only "legal" moves, rearrange the tiles to get y by itself on the left side of the mat. Record each of your moves algebraically.

   c.   Now use your result from part (b) to find the slope and starting value of the line $-6x + 2y = 10$. Did your result match your prediction in part (a)?

3-89.   Many times in real-world situations a formula with more than one variable may not be in the form you need. The previous problem showed that standard form linear equations do not show the slope and y-intercept until they are solved for y, that is, until y is isolated on one side of the equation. The formulas in this problem are used in many different jobs. Sometime you need to solve them for a different variable in order for the formula to be useful. Solve each formula for the given variable.

a. $W = Fd$. Find the force, F, needed to move a piano given the amount of work applied, W, and distance moved, d.

b. $F = \frac{9C}{5} + 32$. Find the temperature in Celsius, C, when given the temperature in degrees Fahrenheit, F.

c. $\rho = \frac{m}{V}$. The symbol ρ is a letter of the Greek alphabet. Sometimes scientists use Greek letters for variables. Find the mass, m, of a precious stone given its density, ρ, and volume, V.

d. $I = \frac{W}{12.6r^2}$. Find, r, the distance to the light bulb, given I, the intensity of light, and W, the wattage of the light bulb.

3-90.   Solve each of the following equations for the indicated variable. Use your Equation Mat if it is helpful. Write down each of your steps algebraically.

a.   Solve for y: $2(y-3) = 4$

b.   Solve for x: $2x - 6y = 12$

c.   Solve for y: $6x + y = 2y + 8$

d.   Solve for x: $3(2x + 4) = 2 + 6x + 10$

3-91.   Solve each of the following equations for the indicated variable. Record your work.

a.   Solve for x: $y = -2x + 5$

b.   Solve for p: $m = 7 - 3(p - m)$

c.   Solve for y: $x^2 + 4y = (x + 6)(x - 2)$

d.   Solve for q: $4(q - 8) = 7q + 5$

3-92.   MORE CLOSED SETS

In Lesson 3.2.3 you were told that whole numbers are said to be a **closed set**
under addition, but are not closed under subtraction. Then you discovered that
integers and polynomials are a closed set under both addition and subtraction.
With your team, explore closure under multiplication as follows:

a.   Investigate with your team if the integers are a closed set under
multiplication. Give examples of your conclusion. If you find that
integers are closed under multiplication, can you explain how you know
all integers are closed under multiplication?

b.   Are one-variable polynomials closed under multiplication? In other
words, if you multiply two polynomials that both have the same variable,
will you always get a polynomial as your answer? Give examples and
explain how you know your answer is true for *all* one-variable
polynomials.

As a starting point, you may want to think about some of the products
below.

i. $(x+2)(3x+4)$ ii. $9x(6-x^2)$

iii. $(3x^2+3)(3x^2+x+1)$ iv. $x(2x^2-12x+7)$

MATH NOTES

METHODS AND MEANINGS

Linear Equations from Slope and/or Points

If you know the slope, m, and y-intercept, $(0, b)$, of a line, you can write the equation of the line as $y = mx + b$.

You can also find the equation of a line when you know the slope and one point on the line. To do so, rewrite $y = mx + b$ with the known slope and substitute the coordinates of the known point for x and y. Then solve for b and write the new equation.

For example, find the equation of the line with a slope of -4 that passes through the point $(5, 30)$. Rewrite $y = mx + b$ as $y = -4x + b$. Substituting $(5, 30)$ into the equation results in $30 = -4(5) + b$. Solve the equation to find $b = 50$. Since you now know the slope and y-intercept of the line, you can write the equation of the line as $y = -4x + 50$.

Similarly you can write the equation of the line when you know two points. First use the two points to find the slope. Then substitute the known slope and either of the known points into $y = mx + b$. Solve for b and write the new equation.

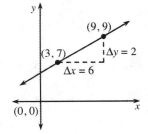

For example, find the equation of the line through $(3, 7)$ and $(9, 9)$. The slope is $\frac{\Delta y}{\Delta x} = \frac{2}{6} = \frac{1}{3}$. Substituting $m = \frac{1}{3}$ and $(x, y) = (3, 7)$ into $y = mx + b$ results in $7 = \frac{1}{3}(3) + b$. Then solve the equation to find $b = 6$. Since you now know the slope and y-intercept, you can write the equation of the line as $y = \frac{1}{3}x + 6$.

Review & Preview

3-93.   Solve each equation. Be sure to find all possible answers and check your solutions.

a. $|x| = 7$

b. $|2x| = 32$

c. $|x + 7| = 10$

d. $|x| = 53.1$

3-94.   Solve each equation below for the indicated variable.

   a. $3x - 2y = 18$ for x b. $3x - 2y = 18$ for y

   c. $rt = d$ for r d. $C = 2\pi r$ for r

3-95.   Evaluate the following expressions.

   a. $-3\frac{2}{9} + 8\frac{7}{9}$ b. $-7\frac{2}{7} - 4\frac{1}{5}$

   c. $1\frac{5}{7} \cdot 3\frac{6}{7}$ d. $-8\frac{1}{7} \div -5\frac{5}{9}$

3-96.   Find the equation of each line described below.

   a.   A line with slope of 0 that passes through the point $(6, -11)$.

   b.   A line that passes through the points $(12, 12)$ and $(20, 6)$.

3-97.   Graph the lines $y = -4x + 3$ and $y = x - 7$ on the same set of axes. Then find their point of intersection.

3-98.   Simplify each expression using the laws of exponents.

   a. $(x^2)(x^2 y^3)$ b. $\frac{x^3 y^4}{x^2 y^3}$

   c. $(2x^2)(-3x^4)$ d. $(2x)^3$

3-99.   One way to solve absolute value equations is to think about "looking inside" the absolute value. The "inside" must be positive or negative, so you should solve the equation both ways. For example, you could record your steps as shown at right.

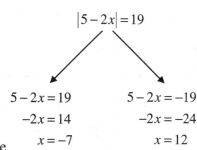

   Solve each equation. Be sure to find all possible answers and check your solutions.

   a. $|9 + 3x| = 39$ b. $|2x + 1| = 10$

   c. $|-3x + 9| = 10$ d. $|3.2x - 4| = -5.7$

3-100.   Find each of the following products by drawing and labeling a generic rectangle or by using the Distributive Property.

a. $5x(x-6)$

b. $-9y(6-3y)$

3-101.   For each generic rectangle below, find the dimensions (length and width). Then write the area as a product of the dimensions and as a sum.

a.

$2x^2$	$10x$

b.

$2x^2$	$10x$
$3x$	15

3-102.   Solve each of the following equations. Be sure to show your work carefully and check your answers.

a. $2(3x-4)=22$

b. $6(2x-5)=-(x+4)$

c. $2-(y+2)=3y$

d. $3+4(x+1)=159$

3-103.   Multiply each of the following expressions. Show all of your work.

a. $(x+3)(4x+5)$

b. $(-2x^2-4x)(3x+4)$

c. $(3y-8)(-x+y)$

d. $(y-4)(3x+5y-2)$

3-104.   Solve each of the following equations for the indicated variable. Show all of your steps.

a. $y=2x-5$ for x

b. $p=-3w+9$ for w

c. $2m-6=4n+4$ for m

d. $3x-y=-2y$ for y

3.3.3 What kinds of equations can I solve now?

Summary of Solving Equations

You have been developing your equation-solving skills in this chapter. Today you will practice solving several types of equations. At the end of the lesson, you will summarize everything you know about solving equations.

3-105. Your teacher will explain the way you will work today on the problems below. As you work, be sure to record all of your steps carefully. Check your solutions, if possible.

a. Solve for c: $E = mc^2$

b. Solve for m: $a = \frac{E}{m}$

c. Solve for x: $-6 = -6(3x - 8)$

d. Solve for y: $3x + 6y = 24$

e. Solve for x: $2 - 3(2x - 1) = 17$

f. Solve for y: $|3 - 5y| = 3$

g. Solve for x: $y = -3x + 4$

h. Solve for x: $x(2x - 1) = 2x^2 + 5x - 12$

i. Solve for w: $2(v - 3) = 1 - (w + 4)$

j. Solve for x: $4x(x + 1) = (2x - 3)(2x + 5)$

3-106. LEARNING LOG

In your Learning Log, write a letter to Clarissa, a new student in class, explaining everything you have learned about how to solve equations. Clarissa does not have algebra tiles, so you will need to show her how to solve *without* the tiles. Make up examples that show all of the different equation-solving skills you have. Be sure to explain your ideas to her thoroughly so she will know what to do on her own. Title this entry "Summary of Solving Equations" and include today's date.

METHODS AND MEANINGS

MATH NOTES

Using Generic Rectangles to Multiply

A generic rectangle can be used to find products because it helps to organize the different areas that make up the total rectangle. For example, to multiply $(2x+5)(x+3)$, a generic rectangle can be set up and completed as shown below. Notice that each product in the generic rectangle represents the area of that part of the rectangle.

	2x	+5
x		
+3		

→

	2x	+5
x	$2x^2$	5x
+3	6x	15

$(2x+5)(x+3) = 2x^2 + 11x + 15$

area as a product   area as a sum

Note that while a generic rectangle helps organize the problem, its size and scale are not important. Some students find it helpful to write the dimensions on the rectangle twice, that is, on both pairs of opposite sides.

Review & Preview

3-107. Solve each equation.

a. $3(x-2) = -6$

b. $2(x+1)+3 = 3(x-1)$

c. $(x+2)(x+3) = (x+1)(x+5)$

d. $|x-5| = 8$

3-108. Find the equation of the line based on the table.

x	3	−2	5	12
y	4	−11	10	31

3-109. Find an equation of the line with slope $\frac{1}{5}$ passing through the point $(10, 9)$.

3-110. This problem is a checkpoint for operations with rational numbers. It will be referred to as Checkpoint 3.

Compute each of the following problems with fractions.

a. $-\frac{2}{3}+\left(-\frac{1}{8}\right)$

b. $3\frac{1}{2}-\left(-1\frac{1}{3}\right)$

c. $\left(-4\frac{1}{5}\right)\left(-\frac{1}{3}\right)$

d. $\left(-\frac{2}{3}\right)\div\left(\frac{1}{4}\right)$

e. $1\frac{3}{4}+\left(-5\frac{1}{3}\right)$

f. $\left(-2\frac{2}{3}\right)\div\left(-1\frac{1}{6}\right)$

Check your answers by referring to the Checkpoint 3 materials located at the back of your book.

If you needed help solving these problems correctly, then you need more practice. Review the Checkpoint 3 materials and try the practice problems. Also consider getting help outside of class time. From this point on, you will be expected to do problems like these quickly and easily.

3-111. Copy and complete these generic rectangles on your paper. Then write the area of each rectangle as a product of the length and width and as a sum of the parts.

a.

6

13x   −21

b.

x

−5

x   +3

c.

16x² −24x 4

d.

3x

−2

x   + 4

3-112. Simplify using only positive exponents.

a. $(3x^2y)(5x)$

b. $(x^2y^3)(x^{-2}y^{-2})$

c. $\frac{x^3}{x^{-2}}$

d. $(2x^{-1})^3$

130

Core Connections Algebra

Chapter 3 Closure   What have I learned?

Reflection and Synthesis

The activities below offer you a chance to reflect about what you have learned during this chapter. As you work, look for concepts that you feel very comfortable with, ideas that you would like to learn more about, and topics you need more help with. Look for connections between ideas as well as connections with material you learned previously.

①   TEAM BRAINSTORM

What have you studied in this chapter? What ideas were important in what you learned? With your team, brainstorm a list. Be as detailed as you can. To help get you started, a list of Learning Log entries and Math Notes boxes are below.

What topics, ideas, and words that you learned *before* this chapter are connected to the new ideas in this chapter? Again, be as detailed as you can.

Now consider the Standards for Mathematical Practice. Obtain the Chapter 3 Closure Resource Page: Standards for Mathematical Practice from your teacher. What Mathematical Practices did you use in this chapter? When did you use them? Give specific examples.

How long can you make your list? Challenge yourselves. Be prepared to share your team's ideas with the class.

Learning Log Entries
- Lesson 3.1.2 – Zero and Negative Exponents
- Lesson 3.2.2 – Area as a Product and as a Sum
- Lesson 3.3.3 – Summary of Solving Equations

Math Notes
- Lesson 3.1.2 – Laws of Exponents
- Lesson 3.2.1 – Using Algebra Tiles to Solve Equations
- Lesson 3.2.2 – Multiplying Algebraic Expressions with Tiles
- Lesson 3.2.3 – Vocabulary for Expressions
- Lesson 3.2.4 – Properties of Real Numbers
- Lesson 3.3.1 – The Distributive Property
- Lesson 3.3.2 – Linear Equations From Slope an/or Points
- Lesson 3.3.3 – Using Generic Rectangles to Multiply

②   **MAKING CONNECTIONS**

Below is a list of the vocabulary used in this chapter. Make sure that you are familiar with all of these words and know what they mean. Refer to the glossary or index for any words that you do not yet understand.

area	terms	Distributive Property
polynomial	expression	"legal" moves
generic rectangles	integer	dimensions
equation	product	algebra tiles
closed sets	sum	**solution**
solve	standard form	evaluate
binomial	length · width	base
exponent		

Make a concept map showing all of the connections you can find among the key words and ideas listed above. To show a connection between two words, draw a line between them and explain the connection, as shown in the model below. A word can be connected to any other word as long as you can justify the connection. For each key word or idea, provide an example or sketch that shows the idea.

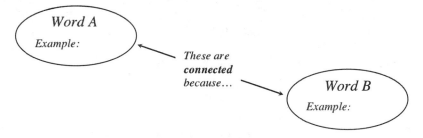

Your teacher may provide you with vocabulary cards to help you get started. If you use the cards to plan your concept map, be sure either to re-draw your concept map on your paper or to glue the vocabulary cards to a poster with all of the connections explained for others to see and understand.

While you are making your map, your team may think of related words or ideas that are not listed here. Be sure to include these ideas on your concept map.

③   PORTFOLIO: EVIDENCE OF MATHEMATICAL PROFICIENCY

Solve the equations in problem 3-105. If you have already solved them, review your work and revise it as needed. Record your work neatly and justify each step as evidence of the mathematics you are now able to do. Carefully show how you check your solutions.

Then show how you applied your understanding of area to use an area model to multiply expressions. For example, the area of the rectangle at right represents the product $(4x + 3)(2x - 7)$. Copy and complete the generic rectangle and write its area as a sum.

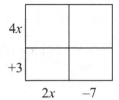

Another student in your class thinks that $(x + y) = x^2 + y^2$. Justify why $(x + y)^2 = x^2 + 2xy + y^2$ so that they are convinced that your answer is correct.

Extend this idea: What if one of the expressions being multiplied has three terms? How can a generic rectangle be used to multiply two expressions such as $(x^2 - 3)(3y + 2x + 1)$?

Now consider the Standards for Mathematical Practice that follow. What Mathematical Practices did you use in this chapter? When did you use them? Give specific examples.

BECOMING MATHEMATICALLY PROFICIENT
The Common Core State Standards For Mathematical Practice

This book focuses on helping you use some very specific
Mathematical Practices. The Mathematical Practices describe ways in
which mathematically proficient students should increasingly engage
with mathematics throughout the year.

Make sense of problems and persevere in solving them:

Making sense of problems and persevering in solving them
means that you can solve realistic problems that are full of
different kinds of mathematics. These types of problems are not
routine, simple, or typical. Instead, they combine lots of math
ideas and real-life situations. You have to stick with challenging problems,
trying different strategies and using all of the resources available to you.

Reason abstractly and quantitatively:

Throughout this course, you are first introduced to new math ideas by discovering
them through real-life situations. Seeing math ideas within a context helps you make
sense of things. Once you learn about a math idea in a practical way, you are able to
think about the concept more generally, or **"reason abstractly."** At that point, you
are often able to use numbers and math symbols to represent the math idea. This is
called **"reasoning quantitatively."**

Construct viable arguments and critique the reasoning of others:

An important practice of mathematics is to **construct viable arguments and critique
the reasoning of others**. In this course, you regularly share information, opinions,
and expertise with your study team. You and your study teams use higher-order,
critical-thinking skills any time you provide clarification, build on each other's ideas,
analyze a problem and come to consensus, and productively criticize each other's
ideas.

Model with mathematics:

When you **model with mathematics** you are taking a complex situation and using
mathematics to represent it, often by making assumptions and approximations to
simplify the situation. Modeling allows you to analyze and describe the situation and
make predictions. For example, you model when you write an equation, or make
graphs or tables or diagrams, to describe a situation. In situations involving the
variability of data, you learn that although a model may not be perfect, it can still be
very useful for describing data and making predictions. In the process of analyzing,
you go back and improve your model by revising your assumptions and
approximations.

Use appropriate tools strategically:

Throughout this course, you have to **use appropriate tools strategically**. Examples of tools include rulers, scissors, diagrams, graph paper, blocks, tiles, calculators, computer software, and websites. Sometimes, different teams decide to use different tools to solve the same problem. Frequently, the lesson concludes with a discussion about which tools are most efficient and productive to solve a given problem.

Attend to precision:

To **attend to precision** means that when solving problems, you need to pay close attention to the details. For example, you need to be aware of the units, or how many digits your answer requires, or how to choose a scale and label your graph. You may need to convert the units to be consistent. Other times, you need to go back and check whether a numerical solution makes sense in the context of the problem.

You need to **attend to the precision** when you communicate your ideas to others. Using the appropriate vocabulary and mathematical language can help to make your ideas and reasoning more understandable to others. This is an important academic and mathematical skill.

Look for and make use of structure:

Looking for and making use of structure is an important part of this course. By being involved in analyzing the structure and in the actual development of math concepts, you gain a deeper, more conceptual, understanding than just being told what the structure is and how to do problems. You often use this practice to bring closure to an investigation.

There are many concepts that you learn by looking at the underlying structure of a math idea and thinking about how it connects to other ideas you have already learned. For example, you use area models to understand the structure of multiplying binomials and connecting that structure to the Distributive Property. You understand the underlying structure of $y = mx + b$ by analyzing growth and starting point of linear functions.

Look for and express regularity in repeated reasoning:

Look for and express regularity in repeated reasoning means that when you are investigating a new mathematical concept, you notice if calculations are repeated in a pattern. Then you look for a way to generalize the method to other situations, or you look for shortcuts. For example, when working with negative or fractional exponents, you repeat exponent patterns that you already know to construct a method for simplifying these types of exponent problems.

WHAT HAVE I LEARNED?

Most of the problems in this section represent typical problems found in this chapter. They serve as a gauge for you. You can use them to determine which types of problems you can do well and which types of problems require further study and practice. Even if your teacher does not assign this section, it is a good idea to try these problems and find out for yourself what you know and what you still need to work on.

Solve each problem as completely as you can. The table at the end of the closure section has answers to these problems. It also tells you where you can find additional help and practice with problems like these.

CL 3-113. Two brothers, Martin and Horace, are in their backyard. Horace is taking down a brick wall on one side of the yard while Martin is building a brick wall on the other side. Martin lays 2 bricks every minute. Meanwhile, Horace takes down 3 bricks each minute from his wall. They both start working at the same time. It takes Horace 55 minutes to finish tearing down his wall.

    a. How many bricks were originally in the wall that Horace started tearing down?

    b. Represent this situation with equations, tables, and a graph.

    c. When did the two walls have the same number of bricks?

CL 3-114. Rewrite each of these products as a sum.

    a. $6x(2x + y - 5)$ b. $(2x^2 - 11)(x^2 + 4)$

    c. $(7x)(2xy)$ d. $(x - 2)(3 + y)$

CL 3-115. Find the missing areas and dimensions for **each generic** rectangle below. Then write each area as a sum and as a **product.**

a.
$$8x \;|\; 16x^2 \qquad | \qquad 1 \qquad | \qquad 1$$

(generic rectangle: top-left cell $16x^2$ with $8x$ to the left, bottom cell labeled 1, bottom dimension 1)

b.
(generic rectangle: top-left cell with $10y$ to the left, bottom-right cell $-12x$, bottom dimensions $2y$ and -3)

CL 3-116. For each equation below, solve for x.

a. $(x-1)(x+7) = (x+1)(x-3)$ b. $2x - 5(x+4) = -2(x+3)$

c. $|x+7| = 11$ d. $|2x-3| = 23$

CL 3-117. For each equation below, solve for y.

a. $6x - 2y = 4$ b. $6x + 3y = 4x - 2y + 8$

c. Find the slope and y-intercepts for **the equations** in parts (a) and (b).

CL 3-118. Simplify each expression.

a. $(5x^3)^2$ b. $\dfrac{14a^3b^2}{21a^4b}$ c. $2m^3n^2 \cdot 3mn^4$

CL 3-119. Determine the equation of each line from **the given representation.**

a.
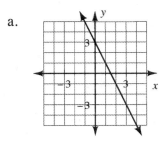

b. A line with a slope $-\frac{2}{3}$ and passes through the point $(-3, 4)$.

c.

x	-4	-3	-2	-1
y	-11	-9	-7	-5

CL 3-120.   Evaluate the following expressions.

       a. $-8\frac{2}{9}+7\frac{3}{5}$ b. $-4\frac{3}{8}-5\frac{3}{8}$

       c. $10\frac{3}{4}\left(-8\frac{4}{9}\right)$ d. $-8\frac{3}{4}\div\left(-\frac{5}{7}\right)$

CL 3-121.   Using your knowledge of exponents, rewrite each expression below so that there are no negative exponents or parentheses remaining.

       a. $\frac{4x^{18}}{(2x^{22})^0}$ b. $(s^4tu^2)(s^7t^{-1})$

       c. $(3w^{-2})^4$ d. m^{-3}

CL 3-122.   Check your answers using the table at the end of the closure section. Which problems do you feel confident about? Which problems were hard? Use the table to make a list of topics you need help on and a list of topics you need to practice more.

Answers and Support for Closure Activity #4
What Have I Learned?

Note: MN = Math Note, LL = Learning Log

Problem	Solution	Need Help?	More Practice
CL 3-113.	a. $55(3) = 165$ bricks	Chapter 2	Problems CL 2-104, CL 2-105, CL 2-106, 3-52, 3-61, and 3-72
	b. Martin's rule: $y = 2x$	LL: 2.3.1	

Horace's rule: $y = 165 - 3x$

Martin's table:

Min.	Bricks
0	0
1	2
2	4
...	...
56	112
57	114

Horace's table:

Min.	Bricks
0	165
1	162
2	159
...	...
54	3
55	0

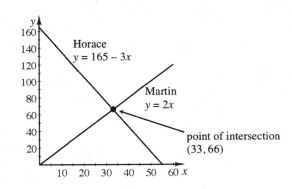

c. After 33 minutes, they will each have 66 bricks.

Problem	Solution	Need Help?	More Practice
CL 3-114.	a. $12x^2 + 6xy - 30x$	Section 3.2	Problems 3-70, 3-81, 3-100, and 3-103
	b. $2x^4 - 3x^2 - 44$	MN: 3.2.2, 3.3.1, and 3.3.3	
	c. $14x^2y$		
	d. $3x + xy - 6 - 2y$	LL: 3.2.2	

Problem	Solution	Need Help?	More Practice
CL 3-115.	a. $(2x+1)(1+8x) = 16x^2 + 10x + 1$ $\begin{array}{c c c} & 2x & 16x^2 \\ 2x & & \\ 1 & 1 & 8x \\ & 1 & 8x \end{array}$	Lesson 3.2.4 MN: 3.3.3 LL: 3.2.2	Problems 3-83, 3-101, and 3-111
	b. $(2y-3)(4x+5) =$ $8xy - 12x + 10y - 15$ $\begin{array}{c c c} & 8xy & -12x \\ 4x & & \\ 5 & 10y & -15 \\ & 2y & -3 \end{array}$		
CL 3-116.	a. $x = \frac{1}{2}$ b. $x = -14$ c. $x = 4, -18$ d. $x = 13, -10$	Lesson 3.3.1 LL: 3.3.3	Problems 3-84, 3-93, 3-102, and 3-107
CL 3-117.	a. $y = 3x - 2$ b. $y = -\frac{2}{5}x + \frac{8}{5}$ c. Part (a): $m = 3, b = -2$ Part (b): $m = -\frac{2}{5}, b = \frac{8}{5}$	Lessons 2.1.4 and 3.3.2 LL: 2.1.4	Problems 3-94 and 3-104
CL 3-118.	a. $25x^6$ b. $\frac{2b}{3a}$ c. $6m^4n^6$	Lesson 3.1.1 MN: 3.1.2	Problems 3-6, 3-12, 3-19, 3-75(b), and 3-98
CL 3-119.	a. $y = -2x + 3$ b. $y = -\frac{2}{3}x + 2$ c. $y = 2x - 3$	Chapter 2 MN: 2.1.4 and 2.2.2 LL: 2.1.3, 2.1.4, 2.3.1, and 2.3.2	Problems 2-73, 2-100, CL 2-101, 3-22, 3-24, 3-38, 3-51, 3-62, and 3-108
CL 3-120.	a. $-\frac{28}{45}$ b. $-9\frac{3}{4}$ c. $-90\frac{7}{9}$ d. $12\frac{1}{4}$	Checkpoint 3	Problems 3-11, 3-37, 3-63, 3-95, and 3-110
CL 3-121.	a. $4x^{18}$ b. $s^{11}u^2$ c. $\frac{81}{w^8}$ d. $\frac{1}{m^3}$	Section 3.1 MN: 3.1.2 LL: 3.1.2	Problems 3-20, 3-75 (a) and (c), and 3-112

SYSTEMS OF EQUATIONS

CHAPTER 4

In Chapter 2, you studied the connections between the multiple representations of linear equations and learned how to write equations from situations. In this chapter, you will learn how to solve word problems by writing a pair of equations, called a system of equations. Then you will solve the system of equations with the same multiple representations you used for solving linear equations: table, graph, and by manipulating the equations.

Along the way, you will develop ways to solve different forms of systems, and will learn how to recognize when one method may be more efficient than another. By the end of this chapter, you will know multiple ways to find the point of intersection of two lines and will be able to solve systems that arise from different situations.

Guiding Question

Mathematically proficient students attend to precision.

As you work through this chapter, ask yourself:

Am I using correct vocabulary and clear explanations in discussions with my team, while paying attention to small details?

Chapter Outline

Section 4.1 In this section, you will write and solve mathematical sentences (such as one- and two-variable equations) to solve situational word problems.

$6x + 2y = 4$

$y = 2x - 7$

Section 4.2 You will develop methods to solve systems of equations in different forms. You will learn what it means for a system to have no solutions or infinite solutions. You will also find ways to know which solving method is most efficient and accurate.

Section 4.3 Section 4.3 provides an opportunity for you to review and extend what you learned in Chapters 1 through 4. You will make important connections between solving equations, multiple representations, and systems of equations.

4.1.1 How can I use variables to solve problems?

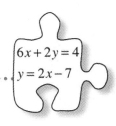

Solving Word Problems by Writing Equations

Today you will learn to translate written information into algebraic symbols and then solve the equations that represent the relationships.

4-1. Match each **mathematical sentence** on the left with its translation on the right.

a. $2z + 12 = 30$

b. $12z + 5(z + 2) = 30$

c. $z + (z - 2) + 5(z - 2) = 30$

d. $z + 12z = 30$

1. A zoo has two fewer elephants than zebras and five times more monkeys than elephants. The total number of elephants, monkeys, and zebras is 30.

2. Zola earned $30 by working two hours and receiving a $12 bonus.

3. Thirty ounces of metal is created by mixing zinc with silver. The number of ounces of silver needed is twelve times the number of ounces of zinc.

4. Eddie, who earns $5 per hour, worked two hours longer than Zach, who earns $12 per hour. Together they earned $30.

4-2. Mathematical sentences, like those in the left column of problem 4-1, are easier to understand when everyone knows what the variables represent. A statement that describes what the variable represents is called a **"let" statement**. For example, for mathematical sentence (a) above, which is matched with translation 2, we could say, "Let z = Zola's rate of pay (in dollars/hour)." Note that a "let" statement always indicates the units of measurement.

Write a "let" statement for each of the mathematical sentences in parts (b) through (d) above.

4-3.   The perimeter of a triangle is 31 cm. Sides #1 and #2 have equal length, while Side #3 is one centimeter shorter than twice the length of Side #1. Let's determine how long each side is:

   a.   Let x represent the length of Side #1. What essential part of this "let" statement is missing? What is the length of Side #2? Side #3?

   b.   Write a mathematical sentence that states that the perimeter is 31 cm.

   c.   Solve the equation you found in part (b) and determine the length of each side. Be sure to label your answers with the appropriate units.

4-4.   THE ENVIRONMENTAL CLUB

Charles and Amy are part of the Environmental Club at school. Their service project for the semester is to get a tree for their school donated and plant it on the school grounds. Charles' uncle owns a tree nursery and is willing to donate a 3-foot tall tree that he says will grow 1.5 feet per year.

Amy goes to another nursery in town, but is only able to get tree seeds donated. According to the seed package, the tree will grow 1.75 feet per year. Charles plants his tree and Amy plants a seed on the same day. Amy thinks that even though her tree will be much shorter than Charles' tree for the first several years, it will eventually be taller because it grows more each year, but she does not know how many years it will take for her tree to get as tall as Charles' tree.

Will the trees ever be the same size? If so, how many years will it take?

Your Task:

   • Represent this problem with tables, equations, and one graph.

   • Use *each* representation to find the solution. Explain how you found the solution in each of the three representations.

Discussion Points

How can the given information be represented with equations?

What is a solution to a two-variable equation?

How can this problem be represented on one graph?

How does the solution appear on the graph?

4-5.   In the previous problem, you wrote equations that were **models** of a real-life situation. **Models** are usually not perfect representations, but they are useful for describing real-life behavior and for making predictions. You predicted when the two trees would be the same height.

  a.   What are an appropriate domain and range for the two models of tree growth?

  b.   Where can you find the *y*-intercepts of the model on the graph, in the table, and in the equation? In the situation of the story, what does the *y*-intercept represent?

4-6.   For the following word problems, write one or two equations. Be sure to define your variable(s) and units of measurement with appropriate "let" statements and label your answers. You do not need to solve the equations yet.

  a.   After the math contest, Basil noticed that there were four extra-large pizzas that were left untouched. In addition, another three slices of pizza were uneaten. If there were a total of 51 slices of pizza left, how many slices does an extra-large pizza have?

  b.   Herman and Jacquita are each saving money to pay for college. Herman currently has $15,000 and is working hard to save $1000 per month. Jacquita only has $12,000 but is saving $1300 per month. In how many months will they have the same amount of savings?

  c.   George bought some CDs at his local store. He paid $15.95 for each CD. Nora bought the same number of CDs from a store online. She paid $13.95 for each CD, but had to pay $8 for shipping. In the end, both George and Nora spent the exact same amount of money buying their CDs! How many CDs did George buy?

4-7.   Solve part (b) of problem 4-6 above. In how many months would they have the same amount of savings? How much savings would they have at that time?

METHODS AND MEANINGS

Line of Best Fit

MATH NOTES

A **line of best fit** is a straight line that represents, in general, data on a scatterplot, as shown in the diagram. This line does not need to touch any of the actual data points, nor does it need to go through the origin. The line of best fit is a model of numerical two-variable data that helps describe the data in order to make predictions for other data.

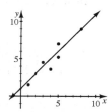

To write the equation of a line of best fit, find the coordinates of any two convenient points on the line (they could be lattice points where the gridlines intersect, or they could be data points, or the origin, or a combination). Then write the equation of the line that goes through these two points.

4-8.   Smallville High School Principal is concerned about his school's Advanced Placement (AP) test scores. He wonders if there is a relationship between the students' performance in class and their AP test scores so he randomly selects a sample of ten students who took AP examinations and compares their final exam scores to their AP test scores.

AP Score	5	1	4	2	1	4	2	1	3	5
Final%	97	70	84	66	62	79	73	63	82	90

Create a scatterplot on graph paper. Draw a line of best fit that represents the data. Refer to the Math Notes box in this lesson. Use the equation of your line of best fit to predict the final exam score of another Smallville HS student who scored a 3 on their AP test.

4-9. Solve for x. Check your solutions, if possible.

    a. $-2(4-3x)-6x=10$ b. $\frac{x-5}{-2} = \frac{x-1}{-3}$

4-10. On the same set of axes, use slope and y-intercept to graph each line in the system shown at right. Then find the point(s) of intersection, if one (or more) exists.

$$y = -x + 2$$
$$y = 3x + 6$$

4-11. A team of students is trying to answer the scientific notation problem $2 \times 10^3 \cdot 4 \times 10^7$.

Jorge thinks they should use a generic rectangle because there are two terms multiplied by two terms.

Cadel thinks the answer is 8×10^{10} but he cannot explain why.

Lauren thinks they should multiply the like parts. Her answer is 8×100^{21}.

Who is correct? Explain why each student is correct or incorrect.

4-12. For each of the following generic rectangles, find the dimensions (length and width) and write the area as the product of the dimensions and as a sum.

a.

$3y^2$	$-12y$

b.

$3y^2$	$-12y$
$5y$	-20

4-13. A **prime number** is defined as a number with exactly two integer factors: itself and 1. Jeannie thinks that all prime numbers are odd. Is she correct? If so, state how you know. If not, provide a counterexample.

4-14. Solve this problem by writing and solving an equation. Be sure to define your variable.

A rectangle has a perimeter of 30 inches. Its length is one less than three times its width. What are the length and width of the rectangle?

4-15.   The basketball **coach** at Washington High School normally starts each game
        with the following **five** players:

            Melinda, Samantha, Carly, Allison, and Kendra

        However, **due to illness**, she needs to substitute Barbara for Allison and
        Lakeisha for **Melinda** at this week's game. What will be the starting roster for
        this upcoming **game**?

4-16.   When Ms. **Shreve** solved an equation in class, she checked her
        solution and **it did** not make the equation true! Examine her
        work below **and find** her mistake. Then find the correct solution.

$$5(2x-1)-3x = 5x+9$$
$$10x-5-3x = 5x+9$$
$$7x-5 = 5x+9$$
$$12x = 4$$
$$x = \tfrac{1}{3}$$

4-17.   Determine **if the statement** below is always, sometimes, or never
        true. Justify **your conclusion**.

$$2(3+5x) = 6+5x$$

4-18.   Find an **equation for** the line passing through the points $(-3,1)$ and $(9,7)$.

4-19.   Multiply each **polynomial**. That is, change each product to a sum.

        a. $(2x+1)(3x-2)$ b. $(2x+1)(3x^2-2x-5)$

4.1.2 How many equations do I need?

$$6x + 2y = 4$$
$$y = 2x - 7$$

One Equation or Two?

In the previous lesson, you created one or two mathematical sentences that represented word problems. Today you will represent a word problem with two equations. You will also explore how to use the Equal Values Method to solve systems containing equations that are not in $y = mx + b$ form.

4-20.   ONE EQUATION OR TWO?

Elsie took all of her cans and bottles from home to the recycling plant. The number of cans was one more than four times the number of bottles. She earned 12¢ for each bottle and 10¢ for each can, and ended up earning $2.18 in all. How many cans and bottles did she recycle?

Solomon decided to solve the problem by writing one equation. He said, *"I can let b represent the number of bottles. Then $4b + 1$ would be the number of cans. My equation would be $12b + 10(4b + 1) = 218$."*

Marcus agreed with Solomon's answer, but said, *"It is easier to solve this problem with two equations. I can let b represent the number of bottles and c represent the number of cans. That way my two equations are $c = 4b + 1$ and $12b + 10c = 218$."*

a.   Solomon's equation has three terms: $12b$, $10(4b + 1)$, and 218. What do each of these terms represent in the problem?

b.   What do the parts of each of Marcus' equations represent?

c.   Do Solomon's equation and Marcus' equations represent the same problem? Why or why not?

d.   Solve this problem using Solomon's equation. Be sure to label your answer. You do not need to solve Marcus' equations.

4-21.   Renard thought that writing two equations for problem 4-20 was easy, but he's not sure if he knows how to solve the system of equations. He wants to use two equations with two variables to solve this problem:

> Ariel bought several bags of caramel candy and taffy. The number of bags of taffy was 5 more than the number of bags of caramels. Taffy bags weigh 8 ounces each, and caramel bags weigh 16 ounces each. The total weight of all of the bags of candy was 400 ounces. How many bags of candy did she buy?

a.   Renard lets t = the number of taffy bags and c = the number of caramel bags. Help him write two equations to represent the information in the problem.

b.   Now Renard is stuck. He says, "If both of the equations were in the form 't = something,' I could set the two equations equal to each other to find the solution." Help him change the equations into a form he can solve.

c.   Solve Renard's equations to find the number of caramel and taffy bags that Ariel bought.

d.   Discuss with your team how you can make sure your solution is correct.

4-22.   When you write equations to solve word problems, you sometimes end up with two equations like Renard's, or like the two equations at right. Notice that the second equation is solved for y, but the first is not. Change the first equation into "y =" form, and then solve this system of equations. Check your solution.

$$x - 2y = 4$$
$$y = -\tfrac{1}{2}x + 4$$

4-23.   A set of two or more equations with the same variables is called a **system of equations**. When you set the two equations equal to each other, like Renard did in problem 4-21, you are using the **Equal Values Method** of solving a system of equations.

There are 21 animals on Farmer Cole's farm – all sheep and chickens. If the animals have a total of 56 legs, how many of each type of animal lives on his farm? Write a system of equations, and use the Equal Values Method to solve it. Be sure to check your answer.

Core Connections Algebra

4-24. Solve the system of equations at right using the Equal Values Method. Check your answer.

$$x + 2y = 14$$
$$-x + 3y = 26$$

METHODS AND MEANINGS

MATH NOTES

The Equal Values Method

The **Equal Values Method** is a method to find the solution to a system of equations. For example, solve the system of equations below:

$$2x + y = 5$$
$$y = x - 1$$

Put both equations into $y = mx + b$ form. The two equations are now $y = -2x + 5$ and $y = x - 1$.

| $2x + y = 5$ | $y = x - 1$ |
| $y = -2x + 5$ | |

Take the two expressions that equal y and set them equal to each other. Then solve this new equation to find x. See the example at right.

$$-2x + 5 = x - 1$$
$$-3x = -6$$
$$x = 2$$

Once you know x, substitute your solution for x into *either* original equation to find y. In this example, the second equation is used.

$$y = x - 1$$
$$y = (2) - 1$$
$$y = 1$$

Check your solution by evaluating for x and y in *both* of the *original* equations.

$2x + y = 5$	$y = x - 1$
$2(2) + 1 = 5$	$1 = 2 - 1$
$5 = 5$	$1 = 1$
✓	✓

4-25.   Write expressions to represent the quantities described below.

    a.   Geraldine is 4 years younger than Tom. If Tom is t years old, how old is Geraldine? Also, if Steven is twice as old as Geraldine, how old is he?

    b.   150 people went to see "Ode to Algebra" performed in the school auditorium. If the number of children that attended the performance was c, how many adults attended?

    c.   The cost of a new CD is $14.95, and the cost of a video game is $39.99. How much would c CDs and v video games cost?

4-26.   Nina has some nickels and 9 pennies in her pocket. Her friend, Maurice, has twice as many nickels as Nina. Together, these coins are worth 84¢. How many nickels does Nina have? Show all of your work and label your answers.

4-27.   Create a table and graph the equation $y = 10 - x^2 + 3x$. Label its x- and y-intercepts.

4-28.   Examine the graphs of each relation below. Decide if each is a function. Then describe the domain and range of each one.

    a.

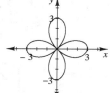

    b.

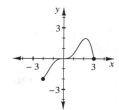

4-29.   What number is not part of the domain of the function $g(x) = \frac{x+2}{x-1}$? How can you tell?

4-30.   If $f(x) = 3x - 9$ and $g(x) = -x^2$, find:

    a. $f(-2)$ b. $g(-2)$ c. x if $f(x) = 0$ d. $g(m)$

4.2.1 How can I solve the system?

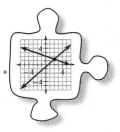

Solving Systems of Equations Using Substitution

In Lesson 4.1.2, you helped Renard develop the Equal Values Method of solving a system of equations. You set both of the equations equal to the same variable. Today you will develop a more efficient method of solving systems that are too messy to solve by setting the equations equal to each other.

4-31. Review what you learned in Lesson 4.1.2 as you solve the system of equations below. Check your solution.

$$y = -x - 7$$
$$5y + 3x = -13$$

4-32. AVOIDING THE MESS

A new method, called the **Substitution Method**, can help you solve the system in problem 4-31 without using fractions. This method is outlined below.

a. If $y = -x - 7$, then does $-x - 7 = y$? That is, can you switch the y and the $-x - 7$? Why or why not?

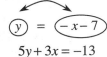

$$5y + 3x = -13$$

b. Since you know that $y = -x - 7$, can you replace the y in the second equation with $-x - 7$ from the top equation? Why or why not?

$$y = \boxed{-x - 7}$$
$$5\,\textcircled{y} + 3x = -13$$

c. Once you replace the y in the second equation with $-x - 7$, you have an equation with only one variable, as shown below. This is called **substitution** because you are substituting for (replacing) y with an expression that it equals. Solve this new equation for x and then use that result to find y in either of the original equations.

$$5(-x - 7) + 3x = -13$$

4-33.   Use the Substitution Method to solve the systems of equations below.

a. $y = 3x$
     $2y - 5x = 4$

b. $x - 4 = y$
     $-5y + 8x = 29$

c. $2x + 2y = 18$
     $x = 3 - y$

d. $c = -b - 11$
     $3c + 6 = 6b$

4-34.   When Mei solved the system of equations below, she got the solution $x = 4$, $y = 2$. *Without solving the system yourself*, can you tell her whether this solution is correct? How do you know?

$$4x + 3y = 22$$
$$x - 2y = 0$$

4-35.   HAPPY BIRTHDAY!

You've decided to give your best friend a bag of marbles for his birthday. Since you know that your friend likes green marbles better than red ones, the bag has twice as many green marbles as red. The label on the bag says it contains a total of 84 marbles.

How many green marbles are in the bag? Write an equation (or system of equations) for this problem. Then solve the problem using any method you choose. Be sure to check your answer when you are finished.

METHODS AND MEANINGS

Describing Association

An association (relationship) between two numerical variables can be described by its form, direction, strength, and outliers.

The shape of the pattern is called the **form** of the association: **linear** or **non-linear**. The form can be made of **clusters** of data.

If one variable increases as the other variable increases, the **direction** is said to be a **positive association**. If one variable increases as the other variable decreases, there is said to be a **negative association**. If there is no apparent pattern in the scatterplot, then the variables have **no association**.

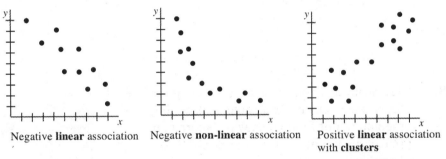

Negative **linear** association   Negative **non-linear** association   Positive **linear** association with **clusters**

Strength is a description of how much scatter there is in the data away from the line of best fit. See some examples below.

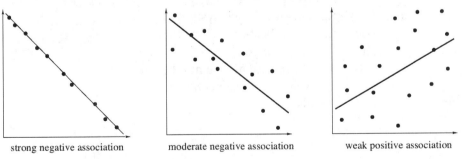

strong negative association   moderate negative association   weak positive association

An **outlier** is a piece of data that does not seem to fit into the overall pattern. There is one obvious outlier in the association graphed at right.

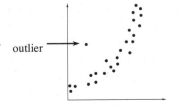

4-36. Ms. Hoang's class conducted an experiment by rolling a marble down different lengths of slanted boards and timing how long it took. The results are shown below. Describe the association. Refer to the Math Notes box in this lesson if you need help remembering how to describe an association.

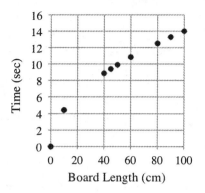

4-37. Solve each equation for the variable. Check your solutions, if possible.

a. $8a + a - 3 = 6a - 2a - 3$

b. $(m+2)(m+3) = (m+2)(m-2)$

c. $\frac{x}{2} + 1 = 6$

d. $4t - 2 + t^2 = 6 + t^2$

4-38. The Fabulous Footballers scored an incredible 55 points at last night's game. Interestingly, the number of field goals was 1 more than twice the number of touchdowns. The Fabulous Footballers earned 7 points for each touchdown and 3 points for each field goal.

a. **Multiple Choice:** Which system of equations below best represents this situation? Explain your reasoning. Assume that t represents the number of touchdowns and f represents the number of field goals.

i. $t = 2f + 1$
    $7t + 3f = 55$

ii. $f = 2t + 1$
    $7t + 3f = 55$

iii. $t = 2f + 1$
     $3t + 7f = 55$

iv. $f = 2t + 1$
    $3t + 7f = 55$

b. Solve the system you selected in part (a) and determine how many touchdowns and field goals the Fabulous Footballers earned last night.

Core Connections Algebra

4-39. Yesterday Mica was given some information and was asked to find a linear equation. But last night her cat destroyed most of the information! At right is all she has left:

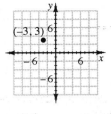

x	y
−3	
−2	1
−1	
0	
1	
2	
3	

a. Complete the table and graph the line that represents Mica's equation.

b. Mica thinks the equation for this graph could be $2x + y = -3$. Is she correct? Explain why or why not. If not, find your own algebraic equation to match the graph and $x \rightarrow y$ table.

4-40. Kevin and his little sister, Katy, are trying to solve the system of equations shown below. Kevin thinks the new equation should be $3(6x - 1) + 2y = 43$, while Katy thinks it should be $3x + 2(6x - 1) = 43$. Who is correct and why?

$$y = 6x - 1$$
$$3x + 2y = 43$$

4-41. Simplify each expression. In parts (c) and (d) write your answers using scientific notation.

a. $5^0 \cdot 2^{-3}$

b. $\dfrac{a^3}{b^{-2}} \cdot \dfrac{ab^2}{a^4}$

c. $2.3 \times 10^{-3} \cdot 4.2 \times 10^2$

d. $(3.5 \times 10^3)^2$

4.2.2 How does a graph show a solution?

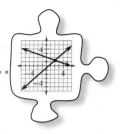

Making Connections: Systems, Solutions, and Graphs

In this chapter you have practiced writing mathematical sentences to represent situations. Often, these sentences give you a system of equations, which you can solve using substitution. Today you will also represent these situations on a graph and will examine more closely the solution to a two-variable equation.

4-42.   THE HILLS ARE ALIVE

The Alpine Music Club is going on its annual music trip. The members of the club are yodelers, and they like to play the xylophone. This year they are taking their xylophones on a gondola to give a performance at the top of Mount Monch.

The gondola conductor charges $2 for each yodeler and $1 for each xylophone. It costs $40 for the entire club, including the xylophones, to ride the gondola. Two yodelers can share a xylophone, so the number of yodelers on the gondola is twice the number of xylophones.

How many yodelers and how many xylophones are on the gondola?

Your Task:

- Represent this problem with a system of equations. Solve the system and explain how its solution relates to the yodelers on the music trip.

- Represent this problem with a graph. Identify how the solution to this problem appears on the graph.

Discussion Points

How can the given information be represented with equations?

What is a solution to a two-variable equation?

How can this problem be represented on a graph?

How does the solution appear on the graph?

4-43.   Start by focusing on one aspect of the problem: the cost to ride the gondola. The conductor charges $2 for each yodeler and $1 for each xylophone. It costs $40 for the entire club, with instruments, to ride the gondola.

   a.   Write an equation with two variables that represents this information. Be sure to define your variables.

   b.   Find a combination of xylophones and yodelers that will make your equation from part (a) true. Is this is the only possible combination?

   c.   List five additional combinations of xylophones and yodelers that could ride the gondola if it costs $40 for the trip. With your team, decide on a good way to organize and share your list.

   d.   Jon says, "I think there could be 28 xylophones and 8 yodelers on the gondola." Is he correct? Use the equation you have written to explain why or why not.

   e.   Helga says, "Each correct combination we found is a *solution* to our equation." Is this true? Explain what it means for something to be a solution to a two-variable equation.

4-44.   Now consider the other piece of information: The number of yodelers is twice the number of xylophones.

   a.   Write an equation (mathematical sentence) that expresses this piece of information.

   b.   List four different combinations of xylophones and yodelers that will make this equation true.

   c.   Put the equation you found in part (a) together with your equation from problem 4-43 and use substitution to solve this system of equations.

   d.   Is the answer you found in part (c) a solution to the first equation you wrote (the equation in part (a) of problem 4-43)? How can you check? Is it a solution to the second equation you wrote (the equation in part (a) of this problem)? Why is this a solution to the *system* of equations?

4-45.   The solution to "The Hills are Alive" problem can also be represented graphically.

   a.   On graph paper, graph the equation you wrote in part (a) of problem 4-43. The points you listed for that equation may help. What is the shape of this graph? Label your graph with its equation.

   b.   Explain how each point on the graph represents a solution to the equation.

   c.   Now graph the equation you wrote in part (a) of problem 4-44 on the same set of axes. The points you listed for that equation may help. Label this graph with its equation.

   d.   Find the intersection point of the two graphs. What is special about this point?

   e.   With your team, find as many ways as you can to express the solution to "The Hills are Alive" problem. Be prepared to share all the different forms you found for the solution with the class.

——————   *Further Guidance*   ——————
section ends here.

4-46.   Consider this system of equations:

$$2x + 2y = 18$$
$$y = x - 3$$

   a.   Use substitution to solve this system.

   b.   With your team, decide how to fill in the rest of the table at right for the equation $2x + 2y = 18$.

   c.   Use your table to make an accurate graph of the equation $2x + 2y = 18$.

x	y
−2	11
−1	
0	
1	
2	
3	

   d.   Now graph $y = x - 3$ on the same set of axes. Find the point of intersection.

   e.   Does the point of intersection you found in part (a) agree with what you see on your graph?

4-47.   The equations of two lines are given below. A table of solutions for the first
         equation has been started below the equation.

$$10x + 4y = -8$$

x	y
−4	8
−2	
0	
2	

$$y = -\tfrac{5}{2}x - 2$$

    a.   Graph both lines. Without actually solving the system of equations,
         predict what the solution to this system will be. Explain.

    b.   Solve the system. Was your prediction in part (a) correct?

4-48.   What is a solution to a two-variable equation? Answer this
         question in complete sentences in your Learning Log. Then
         give an example of a two-variable equation followed by two
         different solutions to it. Finally, make a list of all of the
         ways to represent solutions to two-variable equations. Title
         your entry "Solutions to Two-Variable Equations" and label it
         with today's date.

METHODS AND MEANINGS

The Substitution Method

The **Substitution Method** is a way to change two equations with two variables into one equation with one variable. It is convenient to use when only one equation is solved for a variable.

For example, to solve the system: $x = -3y + 1$

$$4x - 3y = -11$$

Use substitution to rewrite the two equations as one. In other words, replace x in the second equation with $(-3y + 1)$ from the first equation to get $4(-3y+1) - 3y = -11$. This equation can then be solved to find y. In this case, $y = 1$.

$x = \boxed{-3y + 1}$

$$4(\ \ )- 3y = -11$$
$$4(-3y+1) - 3y = -11$$
$$-12y + 4 - 3y = -11$$
$$-15y + 4 = -11$$
$$-15y = -15$$
$$y = 1$$

To find the point of intersection, substitute the value you found into either original equation to find the other value.

In the example, substitute $y = 1$ into $x = -3y + 1$ and write the answer for x and y as an ordered pair.

$$x = -3(1) + 1$$
$$x = -2$$
$$(-2, 1)$$

To check the solution, substitute $x = -2$ and $y = 1$ into *both* of the *original* equations.

$$-2 = -3(1) + 1 \qquad 4(-2) - 3(1) = -11$$
$$-2 = -2 \qquad -11 = -11$$

Review & Preview

4-49. Camila is trying to find the equation of a line that passes through the points $(-1, 16)$ and $(5, 88)$. Does the equation $y = 12x + 28$ work? Justify your answer.

Core Connections Algebra

4-50.   The graph at right contains the lines for $y = x + 2$ and $y = 2x - 1$.

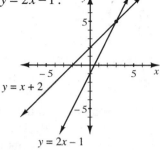

a.   Using the graph, what is the solution to this system?

b.   Solve the system algebraically to confirm your answer to part (a).

4-51.   Hotdogs and corndogs were sold at last night's football game. Use the information below to write mathematical sentences to help you determine how many corndogs were sold.

a.   The number of hotdogs sold was three fewer than twice the number of corndogs. Write a mathematical sentence that relates the number of hotdogs and corndogs. Let h represent the number of hotdogs and c represent the number of corndogs.

b.   A hotdog costs \$3 and a corndog costs \$1.50. If \$201 was collected, write a mathematical sentence to represent this information.

c.   How many corndogs were sold? Show how you found your answer.

4-52.   Copy and complete each of the Diamond Problems below. The pattern used in the Diamond Problems is shown at right.

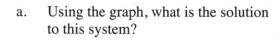

a.   b.   c.   d.

4-53.   Rianna thinks that if $a = b$ and if $c = d$, then $a + c = b + d$. Is she correct?

4-54.   Solve the following equations for x, if possible. Check your solutions.

a. $-(2 - 3x) + x = 9 - x$

b. $\frac{6}{x+2} = \frac{3}{4}$

c. $5 - 2(x + 6) = 14$

d. $\frac{1}{2}x - 4 + 1 = -3 - \frac{1}{2}x$

4.2.3 Can I solve without substituting?

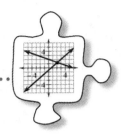

Solving Systems Using Elimination

In this chapter, you have learned the Substitution Method for solving systems of equations. You also studied the Equal Values Method that set two equations equal to each other. But are these methods the best to use for all types of systems? Today you will develop a new solution method that can save time for systems of linear equations in standard form, $ax + by = c$.

4-55.   Jeanette is trying to find the intersection point of these two lines:

$$3y + 2x = -2$$
$$-3y + 5x = 16$$

She has decided to use substitution to find the point of intersection. Her plan is to solve the first equation for y, and then to substitute the result into the second equation. Use Jeanette's idea to solve the system.

4-56.   AVOIDING THE MESS: THE ELIMINATION METHOD

Your class will now discuss a new method, called the **Elimination Method**, to find the solution to Jeanette's problem without the complications and fractions of the previous problem. Your class discussion is outlined below.

a.   Build Jeanette's first equation on an Equation Mat as shown below.

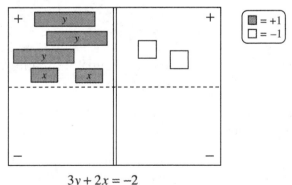

$$3y + 2x = -2$$

Problem continues on next page. →

4-56.   *Problem continued from previous page.*

b.   "Add the same tiles to both sides" is a "legal" tile move. Jeanette can add anything she wants to both sides of the equation. If she wanted to, she could choose to add 16 to both sides. You will see in a moment why that makes sense.

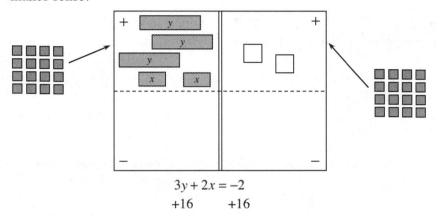

$$3y + 2x = -2$$
$$+16 \qquad +16$$

c.   But 16 is equal to $-3y + 5x$, according to the original equations in problem 4-55. On the left side, instead of adding 16, Jeanette decides to add $-3y + 5x$. After all, 16 is equivalent to $-3y + 5x$.

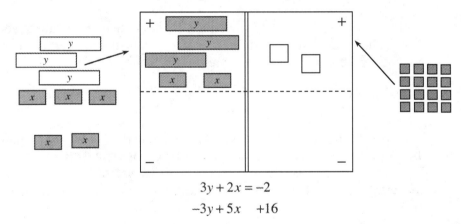

$$3y + 2x = -2$$
$$-3y + 5x \quad +16$$

d.   Write a new equation for the result of Jeanette's addition to both sides of the equation. Notice that you now have only one equation with one variable. What happened to the *y*-terms? Simplify and then solve this new equation for the remaining variable.

e.   Use your solution for *x* to find *y*. Check to be sure your solution makes both original equations true.

f.   Now use algebra tiles and the Elimination Method to solve the system of equations at right for *x* and *y*. Check your solution.

$$2x - y = -2$$
$$-2x + 3y = 10$$

4-57.   Pat was in a fishing competition at Lake
         Pisces. He caught some bass and some
         trout. Each bass weighed 3 pounds, and
         each trout weighed 1 pound. Pat caught a
         total of 30 pounds of fish. He got 5 points
         in the competition for each bass, but since
         trout are endangered in Lake Pisces, he lost
         1 point for each trout. Pat scored a total of
         42 points.

   a.   Write a system of equations representing the information in this problem.

   b.   Is this system a good candidate for the Elimination Method? Why or why
         not?

   c.   Solve this system to find out how many bass and trout Pat caught. Be sure
         to record your work and check your answer by substituting your solution
         into the original equations.

4-58.   ANNIE NEEDS YOUR HELP

         Annie was going to use the Elimination Method. She was ready to add the
         same value to both sides of the equation to eliminate the x-terms when she
         noticed a problem: Both x-terms are positive!

$$2x + 7y = 13$$
$$2x + 3y = 5$$

         With your team, figure out something you could do that would allow you to add
         the value of the second equation to the first equation and eliminate the x-terms.
         Once you have figured out a method, solve the system and check your solution.
         Be ready to share your method with the class.

4-59.   Find the point of intersection of each pair of lines below. Show your steps
         algebraically. Check each solution when you are finished.

   a. $2y - x = 5$ b. $2x - 4y = 14$ c. $3x + 4y = 1$
         $-3y + x = -9$ $4y - x = -3$ $2x + 4y = 2$

METHODS AND MEANINGS

Systems of Linear Equations

A **system of linear equations** is a set of two or more linear equations that are given together, such as the example at right:

If the equations come from a real-world situation, then each variable will represent some type of quantity in both

$$y = 2x$$
$$y = -3x + 5$$

equations. For example, in the system of equations above, y could stand for a number of dollars in *both* equations and x could stand for the number of weeks.

To represent a system of equations graphically, you can simply graph each equation on the same set of axes. The graph may or may not have a **point of intersection**, as shown circled at right.

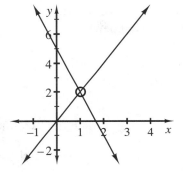

Also notice that the point of intersection lies on *both* graphs in the system of equations. This means that the point of intersection is a **solution** to *both* equations in the system. For example,

$y = 2x$	$y = -3x + 5$
$(2) = 2(1)$	$(2) = -3(1) + 5$
$2 = 2$	$2 = -3 + 5$
	$2 = 2$

the point of intersection of the two lines graphed above is $(1, 2)$. This point of intersection makes both equations true, as shown at right.

The point of intersection makes both equations true; therefore the point of intersection is a solution to both equations. For this reason, the point of intersection is sometimes called a **solution to the system of equations**.

4-60.   Find the point of intersection of each pair of lines, if one exists. If you use an Equation Mat, be sure to record your process on paper. Check each solution, if possible.

a. $x = -2y - 3$
     $4y - x = 9$

b. $x + 5y = 8$
     $-x + 2y = -1$

c. $4x - 2y = 5$
     $y = 2x + 10$

4-61.   Jai was solving the system of equations below when something strange happened.

$$y = -2x + 5$$
$$2y + 4x = 10$$

a.   Solve the system. Explain to Jai what the solution should be.

b.   Graph the two lines on the same set of axes. What happened?

c.   Explain how the graph helps to explain your answer in part (a).

4-62.   On Tuesday the cafeteria sold pizza slices and burritos. The number of pizza slices sold was 20 less than twice the number of burritos sold. Pizza sold for $2.50 a slice and burritos for $3.00 each. The cafeteria collected a total of $358 for selling these two items.

a.   Write two equations with two variables to represent the information in this problem. Be sure to define your variables.

b.   Solve the system from part (a). Then determine how many pizza slices were sold.

4-63.   A local deli sells 4-inch sub sandwiches for $2.95. It has decided to sell a "family sub" that is 50 inches long. How much should it charge? Show all work.

4-64.   Use generic rectangles to multiply each of the following expressions.

  a. $(x+2)(x-5)$ b. $(y+2x)(y+3x)$

  c. $(3y-8)(-x+y)$ d. $(x-3y)(x+3y)$

4-65.   A consumer magazine collected the following data for the fuel efficiency of cars (miles per gallon) compared to weight (thousands of pounds).

$e = 49 - 8.4w$
  w is the weight (1000s of pounds) and e is the fuel efficiency (mpg).

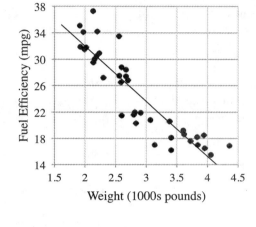

  a.   Describe the association between fuel efficiency and weight.

  b.   Cheetah Motors has come out with a super lightweight sports utility vehicle (SUV) that weighs only 2800 pounds. What does the model predict the fuel efficiency will be?

$4.2.4$ How can I eliminate a variable?

More Elimination

In Lesson 4.2.3, you learned how to use the Elimination Method to solve systems of equations. In this method, you combined two equations in a way that made one variable disappear. This method is particularly useful for solving systems of equations where neither equation is in $y = mx + b$ form.

Today you will practice using the Elimination Method while learning to deal with various complications that systems of equations sometimes present. As you solve these systems, ask your teammates these questions:

How can you create one equation with only one variable?

How can you eliminate one variable?

How do you know your solution is correct?

4-66. Which system of equations below would be easiest to solve using the Elimination Method? Once you have explained your decision, use the Elimination Method to solve this system of equations. (You do not need to solve the other system!) Record your steps and check your solution.

a. $5x - 4y = 37$
    $-8x + 4y = -52$

b. $4 - 2x = y$
    $3y + x = 11$

4-67. Rachel is trying to solve this system:

$$2x + y = 10$$
$$3x - 2y = 1$$

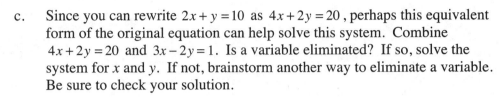

a. Combine these equations. What happened?

b. Is $2x + y = 10$ the same line as $4x + 2y = 20$? That is, do they have the same solutions? Are their graphs the same? Justify your conclusion! Be ready to share your reasoning with the class.

c. Since you can rewrite $2x + y = 10$ as $4x + 2y = 20$, perhaps this equivalent form of the original equation can help solve this system. Combine $4x + 2y = 20$ and $3x - 2y = 1$. Is a variable eliminated? If so, solve the system for x and y. If not, brainstorm another way to eliminate a variable. Be sure to check your solution.

d. Why was the top equation changed? Would a variable have been eliminated if the bottom equation were multiplied by 2 on both sides? Test this idea.

4-68. For each system below, determine:

- Is this system a good candidate for the Elimination Method? Why or why not?

- What is the best way to get one equation with one variable? Carry out your plan and solve the system for both variables.

- Is your solution correct? Verify by substituting your solution into both original equations.

a. $5m + 2n = -10$
$3m + 2n = -2$

b. $6a - b = 3$
$b + 4a = 17$

c. $7x + 4y = 17$
$3x - 2y = -15$

4-69.   Tracy's team was given the following system by their teacher.

$$10x + 4y = -8$$
$$5x + 2y = 10$$

a.   Combine these equations and solve. What happened?

b.   Are these two equations the same line? How can you tell?

c.   How can you explain the solution you got in part (a)?

4-70.   A NEW CHALLENGE

Carefully examine this system:

$$4x + 3y = 10$$
$$9x - 4y = 1$$

With your team, propose a way to combine these equations so that you eventually have one equation with one variable. Be prepared to share your proposal with the class.

METHODS AND MEANINGS

Forms of a Linear Function

MATH NOTES

There are three main forms of a linear function: slope-intercept form, standard form, and point-slope form. Study the examples below.

Slope-Intercept form: $y = mx + b$. The slope is m, and the y-intercept is $(0, b)$.

Standard form: $ax + by = c$

Point-Slope form: $y - k = m(x - h)$. The slope is m, and (h, k) is a point on the line. For example, if the slope is -7 and the point $(20, -10)$ is on the line, the equation of the line can be written $y - (-10) = -7(x - 20)$ or $y + 10 = -7(x - 20)$.

4-71. Solve these systems of equations using any method. Check each solution, if possible.

a. $2x + 3y = 9$
$-3x + 3y = -6$

b. $x = 8 - 2y$
$y - x = 4$

c. $y = -\frac{1}{2}x + 7$
$y = x - 8$

d. $9x + 10y = 14$
$7x + 5y = -3$

4-72. For each line below, make a table and a graph. What do you notice?

a. $y = \frac{2}{3}x - 1$

b. $2x - 3y = 3$

4-73. Find all possible values for x in each equation.

a. $-2|x| = -8$

b. $|x - 3.2| = 4.7$

c. $|9 + 6x| = 4$

c. $|-7x - 7| = 1$

4-74. Aimee thinks the solution to the system below is $(-4, -6)$. Eric thinks the solution is $(8, 2)$. Who is correct? Explain your reasoning.

$$2x - 3y = 10$$
$$6y = 4x - 20$$

4-75. Figure 3 of a tile pattern has 11 tiles, while Figure 4 has 13 tiles. If the tile pattern grows at a constant rate, how many tiles will Figure 50 have?

4-76. Solve each equation for the indicated variable.

a. $y = mx + b$ (for b)

b. $y = mx + b$ (for x)

c. $I = prt$ (for t)

d. $A = p + prt$ (for t)

4.2.5 What is the best method?

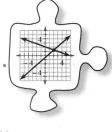

Choosing a Strategy for Solving Systems

When you have a system of equations to solve, how do you know which method to use? Focus today on how to choose a strategy that is the most convenient, efficient, and accurate for a system of equations.

4-77.   Erica works in a soda-bottling factory. As bottles pass her on a conveyer belt, she puts caps on them. Unfortunately, Erica sometimes breaks a bottle before she can cap it. She gets paid 4 cents for each bottle she successfully caps, but her boss deducts 2 cents from her pay for each bottle she breaks.

Erica is having a bad morning. Fifteen bottles have come her way, but she has been breaking some and has only earned 6 cents so far today. How many bottles has Erica capped and how many has she broken?

a.   Write a system of equations representing this situation.

b.   Solve the system of equations using *two* different methods: substitution and elimination. Demonstrate that each method gives the same answer.

4-78.   For each system below, decide which algebraic solving strategy to use. That is, which method would be the most efficient and convenient: the Substitution Method, the Elimination Method, or setting the equations equal to each other (equal values)? Do not solve the systems yet! Be prepared to justify your reasons for choosing one strategy over the others.

a. $x = 4 - 2y$
     $3x - 2y = 4$

b. $3x + y = 1$
     $4x + y = 2$

c. $x = -5y + 2$
     $x = 3y - 2$

d. $2x - 4y = 10$
     $x = 2y + 5$

e. $y = \frac{1}{2}x + 4$
     $y = -2x + 9$

f. $-6x + 2y = 76$
     $3x - y = -38$

g. $5x + 3y = -6$
     $2x - 9y = 18$

h. $x - 3 = y$
     $2(x - 3) - y = 7$

4-79. Your teacher will assign you several systems from problem 4-78 to solve. With your team, use the best strategy to solve each system assigned by your teacher. Be sure to check your solution.

4-80. In your Learning Log, write down everything you know about solving systems of equations. Include examples and explain your reasoning. Title this entry "Solving Systems of Equations" and label it with today's date.

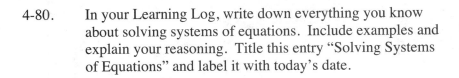

METHODS AND **M**EANINGS

Intersection, Parallel, and Coincide

When two lines lie on the same flat surface (called a plane), they may **intersect** (cross each other) once, an infinite number of times, or never.

For example, if the two lines are **parallel**, then they never intersect. The system of these two lines does not have a solution. Examine the graph of two parallel lines at right. Notice that the distance between the two lines is constant and that they have the same slope but different y-intercepts.

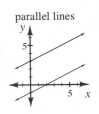

parallel lines

However, what if the two lines lie exactly on top of each other? When this happens, we say that the two lines **coincide**. When you look at two lines that coincide, they appear to be one line. Since these two lines intersect each other at all points along the line, coinciding lines have an infinite number of intersections. The system has an infinite number of solutions. Both lines have the same slope and y-intercept.

While some systems contain lines that are parallel and others coincide, the most common case for a system of equations is when the two lines intersect once, as shown at right. The system has one solution, namely, the point where the lines intersect, (x, y).

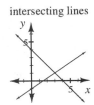

intersecting lines

4-81.   Solve the following systems of equations using any method. Check each
         solution, if possible.

   a. $-2x + 3y = 1$ b. $y = \frac{1}{3}x + 4$
         $2x + 6y = 2$ $x = -3y$

   c. $3x - y = 7$ d. $x + 2y = 1$
         $y = 3x - 2$ $3x + 5y = 8$

4-82.   The Math Club is baking pies for a bake sale. The fruit-pie recipe calls for
         twice as many peaches as nectarines. If it takes a total of 168 pieces of fruit for
         all of the pies, how many nectarines are needed?

4-83.   Candice is solving this system:

$$2x - 1 = 3y$$
$$5(2x - 1) + y = 32$$

   a.   She notices that each equation contains the expression $2x - 1$. Can she
         substitute $3y$ for $2x - 1$? Why or why not?

   b.   Substitute $3y$ for $2x - 1$ in the second equation to create one equation with
         one variable. Then solve for x and y.

4-84.   Find $g(-5)$ for each function below.

   a. $g(x) = x^3 - 2$ b. $g(x) = 7 + \sqrt{4 - x}$

   c. $g(x) = \sqrt[3]{x + (-59)}$ d. $g(x) = -4|x - 1|$

4-85.   Tim is buying snacks for the Mathletes who love microwave popcorn. When Tim looks at the popcorn selection he notices many brands and different prices. He wonders if the cost is related to the quality of the popcorn. To answer his question he purchases a random sample of popcorn bags and records their price. When it is time for the Mathletes meeting he pops each bag in the same microwave, opens each bag and counts the number of unpopped kernels.

Price ($)	2.30	0.60	1.30	1.50	1.70	1.00
# Unpopped	4	30	17	21	15	20

a.   Make a scatterplot on graph paper and draw the line of best fit. Determine the equation of the line of best fit.

b.   Estimate the number of unpopped kernels (after cooking) in a bag that costs $1.19.

4-86.   This problem is part 2 of the checkpoint for solving linear equations (fractional coefficients). It will be referred to as Checkpoint 4.

Solve each equation.

a. $\frac{1}{6}m - 3 = -5$

b. $\frac{2}{3}x - 3 = \frac{1}{2}x - 7$

c. $x + \frac{x}{2} - 4 = \frac{x}{4}$

Check your answers by referring to the Checkpoint 4 materials located at the back of your book.

If you needed help solving these problems correctly, then you need more practice. Review the Checkpoint 4 materials and try the practice problems. Also, consider getting help outside of class time. From this point on, you will be expected to do problems like these quickly and easily.

4.3.1 What can I do now?

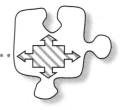

Pulling It All Together

This lesson contains several problems that will require you to use the algebra content you have learned so far in new ways.

Your teacher will describe today's activity. As you solve the problems below, remember to make connections between all of the different topics you have studied in Chapters 1 through 4. If you get stuck, think of what the problem reminds you of. Decide if there is a different way to approach the problem. Most importantly, discuss your ideas with your teammates.

4-87.   Brianna has been collecting insects and measuring the lengths of their legs and antennae. Below is the data she has collected so far.

	Ant	Beetle	Grasshopper
Length of Antenna (x)	2 mm	6 mm	20 mm
Length of Leg (y)	4 mm	10 mm	31 mm

a.   Graph the data Brianna has collected. Put the antenna length on the x-axis and leg length on the y-axis.

b.   Brianna thinks that she has found an algebraic rule relating antenna length and leg length: $4y - 6x = 4$. If x represents the length of the antenna and y represents the leg length, could Brianna's rule be correct? If not, find your own algebraic rule relating antenna length and leg length.

c.   If a ladybug has an antenna 1 mm long, how long does Brianna's rule say its legs will be? Use both the rule and the graph to justify your answer.

4-88. Barry is helping his friend understand how to solve systems of equations. He wants to give her a practice problem that has two lines that intersect at the point $(-3, 7)$. Help him by writing a system of equations that will have $(-3, 7)$ as a solution and demonstrate how to solve it.

4-89. Examine the generic rectangle at right. Determine the missing attributes and then write the area as a product and as a sum.

4-90. One evening, Gemma saw three different phone company ads. TeleTalk boasted a flat rate of 8¢ per minute. AmeriCall charges 30¢ per call plus 5¢ per minute. CellTime charges 60¢ per call plus only 3¢ per minute.

a. Gemma is planning a phone call that will take about 5 minutes. Which phone plan should she use and how much will it cost?

b. Represent each phone plan with a table and a rule. Then graph each plan on the same set of axes, where x represents time in minutes and y represents the cost of the call in cents. If possible, use different colors to represent the different phone plans.

c. How long would a call need to be to cost the same with TeleTalk and AmeriCall? What about AmeriCall and CellTime?

d. Analyze the different phone plans. How long should a call be so that AmeriCall is cheapest?

4-91.   Mary Sue is very famous for her delicious
         brownies, which she sells at football games at
         her Texas high school. The graph at right
         shows the relationship between the number of
         brownies she sells and the amount of money
         she earns.

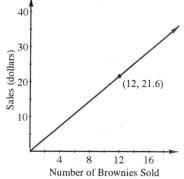

   a.   How much should she charge for
         10 brownies? Be sure to demonstrate
         your reasoning.

   b.   During the last football game, Mary Sue made
         $34.20. How many brownies did she sell?
         Show your work.

4-92.   How many solutions does each equation below have? How can you tell?

   a. $4x - 1 + 5 = 4x + 3$ b. $6t - 3 = 3t + 6$

   c. $6(2m - 3) - 3m = 2m - 18 + m$ d. $10 + 3y - 2 = 4y - y + 8$

4-93.   Anthony has the rules for three lines: A, B, and C. When he solves a system
         with lines A and B, he gets no solution. When he solves a system with lines B
         and C, he gets infinite solutions. What solution will he get when he solves a
         system with lines A and C? Justify your conclusion.

4-94.   Normally, the longer you work for a company, the higher your salary per hour.
         Hector surveyed the people at his company and placed his data in the table
         below.

Number of Years at Company	1	3	6	7
Salary per Hour	$7.00	$8.50	$10.75	$11.50

   a.   How much can Hector expect to make after
         working at the company for 5 years?

   b.   Hector's company is hiring a new
         employee who will work 20 hours a week.
         How much do you expect the new
         employee to earn for the first week?

Core Connections Algebra

4-95.   Dexter loves to find shortcuts. He has proposed a few new moves
to help simplify and solve equations. Examine his work below.
For each Equation Mat, decide if his move is "legal." That is,
decide if the move creates an equivalent equation. Justify your
conclusions using the "legal" moves you already know.

a.
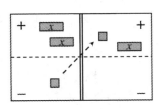

b.
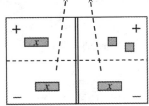

c.
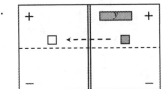

d.
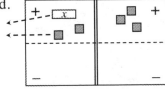

4-96.   Solve the problem below using *two
different methods*.

The Math Club sold roses and tulips
this year for Valentine's Day. The
number of roses sold was 8 more than
4 times the number of tulips sold.
Tulips were sold for $2 each and roses
for $5 each. The club made $414.00.
How many roses were sold?

4-97.   Use substitution to find where the two parabolas below intersect. Then confirm
your solution by graphing both on the same set of axes.

$$y = x^2 + 5$$
$$y = x^2 + 2x + 1$$

4-98.   Find the point of intersection for each set of equations below using any method. Check your solutions, if possible.

   a. $6x - 2y = 10$
         $3x - 5 = y$

   b. $6x - 2y = 5$
         $3x + 2y = -2$

   c. $5 - y = 3x$
         $y = 2x$

   d. $y = \frac{1}{4}x + 5$
         $y = 2x - 9$

4-99.   Consider the equation $-6x = 4 - 2y$.

   a.   If you graphed this equation, what shape would the graph have? How can you tell?

   b.   Without changing the form of the equation, find the coordinates of three points that must be on the graph of this equation. Then graph the equation on graph paper.

   c.   Solve the equation for y. Does your answer agree with your graph? If so, how do they agree? If not, check your work to find the error.

4-100.   A tile pattern has 10 tiles in Figure 2 and increases by 2 tiles for each figure. Find a rule for this pattern and then determine how many tiles are in Figure 100.

4-101.   Make a table and graph the rule $y = -x^2 + x + 2$ on graph paper. Label the x-intercepts.

4-102.   Mr. Greer solved the equation below. However, when he checked his solution, it did not make the original equation true. Find his error and then find the correct solution.

$$4x = 8(2x - 3)$$
$$4x = 16x - 3$$
$$-12x = -3$$
$$x = \frac{-3}{-12}$$
$$x = \frac{1}{4}$$

4-103.   Mr. Saksunn is concerned with his students' scores on the last math test and also concerned about the number of students looking tired in class. He decides to see if there is a relationship between the number of tired or sleepy behaviors (yawns, nodding-off, head on desk) a student exhibits and their test score. He has his assistant observe 10 students and count the number of tired behaviors during one week of class.

Tired Behaviors	2	4	0	2	1	7	0	1	3	6
Test Score	73	63	89	85	90	58	97	90	79	41

a.   Make a scatterplot on graph paper and draw the line of best fit. Determine the equation of the line of best fit.

b.   Using your equation from part (a), estimate the test score of a student who exhibits 5 tired behaviors during Professor Saksunn's math class in a week.

4-104.   Thirty coins, all dimes and nickels, are worth $2.60. How many nickels are there?

4-105.   **Multiple Choice:** Martha's equation has the graph shown at right. Which of these are solutions to Martha's equation? (Remember that more than one answer may be correct.)

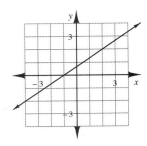

a. $(-4, -2)$ b. $(-1, 0)$

c. $x = 0$ and $y = 1$ d. $x = 2$ and $y = 2$

4-106.   Copy and complete the table below. Then write the corresponding rule.

IN (x)	2	10	6	7	–3	0	–10	100	x
OUT (y)	–7				18	3			

4-107.   Simplify each expression. In parts (c) and (d) write your answers using scientific notation.

   a. $2^3 \cdot 5^{-2}$

   b. $(xy^2)^3 \cdot (x^{-2})$

   c. $3 \times 10^3 \cdot 4 \times 10^5$

   d. $\frac{4 \times 10^2}{5 \times 10^{-2}}$

4-108.   Using the variable x, write an equation that has no solution. Explain how you know it has no solution.

4-109.   If $f(x) = 3 - |x|$ and $g(x) = \sqrt[3]{x} + 5$, then find:

   a. $f(-5)$

   b. $g(64)$

   c. $f(0)$

   d. $f(2)$

   e. $g(-8)$

   f. $g(0)$

4-110.   **Multiple Choice:** Which equation below could represent a tile pattern that grows by 3 and has 9 tiles in Figure 2?

   a. $3x + y = 3$ b. $-3x + y = 9$ c. $-3x + y = 3$ d. $2x + 3y = 9$

4-111.   Solve the systems of equations below using the method of your choice. Check your solutions, if possible.

   a. $y = 7 - 2x$
        $2x + y = 10$

   b. $3y - 1 = x$
        $4x - 2y = 16$

4-112.   Decide if the statement below is true or false. Justify your response.

"The expression $(x+3)(x-1)$ is equivalent to $(x-1)(3+x)$."

4-113.   Find each of the following products by drawing and labeling a generic rectangle or by using the Distributive Property.

a. $(x+5)(x+4)$ b. $2y(y+3)$

4-114.   Solve each equation below for the indicated variable, if possible. Show all steps.

a.   Solve for x: $2x+22=12$ b.   Solve for y: $2x-y=3$

c.   Solve for x: $2x+15=2x-15$ d.   Solve for y: $6x+2y=10$

4-115.   **Consecutive integers** are integers that are in order without skipping, such as 3, 4, and 5. Find three consecutive numbers with a sum of 54.

Chapter 4 Closure   What have I learned?

Reflection and Synthesis

The activities below offer you a chance to
reflect about what you have learned during this
chapter. As you work, look for concepts that
you feel very comfortable with, ideas that you
would like to learn more about, and topics you
need more help with. Look for connections
between ideas as well as connections with
material you learned previously.

①   TEAM BRAINSTORM

What have you studied in this chapter? What ideas were important in what you
learned? With your team, brainstorm a list. Be as detailed as you can. To help
get you started, a list of Learning Log entries and Math Notes boxes are below.

What topics, ideas, and words that you learned *before* this chapter are connected
to the new ideas in this chapter? Again, be as detailed as you can.

How long can you make your list? Challenge yourselves. Be prepared to share
your team's ideas with the class.

Learning Log Entries
- Lesson 4.2.2 – Solutions to Two-Variable Equations
- Lesson 4.2.5 – Solving Systems of Equations

Math Notes
- Lesson 4.1.1 – Line of Best Fit
- Lesson 4.1.2 – The Equal Values Method
- Lesson 4.2.1 – Describing Association
- Lesson 4.2.2 – The Substitution Method
- Lesson 4.2.3 – Systems of Linear Equations
- Lesson 4.2.4 – Forms of a Linear Function
- Lesson 4.2.5 – Intersection, Parallel, and Coincide

②   MAKING CONNECTIONS

Below is a list of the vocabulary used in this chapter. Make sure that you are familiar with all of these words and know what they mean. Refer to the glossary or index for any words that you do not yet understand.

infinite solutions	coincide	Elimination Method
Equal Values Method	equation	graph
"let" statement	no solution	mathematical sentence
model	$y = mx + b$	parallel
point of intersection	situation	solution
standard form	Substitution Method	system of equations
table		

Make a concept map showing all of the connections you can find among the key words and ideas listed above. To show a connection between two words, draw a line between them and explain the connection, as shown in the model below. A word can be connected to any other word as long as you can justify the connection. For each key word or idea, provide an example or sketch that shows the idea.

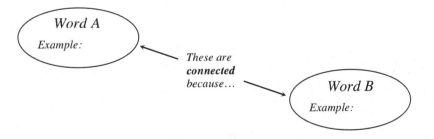

Your teacher may provide you with vocabulary cards to help you get started. If you use the cards to plan your concept map, be sure either to re-draw your concept map on your paper or to glue the vocabulary cards to a poster with all of the connections explained for others to see and understand.

While you are making your map, your team may think of related words or ideas that are not listed here. Be sure to include these ideas on your concept map.

③   PORTFOLIO: EVIDENCE OF MATHEMATICAL PROFICIENCY

Copy all your work from problem 4-36 into your portfolio. This will provide evidence of your early understanding of describing an association. After Chapter 6, you can compare your work on this problem to other statistics problems to see how much your understanding has grown.

Your teacher may have also assigned some or all of the problems from Lesson 4.3.1 as portfolio entries. Make sense of the problems by making connections between all of the topics you have studied in Chapters 1 through 4 and in previous courses. Show all your work, explain your reasoning, and make viable arguments for your answers. Pay attention to precision.

Alternatively, your teacher may ask you to include all your work from problem 4-77. Obtain the Chapter 4 Closure Resource Page: Systems of Equations Graphic Organizer from your teacher and complete it for problem 4-77. Then include your work for problems 4-78 and 4-79. Justify your reasons for choosing one strategy over the others. Show all of your work and be sure to check your solutions.

④   WHAT HAVE I LEARNED?

Most of the problems in this section represent typical problems found in this chapter. They serve as a gauge for you. You can use them to determine which types of problems you can do well and which types of problems require further study and practice. Even if your teacher does not assign this section, it is a good idea to try these problems and find out for yourself what you know and what you still need to work on.

Solve each problem as completely as you can. The table at the end of the closure section has answers to these problems. It also tells you where you can find additional help and practice with problems like these.

CL 4-116. Solve the system of equations shown at right.
$$y = 3x + 2$$
$$6x - 2y = 8$$

    a.   Describe what happened when you tried to solve the system.

    b.   Graph the system of equations. How does the graph of the system explain what happened with the equations?

CL 4-117. Solve the system of equations shown at right.
$$18x - 3y = 9$$
$$y = 6x - 3$$

    a.   Describe what happened when you tried to solve the system.

    b.   Graph the system of equations. How does the graph of the system explain what happened with the equations?

CL 4-118. Solve these systems of equations using any method.

    a. $y = 3x + 7$ b. $3x - y = 17$ c. $x = 3y - 5$
            $y = -4x + 21$ $-x + y = -7$ $2x + 12y = -4$

CL 4-119. Bob climbed down a ladder from his roof, while Roy climbed up another ladder next to him. Each ladder had 30 rungs. Their friend Jill recorded the following information about Bob and Roy:

Bob went down 2 rungs every second.

Roy went up 1 rung every second.

At some point, Bob and Roy were at the same height. Which rung were they on?

CL 4-120. Solve for x.

    a. $6x - 11 = 4x + 12$ b. $2(3x - 5) = 6x - 4$

    c. $(x - 3)(x + 4) = x^2 + 4$ d. $\frac{x}{25} = \frac{7}{10}$

    e. $\frac{2}{3}x + 3 = \frac{1}{4}x - 7$ f. $x + \frac{x}{3} = 4$

CL 4-121.   Solve the equations in parts (a) and (b) for y.

   a. $-6x - 2y = 8$ b. $2x^2 + 2y = 4x + 2x^2 - 7$

   c.   For each of the two solved equations, find the y-intercept and slope. Justify your answers.

CL 4-122.   Leo solved a system of equations by graphing and the graph is shown at right.

   a.   Estimate the solution from the graph.

   b.   What is the equation of each line in the system?

   c.   Solve the system algebraically. How accurate was your estimate?

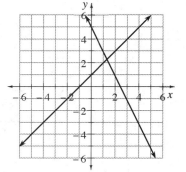

CL 4-123.   As treasurer of his school's FFA club, Kenny wants to buy gifts for all 18 members. He can buy t-shirts for $9 and sweatshirts for $15. The club has only $180 to spend. If Kenny wants to spend all of the club's money, how many of each type of gift can he buy?

   a.   Write a system of equations representing this problem.

   b.   Solve your system of equations and figure out how many of each type of gift Kenny should buy.

CL 4-124.   Simplify each expression to one without zero or negative exponents. In part (d), write the answer in scientific notation.

   a. 3^{-2} b. $a^3 b^2 (b^{-1})^3$ c. $\dfrac{x^2 y^3}{x^2 y^{-1}}$ d. $\dfrac{4 \times 10^5}{8 \times 10^7}$

CL 4-125.   Rewrite each expression below as a product and as a sum.

   a. $(x + 7)(2x - 5)$ b. $5x(y - 7)$ c. $(3x - 7)(x^2 - 2x + 11)$

Core Connections Algebra

CL 4-126. Check your answers using the table at the end of the closure section. Which problems do you feel confident about? Which problems were hard? Use the table to make a list of topics you need help on and a list of topics you need to practice more.

Answers and Support for Closure Activity #4
What Have I Learned?

Note: MN = Math Note, LL = Learning Log

Problem	Solution	Need Help?	More Practice
CL 4-116.	a. Setting the two equations equal to each other results in an answer that is not possible, so no solution. b. There can be no intersection because the lines are parallel.	Section 4.2 MN: 4.2.3 and 4.2.5 LL: 4.2.2 and 4.2.5	Problems 4-60(c), 4-69, and 4-81
CL 4-117.	a. Setting the two equations equal to each other results in an answer that is all real numbers. b. The two lines coincide is why the answer is all numbers.	Section 4.2 MN: 4.2.3 and 4.2.5 LL: 4.2.2 and 4.2.5	Problems 4-47, 4-61, 4-74, 4-81, 4-98, and 4-111
CL 4-118.	a. $x = 2$, $y = 13$ b. $x = 5$, $y = -2$ c. $x = -4$, $y = \frac{1}{3}$	Section 4.2 MN: 4.1.2, 4.2.2 and 4.2.3 LL: 4.2.2 and 4.2.5	Problems 4-60, 4-71, 4-81, 4-98, and 4-111
CL 4-119.	They were on the 10th rung.	Chapter 4 MN: 4.2.3 LL: 4.2.5	Problems 4-25, 4-26, 4-38, 4-51, 4-82, and 4-104

Problem	Solution	Need Help?	More Practice
CL 4-120.	a. $x = 11.5$ b. no solution c. $x = 16$ d. $x = 17.5$ e. $x = -24$ f. $x = 3$	Lesson 3.2.1, Checkpoints 2 and 4	Problems CL 2-107, CL 3-116, 4-9, 4-37, 4-54, and 4-86
CL 4-121.	a. $y = -3x - 4$ b. $y = 2x - \frac{7}{2}$ c. (a) y-intercept: $(0, -4)$, slope: -3 (b) y-intercept: $(0, -3.5)$, slope: 2	Lessons 2.1.4 and 3.2.2	Problems CL 3-117, 4-99, and 4-114
CL 4-122.	b. $y = -2x + 5$ and $y = x + 1$ c. $\left(1\frac{1}{3}, 2\frac{1}{3}\right)$	Section 4.2 MN: 4.2.1, 4.2.2, and 4.2.3 LL: 4.2.5	Problem 4-40, 4-60, 4-71, 4-81, 4-98, and 4-111
CL 4-123.	a. $9x + 15y = 180$, $x + y = 18$ b. 15 t-shirts, 3 sweatshirts	Chapter 4 MN: 4.2.3 LL: 4.2.5	Problems 4-25, 4-26, 4-38, 4-51, 4-82, and 4-104
CL 4-124.	a. $\frac{1}{9}$ b. $\frac{a^3}{b}$ c. y^4 d. 5×10^{-3}	Section 3.1	Problems CL 3-121, 4-11, 4-41, and 4-107
CL 4-125.	a. $2x^2 + 9x - 35$ b. $5xy - 35x$ c. $3x^3 - 13x^2 + 47x - 77$	Section 3.2 MN: 3.3.3 LL: 3.2.2	Problems CL 3-114, 4-19, 4-64, and 4-102

SEQUENCES

5

CHAPTER 5   Sequences

Chapter 5 provides you an opportunity to review and strengthen your algebra skills while you learn about arithmetic and geometric sequences. Early in the chapter, you will find yourself using familiar strategies such as looking for patterns and making tables to write algebraic equations describing sequences of numbers. Later in the chapter, you will develop shortcuts for writing equations for certain kinds of sequences.

Guiding Question

Mathematically proficient students look for and express regularity in repeated reasoning.

As you work through this chapter, ask yourself:

When patterns are repeated, can I find shortcuts that lead to equations?

Chapter Outline

Section 5.1 This section begins with lessons that ask you to describe the growth of a rabbit population and the decreasing rebound height of a bouncing ball. You will use tables, graphs, and equations to represent the growth.

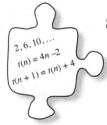

Section 5.2 You will do an investigation where you categorize several sequences. You will also learn some of the specialized vocabulary used when discussing sequences. You will create multiple representations of arithmetic sequences, including equations for sequences that depend on previous terms.

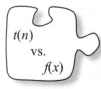

Section 5.3 In this section you will compare the growth of various sequences and recognize growth by multiplication and growth by addition. Then you will create multiple representations of geometric sequences and compare sequences to functions.

5.1.1 How does the pattern grow?

Representing Exponential Growth

So far in this course, you have been investigating the family of linear functions using multiple representations (especially tables, graphs, and equations). In this chapter, you will learn about a new family of functions and the type of growth it models.

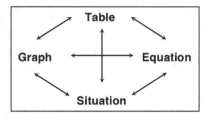

5-1.   MULTIPLYING LIKE BUNNIES

In the book *Of Mice and Men* by John Steinbeck, two good friends named Lenny and George dream of raising rabbits and living off the land. What if their dream came true?

Suppose Lenny and George started with two rabbits and that in each month following those rabbits have two babies. Also suppose that every month thereafter, each pair of rabbits has two babies.

Your Task: With your team, determine how many rabbits Lenny and George would have after one year (12 months). Represent this situation with a written description of the pattern of growth, a diagram, and a table. What patterns can you find and how do they compare to other patterns that you have investigated previously?

Discussion Points

What strategies could help us keep track of the total number of rabbits?

What patterns can we see in the growth of the rabbit population?

How can we predict the total number of rabbits after many months have passed?

5-2. How can you determine the number of rabbits that will exist at the end of one year? Consider this as you answer the questions below.

   a. Draw a diagram to represent how the total number of rabbits is growing each month. How many rabbits will Lenny and George have after three months?

   b. As the number of rabbits becomes larger, a diagram becomes too cumbersome to be useful. A table might work better. Organize your information in a table showing the total number of rabbits for the first several months (at least 6 months). What patterns can you find in your table? Describe the pattern of growth in words.

   c. If you have not done so already, use your pattern to determine the number of rabbits that Lenny and George would have after one year (12 months) have passed.

   d. How does the growth in the table that you created compare to the growth patterns that you have investigated previously? How is it similar and how is it different?

————— *Further Guidance* —————
section ends here.

5-3. Lenny and George want to raise as many rabbits as possible, so they have a few options to consider. They could start with a larger number of rabbits, or they could raise a breed of rabbits that reproduces faster. How do you think that each of these options would change the pattern of growth you observed in the previous problem? Which situation might yield the largest rabbit population after one year?

   a. To help answer these questions, model each case below with a table for the first five months.

      Case 2: Start with 10 rabbits; each pair has 2 babies per month.

      Case 3: Start with 2 rabbits; each pair has 4 babies per month.

      Case 4: Start with 2 rabbits; each pair has 6 babies per month.

   b. Which case would appear to give Lenny and George the most rabbits after one year? How many rabbits would they have in that case?

5-4.   A NEW FAMILY

Look back at the tables you created in problems 5-1 and 5-3.

a.   What pattern do they all have in common? Functions that have this pattern are called **exponential functions**.

b.   Obtain the Lesson 5.1.1 Resource Page from your teacher. Graph the data for Case 2. Give a complete description of the graph.

5-5.   LEARNING LOG

To represent the growth in number of rabbits in problems 5-1 and 5-3, you discovered a new function family that is not linear. Functions in this new family are called exponential functions. Throughout this chapter and later in Chapter 7, you will learn more about this special family of functions.

Write a Learning Log entry to record what you have learned so far about exponential functions. For example, what do their graphs look like? What patterns do you observe in their tables? Title this entry "Exponential Functions" and include today's date.

MᴇᴛHODS AND Mᴇᴀɴɪɴɢs

The Elimination Method

When solving a system of equations, it may be easier to eliminate one of the variables by adding multiples of the two equations. This process is called **elimination**.

The first step is to rewrite the equations so that the x and y variables are lined up vertically. Next, decide what number to multiply each equation by, if necessary, in order to make the coefficients of either the x-terms or the y-terms add up to zero. Be sure that you can justify each step in the solution.

For example, consider the system at right.

$$10y - 3x = 14$$
$$4y + 2x = -4$$

You can eliminate the x-terms by multiplying the top equation by 2 and the bottom equation by 3 and then adding the equations, as shown at right.

$$(10y - 3x = 14) \cdot 2 \rightarrow 20y - 6x = 28$$
$$(4y + 2x = -4) \cdot 3 \rightarrow \underline{12y + 6x = -12}$$

Add the resulting equations: $32y = 16$

Divide: $y = 0.5$

Finally, substitute 0.5 for y in either original equation:

Thus, the solution to the original system is $(-3, 0.5)$.

$$10(0.5) - 3x = 14$$
$$5 - 3x = 14$$
$$-3x = 9$$
$$x = -3$$

Check your solution by evaluating for x and y in *both* of the *original* equations.

5-6. What if the data for Lenny and George (from problem 5-1) matched the data in each table below? Assuming that the growth of the rabbits multiplies as it did in problem 5-1, complete each of the following tables. Show your thinking or give a brief explanation of how you know what the missing entries are.

a.
Months	Rabbits
0	4
1	12
2	36
3	
4	

b.
Months	Rabbits
0	6
1	
2	24
3	
4	96

5-7. Solve the following systems of equations algebraically. Then graph each system to confirm your solution.

a. $x + y = 3$
   $x = 3y - 5$

b. $x - y = -5$
   $y = -2x - 4$

5-8. For the function $f(x) = \frac{6}{2x-3}$, find the value of each expression below.

a. $f(1)$ b. $f(0)$ c. $f(-3)$ d. $f(1.5)$

e. What value of x would make $f(x) = 4$?

5-9. Benjamin is taking Algebra 1 and is stuck on the problem shown below. Examine his work so far and help him by showing and explaining the remaining steps.

Original problem: Simplify $(3a^{-2}b)^3$.

He knows that $(3a^{-2}b)^3 = (3a^{-2}b)(3a^{-2}b)(3a^{-2}b)$. Now what?

5-10.   Simplify each expression below. Assume that the denominator in part (b) is not equal to zero.

   a. $(x^3)(x^{-2})$ b. $\dfrac{y^5}{y^{-2}}$ c. 4^{-1} d. $(4x^2)^3$

5-11.   The equation of a line describes the relationship between the x- and y-coordinates of the points on the line.

   a.   Plot the points $(3, -1)$, $(3, 2)$, and $(3, 4)$ and draw the line that passes through them. State the coordinates of two more points on the line. Then answer this question: What will be true of the coordinates of any other point on this line? Now write an equation that says exactly the same thing. (Do not worry if it is very simple! If it accurately describes all the points on this line, it is correct.)

   b.   Plot the points $(5, -1)$, $(1, -1)$, and $(-3, -1)$. What is the equation of the line that goes through these points?

   c.   Choose any three points on the y-axis. What must be the equation of the line that goes through those points?

5-12.   Jill is studying a strange bacterium. When she first looks at the bacteria, there are 1000 cells in her sample. The next day, there are 2000 cells. Intrigued, she comes back the next day to find that there are 4000 cells!

   a.   Should the graph of this situation be linear or curved?

   b.   Create a table and graph for this situation. The inputs are the days that have passed after she first began to study the sample, and the outputs are the number of cells of bacteria.

5-13.   Write each expression below in a simpler form.

   a. $\dfrac{5^{723}}{5^{721}}$ b. $\dfrac{3^{300}}{3^{249}}$ c. $\left(\dfrac{3 \cdot 4^3}{3^{-2} \cdot 4^{-7}}\right)^0$ d. $\left(\dfrac{4 \times 10^3}{10^{-2}}\right)^2$

200   *Core Connections Algebra*

5-14. Jackie and Alexa were working on homework together when Jackie said, *"I got x = 5 as the solution, but it looks like you got something different. Which solution is right?"*

$$(x+4)^2 - 2x - 5 = (x-1)^2$$
$$x^2 + 16 - 2x - 5 = x^2 + 1$$
$$16 - 2x - 5 = 1$$
$$11 - 2x = 1$$
$$-2x = -10$$
$$x = 5$$

"I think you made a mistake," said Alexa. Did Jackie make a mistake? Help Jackie figure out whether she made a mistake and, if she did, explain her mistake and show her how to solve the equation correctly. Jackie's work is shown above right.

5-15. Solve each of the following equations.

a. $\frac{m}{6} = \frac{15}{18}$

b. $\frac{\pi}{7} = \frac{a}{4}$

5-16. Write the equation of each line described below.

a. A line with slope –2 and *y*-intercept 7.

b. A line with slope $-\frac{3}{2}$ and *x*-intercept $(4, 0)$.

5-17. The dartboard shown at right is in the shape of an equilateral triangle. It has a smaller equilateral triangle in the center, which was made by joining the midpoints of the three edges. If a dart hits the board at random, what is the probability that:

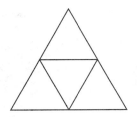

a. The dart hits the center triangle?

b. The dart misses the center triangle but hits the board?

5.1.2 How high will it bounce?

Rebound Ratios

Many games depend on how a ball bounces. For example, if different basketballs rebounded differently, one basketball would bounce differently off of a backboard than another would, and this could cause basketball players to miss their shots. For this reason, manufacturers have to make balls' bounciness conform to specific standards. In this lesson, you will investigate the relationship between the height from which you drop a ball and the height to which it rebounds.

5-18. Listed below are "bounciness" standards for different kinds of balls.

- Tennis balls: Must rebound approximately 111 cm when dropped from 200 cm.

- Soccer balls: Must rebound approximately 120 cm when dropped from 200 cm onto a steel plate.

- Basketballs: Must rebound approximately 53.5 inches when dropped from 72 inches onto a wooden floor.

- Squash balls: Must rebound approximately 29.5 inches when dropped from 100 inches onto a steel plate at 70° F.

Discuss with your team how you can measure a ball's bounciness. Which ball listed above is the bounciest? Justify your answer.

5-19.   THE BOUNCING BALL

How can you determine if a ball meets expected standards?

Your Task: With your team, find the rebound ratio for a ball. Your teacher will provide you with a ball and a measuring device. You will be using the same ball again later, so make sure you can identify which ball your team is using. Before you start your experiment, discuss the following questions with your team.

What do we need to measure?

How should we organize our data?

How can we be confident that our data is accurate?

You should choose one person in your team to be the recorder, one to be the ball dropper, and two to be the spotters. When you are confident that you have a good plan, ask your teacher to come to your team and approve your plan.

5-20.   MODELING YOUR DATA

Work with your team to model the data you collected by considering parts (a) through (c) below.

a.   In problem 5-19, does the height from which the ball is dropped depend on the rebound height, or is it the other way around? With your team, decide which is the independent variable and which is the dependent variable.

b.   Graph your results on a full sheet of graph paper. Draw a line that best fits your data. Should this line go through the origin? Why or why not? Justify your answer in terms of what the origin represents in the context of this problem.

c.   Find an equation for your line.

5-21.   What is the rebound ratio for your team's ball? How is the rebound ratio reflected in the graph of your line of best fit? Where is it reflected in the equation for your data? Where is it reflected in your table?

Save your data and your graph in a safe place. You will need them for the next lesson.

METHODS AND MEANINGS

Continuous and Discrete Graphs

MATH NOTES

When the points on a graph are connected, and it *makes sense* to connect them, the graph is said to be **continuous**. If the graph is not continuous, and is just a sequence of separate points, the graph is called **discrete**.

For example, the graph below left represents the cost of buying x shirts, and it is discrete because you can only buy whole numbers of shirts. The graph farthest right represents the cost of buying x gallons of gasoline, and it is continuous because you can buy any (non-negative) amount of gasoline.

Discrete Graph

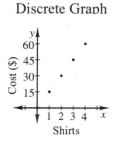

Continuous Graph

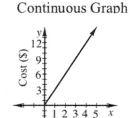

Review & Preview

5-22. Solve each system of equations below.

a. $y = 3x + 1$
$x + 2y = -5$

b. $2x + 3y = 9$
$x - 2y = 1$

5-23. Solve each equation for the indicated variable.

a. $t = an + b$ (for b)

b. $\frac{y}{3} - a = b$ (for y)

c. $m = \frac{y}{x}$ (for y)

d. $m = \frac{y}{x}$ (for x)

5-24. Simplify each expression below.

a. $\frac{6x^2 y^3}{3xy}$

b. $(-mn)^3$

c. $(mn)^{-3}$

d. $\frac{3.2 \times 10^{-2}}{8 \times 10^3}$

5-25.   Determine the domain and range of each of the following graphs.

a.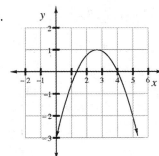

b.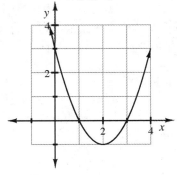

c.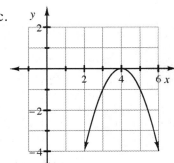

d.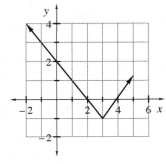

5-26.   The graph at right compares the age and the number of pets for a certain population.

Describe the association for this population.

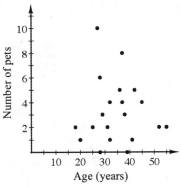

5-27.   At an aunt's wedding, Nicolas collected data about an ice sculpture that was about to completely melt. A graph of his data is shown at right.

a.   Calculate the equation of a line of best fit.

b.   Based on your equation, how tall was the ice sculpture one hour before Nicolas started measuring?

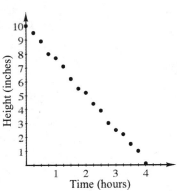

5.1.3 What is the pattern?

The Bouncing Ball and Exponential Decay

In Lesson 5.1.2, you found that the relationship between the height from which a ball is dropped and its rebound height is determined by a constant multiplier. In this lesson, you will continue this investigation by exploring the mathematical relationship between how many times a ball has bounced and the height of each bounce.

5-28. Consider the work you did in Lesson 5.1.2, in which you found the rebound ratio for a ball.

a. What was the rebound ratio for the ball your team used?

b. Did the height you dropped the ball from affect this ratio?

c. If you were to use the same ball again and drop it from *any* height, could you predict its rebound height? Explain how you would do this.

5-29. A MODEL FOR MANY BOUNCES

Imagine that you drop the ball you used in problem 5-19 from a height of 200 cm, but this time you let it bounce repeatedly.

a. As a team, discuss this situation. Then sketch a picture showing what this situation would look like. Your sketch should show a minimum of 6 bounces after you release the ball.

b. Predict your ball's rebound height after each successive bounce if its starting height is 200 cm. Create a table with these predicted heights.

c. What are the independent and dependent variables in this situation?

d. Graph your predicted rebound heights.

e. Should the points on your graph be connected? How can you tell?

5-30.   TESTING THE MANY-BOUNCE MODEL

Now you will test the accuracy of the
predictions you made in problem 5-29.

Your Task: Test your predictions by collecting
experimental data. Use the same team roles as
you used in problem 5-19. Drop your ball,
starting from an initial height of 200 cm, and
record your data in a table. Then compare your
experimental data to your predictions using
your table and your graph. How do they compare? What might cause your
experimental data to be different from your predictions? Do you think that your
table and graph model the situation appropriately? Why or why not?

These suggestions will help you gather accurate data:

- Have a spotter catch the ball just as it reaches the top of its first rebound
  and have the spotter "freeze" the ball in place.

- Record the first rebound height and then drop the ball again from that
  new height.

- Catch and "freeze" it again at the second rebound height.

- Repeat this process until you have collected at least six data points (or
  until the height of the bounce is so small that it is not reasonable to
  continue).

5-31.   Compare your graph for the height of successive bounces in problem 5-29 to the
graph for drop height versus bounce height that you investigated in Lesson
5.1.2.

a.   Can you use the same kind of equation to model the two situations? That
is, what family of functions do you think would make the best fit for each
data set? Discuss this with your team and be ready to report and justify
your choice.

b.   Describe how the pattern of growth for successive bounces is the same as
or different from other models that you have looked at previously.

5-32.   If you continued to let your ball bounce uninterrupted, how high would the ball
be after 12 bounces? Would the ball ever stop bouncing? Explain your answer
in terms of both your experimental data and your equation.

5-33.   Notice that your investigations of rebound patterns in Lessons 5.1.2 and 5.1.3 involved both a linear and an exponential model. Look back over your work and discuss with your team why each model was appropriate for its specific purpose. Be prepared to share your ideas with the class.

5-34.   DeShawna and her team gathered data for their ball and recorded it in the table shown at right.

Drop Height	Rebound Height
150 cm	124 cm
70 cm	59 cm
120 cm	100 cm
100 cm	83 cm
110 cm	92 cm
40 cm	33 cm

a.   What is the rebound ratio for their ball?

b.   Predict how high DeShawna's ball will rebound if it is dropped from 275 cm. Look at the precision of DeShawna's measurements in the table. Round your calculation to a reasonable number of decimal places.

c.   Suppose the ball is dropped and you notice that its rebound height is 60 cm. From what height was the ball dropped? Use an appropriate precision for your answer.

d.   Suppose the ball is dropped from a window 200 meters up the Empire State Building. What would you predict the rebound height to be after the first bounce?

e.   How high would the ball in part (d) rebound after the second bounce? After the third bounce?

5-35.   Look back at the data given in problem 5-18 that describes the rebound ratio for an official tennis ball. Suppose you drop such a tennis ball from an initial height of 10 feet.

a.   How high would it rebound after the first bounce?

b.   How high would it rebound after the second bounce?

c.   How high would it rebound after the fifth bounce?

5-36.   Solve the following systems of equations algebraically and then confirm your solutions by graphing.

a. $y = 3x - 2$
      $4x + 2y = 6$

b. $x = y - 4$
      $2x - y = -5$

5-37.   Lona received a stamp collection from her grandmother. The collection is in a leather book and currently has 120 stamps. Lona joined a stamp club, which sends her 12 new stamps each month. The stamp book holds a maximum of 500 stamps.

a.   Complete the table at right.

b.   How many stamps will Lona have in one year from now?

c.   Write an equation using function notation to represent the total number of stamps that Lona has in her collection after n months. Let the total be represented by $t(n)$.

Month	Stamps
0	120
1	132
2	
3	
4	
5	

d.   Solve your equation from part (c) for n when $t(n) = 500$. Will Lona be able to fill her book exactly with no stamps remaining? How do you know? When will the book be filled?

5-38.   Use slope to determine whether the points $A(3, 5)$, $B(-2, 6)$, and $C(-5, 7)$ are on the same line. Justify your conclusion algebraically.

5-39.   Serena wanted to examine the graphs of the equations below on her graphing calculator. Rewrite each of the equations in **y-form** (when the equation is solved for y) so that she can enter them into the calculator.

a. $5 - (y - 2) = 3x$

b. $5(x + y) = -2$

5.2.1 How can I describe a sequence?

Generating and Investigating Sequences

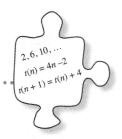

In the bouncing ball activity from Lessons 5.1.2 and 5.1.3, you used multiple representations (a table, an equation, and a graph) to represent a discrete situation involving a bouncing ball (a situation). Today you will learn about a new way to represent a discrete pattern, called a sequence.

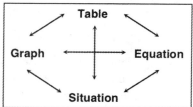

5-40.   Samantha was thinking about George and Lenny and their rabbits. When she listed the number of rabbits George and Lenny could have each month, she ended up with the ordered list below, called a **sequence**.

$$2, 6, 18, 54, \ldots$$

She realized that she could represent this situation using a sequence-generating machine that would generate the number of rabbits each month by doing something to the previous month's number of rabbits. She tested her generator by putting in a **first term** of 2 and she recorded each output before putting it into the next machine. Below is the diagram she used to explain her idea to her teammates.

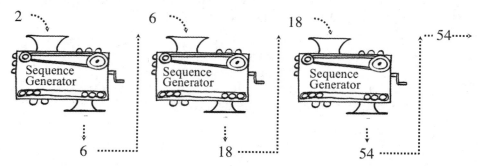

a.   What does Samantha's sequence generator seem to be doing to each input?

b.   What are the next two terms of Samantha's sequence? Show how you got your answer.

c.   Samantha decided to use the same sequence generator, but this time she started with a first term of 5. What are the next four terms in this new sequence?

Core Connections Algebra

5-41.   SEQUENCE FAMILIES

Samantha and her teacher have been busy creating new sequence generators and the sequences they produce. Below are the sequences Samantha and her teacher created.

a. $-4, -1, 2, 5, \ldots$ b. $1.5, 3, 6, 12, \ldots$

c. $0, 1, 4, 9, \ldots$ d. $2, 3.5, 5, 6.5, \ldots$

e. $1, 1, 2, 3, 5, 8, \ldots$ f. $9, 7, 5, 3, \ldots$

g. $48, 24, 12, \ldots$ h. $27, 9, 3, 1, \ldots$

i. $8, 2, 0, 2, 8, 18, \ldots$ j. $\frac{5}{4}, \frac{5}{2}, 5, 10, \ldots$

Your teacher will give your team a set of Lesson 5.2.1A Resource Pages with the above sequences on strips so that everyone in your team can see and work with them in the middle of your workspace.

Your Task: Working together, organize the sequences into families of similar sequences. Your team will need to decide how many families to make, what common features make the sequences a family, and what characteristics make each family different from the others. Follow the directions below. As you work, use the following questions to help guide your team's discussion.

Discussion Points

How can we describe the pattern?

How does it grow?

What do they have in common?

(1)   As a team, initially sort the sequence strips into groups based on your first glance at the sequences. Remember that you can sort the sequences into more than two families. You will have a chance to revise your groups of sequences throughout this activity, so just sort them in a way that makes sense to start out with. Which seem to behave similarly? Record your groupings and what they have in common before proceeding.

(2)   If one exists, find a sequence generator (growth pattern) for each sequence and write it on the strip. You can express the sequence generator either in symbols or in words. Also record the next three terms in each sequence on the strips. Do your sequence families still make sense? If so, what new information do you have about your sequence families? If not, reorganize the strips and explain how you decided to group them.

Problem continues on next page. →

5-41.   *Problem continued from previous page.*

(3)   Get a set of Lesson 5.2.1B Resource Pages for your team. Then record each sequence in a table. Your table should compare the **term number**, n, to the value of each **term**, $t(n)$. This means that your sequence itself is a list of *outputs* of the relationship and the *inputs* are a list of integers! The first term in a sequence is always $n = 1$. Attach the table to the sequence strip it represents. Do your sequence families still make sense? Record any new information or reorganize your sequence families if necessary.

(4)   Now graph each sequence on a Lesson 5.2.1C Resource Page. Include as many terms as will fit on the existing set of axes. Be sure to decide whether your graphs should be discrete or continuous. Use color to show the growth between the points on each graph. Attach the graph to the sequence strip it represents. Do your sequence families still make sense? Record any new information and reorganize your sequence families if necessary.

5-42.   Choose one of the families of sequences you created in problem 5-41. With your team, write clear summary statements about this family of sequences. Refer to the Discussion Points in problem 5-41 to help you write summary statements. Be sure to use multiple representations to justify each statement. Be prepared to share your summary statements with the class.

5-43.   Some types of sequences have special names.

a.   When the sequence generator *adds* a constant to each previous term, it is called an **arithmetic sequence**. Which of your sequences from problem 5-41 fall into this family? Should you include the sequence labeled (f) in this family? Why or why not?

Sequence Generator

b.   When the sequence generator *multiplies* a constant times each previous term, it is called a **geometric sequence**. Which of the sequences from problem 5-41 are geometric? Should sequence (h) be in this group? Why or why not?

5-44.   Find the slope of the line you would get if you graphed each sequence listed below and connected the points.

   a.   5, 8, 11, 14, ...   b.   3, 9, 15, ...

   c.   26, 21, 16, ...   d.   7, 8.5, 10, ...

5-45.   For the line passing through the points (–2,1) and (2,–11):

   a.   Calculate the slope of the line.

   b.   Find an equation of the line.

5-46.   Allie is making 8 dozen chocolate-chip muffins for the Food Fair at school. The recipe she is using makes 3 dozen muffins. If the original recipe calls for 16 ounces of chocolate chips, how many ounces of chocolate chips does she need for her new amount? (Allie buys her chocolate chips in bulk and can measure them to the nearest ounce.)

5-47.   The area of a square is 225 square centimeters.

   a.   Make a diagram and determine the length of each side.

   b.   Use the Pythagorean Theorem to find the length of the square's diagonal.

5-48.   Refer to sequences (c) and (i) in problem 5-41.

   a.   How are these two sequences similar?

   b.   The numbers in the sequence in part (e) from problem 5-41 are called **Fibonacci numbers**. They are named after an Italian mathematician who discovered the sequence while studying how fast rabbits could breed. What is different about this sequence than the other three you discovered?

5-49.   Chelsea dropped a bouncy ball off the roof while Nery recorded its rebound height. The table at right shows their data. Note that the 0 in the "Bounce" column represents the starting height.

Bounce	Rebound Height
0	800 cm
1	475 cm
2	290 cm
3	175 cm
4	100 cm
5	60 cm

a.   To what family does the function belong? Explain how you know.

b.   Show the data as a sequence. Is the sequence arithmetic, geometric, quadratic, or something else? Justify your answer.

5-50.   For the function $f(x) = \sqrt{3x - 2}$, find the value of each expression below.

a. $f(1)$ b. $f(9)$ c. $f(4)$ d. $f(0)$

e.   What value of x makes $f(x) = 6$?

5-51.   Simplify each expression below.

a. $y + 0.03y$ b. $z - 0.2z$ c. $x + 0.002x$

5-52.   A tank contains 8000 liters of water. Each day, half of the water in the tank is removed. How much water will be in the tank at the end of:

a.   The 4th day?   b.   The 8th day?

5-53.   Solve each system.

a. $y + 3x = -10$ b. $6x = 7 - 2y$
       $5x - y = 2$ $4x + y = 4$

5-54.   Draw a slope triangle and use it to find the equation of the line shown in the graph at right.

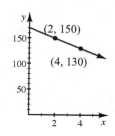

5-55. This problem is a checkpoint for laws of exponents and scientific notation. It will be referred to as Checkpoint 5A.

Simplify each expression. In parts (e) through (f) write the final answer in scientific notation.

a. $4^2 \cdot 4^5$

b. $(5^0)^3$

c. $x^{-5} \cdot x^3$

d. $(x^{-1} \cdot y^2)^3$

e. $(8 \times 10^5) \cdot (1.6 \times 10^{-2})$

f. $\dfrac{4 \times 10^3}{5 \times 10^5}$

Check your answers by referring to the Checkpoint 5A materials located at the back of your book.

If you needed help solving these problems correctly, then you need more practice. Review the Checkpoint 5A materials and try the practice problems. Also, consider getting help outside of class time. From this point on, you will be expected to do problems like these quickly and easily.

5.2.2 How do arithmetic sequences work?

Generalizing Arithmetic Sequences

In Lesson 5.2.1, you learned how to identify arithmetic and geometric sequences. Today you will solve problems involving arithmetic sequences. Use the questions below to help your team stay focused and start mathematical conversations.

What type of sequence is this? How do we know?

How can we find the equation?

Is there another way to see it?

5-56.   LEARNING THE LANGUAGE OF SEQUENCES

Sequences have their own notation and vocabulary that help describe them, such as "term" and "term number." The questions below will help you learn more of this vocabulary and notation.

Consider the sequence $-9, -5, -1, 3, 7, \ldots$ as you complete parts (a) through (i) below.

a.   Is this sequence arithmetic, geometric, or neither? How can you tell?

b.   What is the first term of the sequence?

c.   When the sequence generator adds a number to each term, the value that is added is known as the **common difference**. It is the difference between each term and the term before it.

      What is the sequence generator?

d.   Record the sequence in a table. Remember a sequence table compares the term number, n, to the value of each term, $t(n)$.

e.   What is $t(n)$ when $n = 0$?

f.   Graph the sequence. Should the graph be continuous or discrete? Why?

g.   Write an equation (beginning $t(n) =$) for the nth term of this sequence.

h.   What is the domain for the sequence equation that you have written?

i.   How is the **common difference** related to the graph and the equation? Why does this make sense?

5-57.   Consider the sequence $t(n) = -4, -1, 2, 5, \ldots$

a.   If the first term is $t(1)$, what is $t(0)$ for this sequence? What is the common difference?

b.   Write an equation for $t(n)$. Verify that your equation works for each of the first 4 terms of the sequence.

c.   Is it possible for $t(n)$ to equal 42? Justify your answer.

d.   For the function $f(x) = 3x - 7$, is it possible for $f(x)$ to equal 42? Explain.

e.   Explain the difference between $t(n)$ and $f(x)$ that makes your answers to parts (b) and (c) different.

5-58.   Trixie wants to create an especially tricky arithmetic sequence. She wants the 5th term of the sequence to equal 11 and the 50th term to equal 371. That is, she wants $t(5) = 11$ and $t(50) = 371$. Is it possible to create an arithmetic sequence to fit her information? If it is possible, find the sequence generator, the initial value $t(0)$, and then find the equation for the arithmetic sequence. If it is not possible, explain why not.

5-59.   Seven years ago, Kodi found a box of old baseball cards in the garage. Since then, he has added a consistent number of cards to the collection each year. He had 52 cards in the collection after 3 years and now has 108 cards.

   a.   How many cards were in the original box? Is this $t(0)$ or $t(1)$? Write the first few terms of the sequence.

   b.   Kodi plans to keep the collection for a long time. How many cards will the collection contain 10 years from now?

   c.   Write an equation that determines the number of cards in the collection after n years. What does each number in your equation represent?

5-60.   Trixie now wants an arithmetic sequence with a sequence generator of –17 and a 16th term of 93. (In other words, $t(16) = 93$.) Is it possible to create an arithmetic sequence to fit her information? If it is possible, find the equation. If it is not possible, explain why not.

5-61.   Your favorite radio station, WCPM,
is having a contest. The DJ poses a
question to the listeners. If the caller
answers correctly, he or she wins the
prize money. If the caller answers
incorrectly, $20 is added to the prize
money and the next caller is eligible
to win. The current question is
difficult, and no one has won for two
days.

a.   Lucky you! Fourteen people
already called in today with
incorrect answers, so when you
called (with the right answer, of
course) you won $735! How
much was the prize worth at the
beginning of the day today?

b.   Suppose the contest always starts with $100. How many people would
have to guess incorrectly for the winner to get $1360?

5-62.   Trixie is at it again. This time she wants an arithmetic sequence that has a graph
with a slope of 22. She also wants $t(8) = 164$ and the 13th term to have a value
of 300. Is it possible to create an arithmetic sequence to fit her information? If
it is possible, find the equation. If it is not possible, explain why not.

5-63.   Find the equation for each arithmetic sequence represented by the tables below.

a.

n	$t(n)$
7	54
3	10
19	186
16	153
40	417

b.

n	$t(n)$
100	10
70	100

5-64.   Trixie exclaimed, *"Hey! Arithmetic sequences are just another name for linear
functions."* What do you think? Justify your idea based on multiple
representations.

Core Connections Algebra

5-65. Determine whether 447 is a term of each sequence below. If so, which term is it?

a. $t(n) = 5n - 3$

b. $t(n) = 24 - 5n$

c. $t(n) = -6 + 3(n-1)$

d. $t(n) = 14 - 3n$

e. $t(n) = -8 - 7(n-1)$

5-66. Choose one of the sequences in problem 5-65 for which you determined that 447 is *not* a term. Write a clear explanation describing how you can be sure that 447 is not a term of the sequence.

5-67. Find the sequence generator for each sequence listed below. Write an equation for the nth term in each sequence below, keeping in mind that the first term of each sequence is $t(1)$.

a. $4, 7, 10, 13, \ldots$

b. $3, 8, 13, \ldots$

c. $24, 19, 14, \ldots$

d. $7, 9.5, 12, \ldots$

5-68. Great Amusements Park has been raising its ticket prices every year, as shown in the table at right.

a. Describe how the ticket prices are growing.

b. What will the price of admission be in year 6?

Year	Price
0	$50
1	$55
2	$60.50
3	$66.55

5-69. Solve the system at right for m and b.

$$1239 = 94m + b$$
$$810 = 61m + b$$

5-70. Write an equation or system of equations and solve the problem below.

The French club sold rose bouquets and chocolate hearts for Valentine's Day. The roses sold for $5 and the hearts sold for $3. The number of bouquets sold was 15 more than the number of hearts sold. If the club collected a total of $339, how many of each gift was sold?

5.2.3 How else can I write the equation?

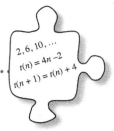

Recursive Sequences

In this chapter you have been writing equations for arithmetic sequences so that you could find the value of any term in the sequence, such as the 100th term, directly. Today you will investigate recursive sequences. A term in a recursive sequence depends on the term(s) before it.

5-71.   Look at the following sequence:

$$-8, -2, 4, 10, \ldots$$

a.   What are two ways that you could find the 10th term of the sequence? What is the 10th term?

b.   If you have not done so already, write an equation that lets you find the value of any term $t(n)$. This kind of equation is called an **explicit equation**.

c.   The next term after $t(n)$ is called $t(n+1)$. Write an equation to find $t(n+1)$ if you know what $t(n)$ is. An equation that depends on knowing other terms is called a **recursive equation**.

5-72.   Alejandro used his recursive equation, $t(n + 1) = t(n) + 6$, from part (c) of problem 5-71 to write the following sequence:

$$0, 6, 12, 18, 24$$

a.   Does Alejandro's sequence match the recursive equation from problem 5-71?

b.   If Alejandro did not make a mistake when writing his recursive equation, why did he get a different sequence than the one from problem 5-71? How can you mathematically write down the information he needs so that he can write the correct sequence?

5-73.   Avery and Collin were trying to challenge each other with equations for sequences. Avery wrote:

$$t(n+1) = t(n)^2 - 1$$
$$t(1) = 3$$

a.   Help Collin write the first 4 terms of this sequence.

b.   Is Avery's sequence arithmetic, geometric, or some other kind of sequence? How do you know?

c.   Describe to Collin how he could find the 10th term of this sequence. You do not need to actually find the 10th term.

5-74.   Avery and Collin were still at it.

a.   Collin wrote: $t(2) = 19$
$$t(n+1) = t(n) - 2$$

Help Avery write an explicit equation. Is the sequence arithmetic, geometric, or neither?

b.   Then Avery wrote $t(n) = 6n + 8$. Help Collin write a recursive equation.

5-75.   The Fibonacci sequence is a famous sequence that appears many times in mathematics. It can describe patterns found in nature, such as the number of petals on flowers, the arrangements of seeds in sunflowers, or scales on pinecones. It is named after Leonardo of Pisa, who was known as Fibonacci. He introduced the sequence to Western European mathematicians in 1202, though it had been described earlier by others including mathematicians in India.

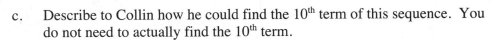

The equation that describes the Fibonacci sequence can be written as:

$$t(1) = 1$$
$$t(2) = 1$$
$$t(n+1) = t(n) + t(n-1)$$

a.   Write the first 10 terms of the Fibonacci sequence.

b.   Is the Fibonacci sequence arithmetic, geometric, or neither?

c.   Describe what you would need to do in order to find the 100th term of the Fibonacci sequence. Do not actually calculate the 100th term.

5-76. Avery and Collin were trying to challenge each other with equations for sequences. Avery was looking at an explicit equation that Collin wrote.

$$t(n) = 4.5n - 8$$

a. Write the first 4 terms for the sequence.

b. What would Avery do to write the 15th term of this sequence?

5-77. Write both an explicit equation and a recursive equation for the sequence: 5, 8, 11, 14, 17, ...

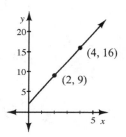

5-78. Draw a slope triangle and use it to find the equation of the line shown in the graph at right.

5-79. Find the following products.

a. $(4x + 5)(4x - 5)$

b. $(4x + 5)^2$

5-80. Write an equation or system of equations to solve the problem below.

Apollo and Zeus are both on diets. Apollo currently weighs 105 kg and is gaining 2 kg per month. Zeus currently weighs 130 kg and is losing 3 kg per month. In how many months will they weigh the same?

5-81. Solve each system.

a. $6x - 2y = 10$
   $3x - 2 = y$

b. $3x - 9y = 3$
   $2x = 16 - y$

5.3.1 What is the rate of change?

Patterns of Growth in Tables and Graphs

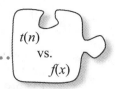

So far in this chapter you have looked at several types of sequences and compared linear and exponential growth patterns in situations, tables, and graphs. In this lesson you will compare patterns of growth rates to each other. This work will also help you write equations for exponential sequences in the next lesson.

5-82.   **PATTERNS OF GROWTH**

Sequence A	
n	$t(n)$
1	27
2	54
3	81
4	108

Sequence B	
n	$t(n)$
1	9
2	36
3	81
4	144

Sequence C	
n	$t(n)$
1	6
2	12
3	24
4	48

Your Task:

- Represent these three sequences on a graph (the Lesson 5.3.1A Resource Page). Use a different color for each sequence. Although the graph is discrete, connect the lines so you can see the trends easier.

- Consider the discussion points below for each sequence as you investigate the growth of these three sequences. You can discuss the sequences in any order.

- Be prepared to share your results with the class.

Discussion Points

How do the inputs, n, and the outputs of the sequence generator, $t(n)$, increase?

How does the sequence grow? Is the rate of change constant or changing? How? (You can make growth triangles to help answer this question.)

If you knew a specific term, how would you find the next term? For example, if you knew the 10th term, could you find the 11th term?

Which family of functions best models each sequence?

5-83.   GROWTH RATES IN SEQUENCES

Consider how fast each of the sequences is
growing by looking at the tables and the graph.
Do not make any additional computations. Instead
make conjectures based on the tables and graphs.

a.   If n represents the number of years, and $t(n)$
       represents the amount of money in your
       savings account, which account would you want, Sequence A, B, or C?

b.   Would your answer change if you kept the account for many years?

c.   Obtain the Lesson 5.3.1B Resource Page from your teacher. Extend the
       tables and the graph to $n = 7$. The table for Sequence B has been
       completed for you.

d.   Based on your new graph, do you want to change your answer to part (b)?
       Why or why not?

5-84.   WHICH GROWS THE MOST?

a.   Will an exponentially growing bank account eventually contain more
       money than a linearly growing bank account for the same amount of initial
       savings, no matter how fast (steep) the rate of growth of the linear account?
       Use the slope triangles on your graph from problem 5-83 to help you
       explain.

b.   How does the growth of a quadratic sequence like Sequence B compare to
       exponential growth?

5-85.   Identify the following sequences as linear, exponential, or other. For the linear
and exponential sequences, identify the rate of change and whether it is a
constant that is added or multiplied.

a.   12, 144, 1728, ...   b.   0, 5, 10, 15, 20, 25, ...

c.   0, 4, 16, 36, 64, ...   d.   1.5, 2.25, 3.375, 5.0625, ...

5-86.   Solve the system of equations at right. $y = -x - 2$

$5x - 3y = 22$

5-87.   Write the first five terms of each sequence.

   a. $t(1) = -3$

         $t(n+1) = -2 \cdot t(n)$

   b. $t(1) = 8$

         $t(n+1) = t(n) - 5$

   c. $t(1) = 2$

         $t(n+1) = (t(n))^{-1}$

5-88.   The graph at right compares the gas mileage to the weight of numerous vehicles.

         Describe the association between these two quantities.

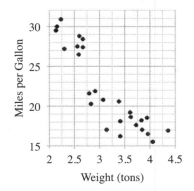

5-89.   Find the missing areas and dimensions for each generic rectangle below. Then write each area as a sum and as a product.

   a.

   b.

5-90.   This problem is a checkpoint for writing the equation of a line. It will be referred to as Checkpoint 5B.

         Use the given information to find an equation of the line.

   a.   Slope 2 and passing through $(10, 17)$.

   b.   Passing through $(1, -4)$ and $(-2, 5)$.

   c.
x	-6	-3	0	3	6
y	-6	-4	-2	0	2

   d.
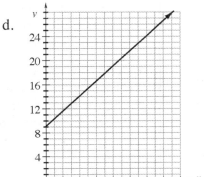

         Check your answers by referring to the Checkpoint 5B materials located at the back of your book.

         If you needed help solving these problems correctly, then you need more practice. Review the Checkpoint 5B materials and try the practice problems. Also, consider getting help outside of class time. From this point on, you will be expected to do problems like these quickly and easily.

5.3.2 How can I use a multiplier?

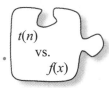

Using Multipliers to Solve Problems

In the past few lessons, you have investigated sequences that grow by adding (arithmetic) and sequences that grow by multiplying (geometric). In today's lesson, you will learn more about growth by multiplication as you use your understanding of geometric sequences and multipliers to solve problems. As you work, use the following questions to move your team's discussion forward:

> What type of sequence is this? How do we know?

> How can we describe the growth?

> How can we be sure that our multiplier is correct?

5-91. Thanks to the millions of teens around the world seeking to be just like their math teachers, industry analysts predict that sales of the new πPhone will skyrocket!

πPHONES SWEEP THE NATION
Millions demand one!

(API) – Teenagers and Hollywood celebrities flocked to an exclusive shop in Beverly Hills, California yesterday, clamoring for the new πPhone. The store expects to start by selling 100 and expects to sell an average of 15% more each week after that.

"I plan to stand in line all night!" said Nelly Hillman. "As soon as I own one, I'll be cooler than everyone else."

Across the globe, millions of fans

a. The article provides a model for how many πPhones the store expects to sell. They start by selling 100 πPhone pre-orders in week zero. Predict the number sold in the 4th week.

b. If you were to write the number of πPhones the store received each week as a sequence, would your sequence be arithmetic, geometric, or something else? Justify your answer.

c. The store needs to know how many phones to order for the last week of the year. If you knew the number of πPhones sold in week 51 how could you find the sales for week 52? Write a recursive equation to show the predicted sales of πPhones in the nth week.

d. Write an explicit equation that starts with "$t(n) = $" to find the number of πPhones sold during the nth week without finding all of the weeks in between.

e. How many πPhones will the store predict it sells in the 52nd week?

5-92. A new πRoid, a rival to the πPhone, is about to be introduced. It is cheaper than the πPhone, so more are expected to sell. The manufacturer plans to make and then sell 10,000 pre-orders in week zero and expects sales to increase by 7% each week.

    a. Write an explicit and a recursive equation for the number of πRoids sold during the nth week.

    b. What if the expected weekly sales increase were 17% instead of 7%? Now what would the new explicit equation be? How would it change the recursive equation?

5-93. Oh no! Thanks to the lower price, 10,000 πRoids were made and sold initially, but after that, weekly sales actually decreased by 3%.

Find an explicit and a recursive equation that models the product's actual weekly sales.

5-94. In a geometric sequence, the sequence generator is the number that one term is multiplied by to generate the next term. Another name for this number is the **multiplier**.

    a. Look back at your work for problems 5-92 and 5-93. What is the multiplier in each of these three situations?

    b. What is the multiplier for the sequence 8, 8, 8, 8, ... ?

    c. Explain what happens to the terms of the sequence when the multiplier is less than 1, but greater than zero. What happens when the multiplier is greater than 1? Add this description to your Learning Log. Title this entry "Multipliers" and add today's date.

5-95.   MULTIPLE REPRESENTATIONS ON THE GRAPHING CALCULATOR

a.   According to the model in problem 5-93, how many
     weeks will it take for the weekly sales to drop to only one
     πRoid per week? Make a conjecture.

b.   Before calculating the exact answer to the question in
     part (a), become comfortable with using your graphing
     calculator. On your calculator, make a graph for the sales
     of πPhones (problem 5-91) for the first year. Sketch the
     graph on your paper. Make sure you show the scale of the axes on your
     sketch.

c.   Use the table on your calculator to determine where, if at all, the graph in
     part (b) crosses the x-axis.

d.   Enter the explicit equations for both problems 5-91, $t(n) = 100 \cdot 1.15^n$, and
     5-92, $t(n) = 10,000 \cdot 1.07^n$, in your calculator. Use your table to find the
     number of weeks it takes for sales in the first equation to exceed the sales
     in the second equation.

e.   Make a sketch of the graph of both equations in part (d). Be sure to show
     the point of intersection. Label the scale on both axes.

f.   Now use your calculator to answer the question in part (a). How close was
     your conjecture?

.

5-96.   Write an explicit and a recursive equation for each table below. Be sure to check that your equations work for all of the entries in the table.

a.

n	t(n)
0	1600
1	2000
2	2500
3	3125
4	3906.25

b.

n	t(n)
0	3906.25
1	3125
2	2500
3	2000
4	1600

c.

n	t(n)
0	50
1	72
2	103.68
3	149.2992

d.

n	t(n)
0	
1	50
2	
3	72
4	
5	103.68
6	
7	149.2992

e.   How are the tables in (a) and (b) related? How are the multipliers for (a) and (b) related? Why does this make sense?

f.   What strategies did you use to find the equation for part (d)? How is the table in part (d) related to the one in part (c)?

g.   In part (d), why is term 2 *not* 61?

5-97.   PERCENTS AS MULTIPLIERS

What a deal! Just deShirts is having a 20% off sale. Trixie rushes to the store and buys 14 shirts. When the clerk rings up her purchases, Trixie sees that the clerk has added the 5% sales tax first, before taking the discount. Trixie wonders whether adding the sales tax before the discount makes her final cost more than adding the sales tax after the discount. Without making any calculations, make a conjecture. Is Trixie getting charged more when the clerk adds sales tax first? The next few problems will help you figure it out for sure.

5-98.   Karen works for a department store and receives a 20% discount on any
         purchases that she makes. The department store is having a clearance sale, and
         every item will be marked 30% off the regular price. Karen has decided to buy
         the $100 dress she's been wanting. When she includes her employee discount
         with the sale discount, what is the total discount she will receive? Does it
         matter what discount she takes first? Use the questions below to help you
         answer this question.

    a.   Use the grids like the ones below to picture another way to think about this
         situation. Using graph paper, create two 10-by-10 grids (as shown below)
         to represent the $100 price of the dress.

         CASE 1: 20% discount first   **CASE 2:** 30% discount first

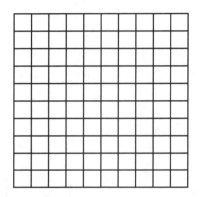   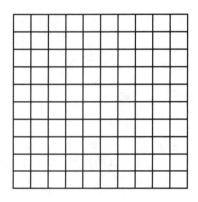

    b.   Use the first grid to represent the 20% discount followed by the 30%
         discount (Case 1). Use one color to shade the number of squares that
         represent the first 20% discount. For whatever is left (unshaded), find the
         30% discount and use another color to shade the corresponding number of
         squares to represent this second discount. Then repeat the process (using
         the other grid) for the discounts in reverse order (Case 2).

    c.   How many squares remain after the first discount in Case 1? In Case 2?

    d.   How many squares remain after the second discount in Case 1? In Case 2?

    e.   Explain why these results make sense.

5-99.   Suppose that Trixie's shirts cost x dollars in problem 5-97.

      a.   If x represents the cost, how could you represent the tax? How could you represent the cost plus the tax?

      b.   How could you represent the discount? How could you represent the cost of the shirt after the discount?

      c.   Did Trixie get charged more because the clerk added the sales tax first? Justify your reasoning.

5-100.   Remember the "Multiplying Like Bunnies" problem at the beginning of this chapter? In that problem, Lenny and George started with 2 rabbits and each month the number of rabbits that they had doubled since each pair of rabbits produced another pair of rabbits.

      a.   Find an equation for this situation. Let y represent the number of rabbits after x months.

      b.   Lenny and George now have over 30 million rabbits. How many months have passed?

      c.   With 30 million rabbits, the bunny farm is getting overcrowded and some of the rabbits are dying from a contagious disease. The rabbits have stopped reproducing, and the disease is reducing the total rabbit population at a rate of about 30% each month. If this continues, then in how many months will the population drop below 100 rabbits?

METHODS AND MEANINGS

Types of Sequences

An **arithmetic sequence** is a sequence with an addition (or subtraction) **sequence generator**. The number added to each term to get the next term is called the **common difference..**

A **geometric sequence** is a sequence with a multiplication (or division) generator. The number multiplied by each term to get the next term is called the **common ratio** or the **multiplier**.

A multiplier can also be used to increase or decrease by a given percentage. For example, the multiplier for an increase of 7% is 1.07. The multiplier for a decrease of 7% is 0.93.

A **recursive sequence** is a sequence in which each term depends on the term(s) before it. The equation of a recursive sequence requires at least one term to be specified. A recursive sequence can be arithmetic, geometric, or neither.

For example, the sequence $-1, 2, 5, 26, 677, \ldots$ can be defined by the **recursive equation**:

$$t(1) = -1, \quad t(n+1) = \big(t(n)\big)^2 + 1$$

An alternative notation for the equation of the sequence above is:

$$a_1 = -1, \quad a_{n+1} = (a_n)^2 + 1$$

Review & Preview

5-101.   For each table below, find the missing entries and write an equation.

a.

Month (x)	0	1	2	3	4	5	6
Population (y)	2	8	32				

b.

Year (x)	0	1	2	3	4	5	6
Population (y)	5	6	7.2				

5-102.   Convert each percent increase or decrease into a multiplier.

    a.   3% increase   b.   25% decrease

    c.   13% decrease   d.   2.08% increase

5-103.   Mr. C is such a mean teacher! The next time Mathias gets in trouble, Mr. C has designed a special detention for him. Mathias will have to go out into the hall and stand exactly 100 meters away from the exit door and pause for a minute. Then he is allowed to walk exactly halfway to the door and pause for another minute. Then he can again walk exactly half the remaining distance to the door and pause again, and so on. Mr. C says that when Mathias reaches the door he can leave, *unless* he breaks the rules and goes more than halfway, even by a tiny amount. When can Mathias leave? Prove your answer using multiple representations.

5-104.   Simplify each expression.

    a. $(2m^3)(4m^2)$ b. $\dfrac{6y^5}{3y^2}$ c. $\dfrac{-4y^2}{6y^7}$ d. $(-2x^2)^3$

5-105.   For this problem, refer to the sequences graphed below.

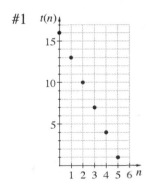 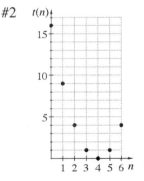 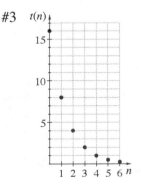

    a.   Identify each sequence as arithmetic, geometric, or neither.

    b.   If it is arithmetic or geometric, describe the sequence generator.

5-106.   Read the Math Notes box in this lesson for information about an alternative notation for sequences and write the first 5 terms of these sequences.

a. $a_n = 2n - 5$

b. $a_1 = 3$
$a_{n+1} = -2 \cdot a_n$

5-107.   Solve each equation.

a. $(x+2)(x+3) = x^2 - 10$

b. $\frac{1}{2}x + \frac{1}{3}x - 7 = \frac{5}{6}x$

c. $|2x - 1| = 9$

d. $\frac{x+1}{3} = \frac{x}{2}$

5-108.   For each sequence defined recursively, write the first 5 terms and then define it explicitly.

a. $t(1) = 12$
$t(n+1) = t(n) - 5$

b. $a_1 = 32$
$a_{n+1} = \frac{1}{2} a_n$

5-109.   **Multiple Choice:** Which line below is parallel to $y = -\frac{2}{3}x + 5$?

a. $2x - 3y = 6$

b. $2x + 3y = 6$

c. $3x - 2y = 6$

d. $3x + 2y = 6$

5-110.   The graph at right shows a comparison of the length of several gold chain necklaces (including the clasp) to the total mass.

a. Write an equation for the line of best fit.

b. Based on your equation, what would you expect to be the mass of a 26 inch chain?

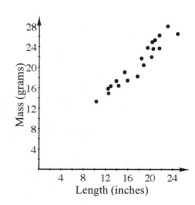

234

5.3.3 Is it a function?

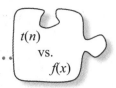

$t(n)$

vs.

$f(x)$

Comparing Sequences to Functions

Throughout this chapter, you have been learning about sequences. In Chapter 1, you started to learn about functions. But what is the difference between them? In this lesson, you will compare and contrast sequences with functions. By the end of the lesson, you will be able to answer these questions:

Is a sequence different from a function?

What is the difference between a sequence $t(n)$ and the function $f(x)$ with the same equation?

5-111.   Consider sequence $t(n)$ below.

$$-5, -1, 3, 7, \ldots$$

a.   Create multiple representations, namely, a table, a graph and an equation (recursive or explicit), for the sequence $t(n)$.

b.   Is it possible for the equation representing $t(n)$ to equal 400? Justify your answer.

c.   Create the same multiple representations as you did in part (a) for the function $f(x) = 4x - 9$. How are $f(x)$ and $t(n)$ different? How can you see their differences in each of the representations?

d.   For the function $f(x) = 4x - 9$, is it possible for $f(x)$ to equal 400? Explain why or why not.

5-112.   Let us consider the difference between $t(n) = 2 \cdot 3^n$ and $f(x) = 2 \cdot 3^x$.

a.   Is $f(x) = 2 \cdot 3^x$ a function? Why or why not? Is $t(n) = 2 \cdot 3^n$ a function?

b.   Is it possible for $t(n)$ to equal 1400? If so, find the value of n that makes $t(n) = 1400$. If not, justify why not.

c.   Is it possible for $f(x)$ to equal 1400? Be prepared to share your solving strategy with the class.

d.   How are the functions similar? How are they different?

5-113.   LEARNING LOG

Is a sequence a function? Justify your answer completely. If so, what makes it different from the functions that are usually written in the form $f(x) =$ _____ ? If not, why not? Be prepared to share your ideas with the class. After a class discussion about these questions, answer the questions in your Learning Log. Title this entry "Sequences vs. Functions" and label it with today's date.

5-114.   Janine was working on her homework but lost part of it. She knew that one output of $p(r) = 2 \cdot 5^r$ is 78,000, but she could not remember if $p(r)$ is a sequence or if it is a regular function. With your team, help her figure it out. Be sure to justify your decision.

5-115.   **Additional Challenge:** Khalil is working with a geometric sequence. He knows that $t(0) = 3$ and that the sum of the first three terms ($t(0)$, $t(1)$, and $t(2)$) is 63. Help him figure out the sequence. Be prepared to share your strategies with the class.

5-116.   **Additional Challenge:** Discuss with your team how you can use your graphing calculator to solve each of the following equations for x, accurate to the nearest 0.01.

a. $200(0.5)^x = 3.125$ b. $318 = 6 \cdot 3^x$

5-117.   Is it possible for the sequence $t(n) = 5 \cdot 2^n$ to have a term with the value of 200? If so, which term is it? If not, justify why not.

5-118.   Is it possible for the function $f(x) = 5 \cdot 2^x$ to have an output of 200? If so, what input gives this output? If not, justify why not.

5-119.   Consider the following sequences as you complete parts (a) through (c) below.

Sequence 1	Sequence 2	Sequence 3
$2, 6, \ldots$	$24, 12, \ldots$	$1, 5, \ldots$

a.   Assuming that the sequences above are arithmetic with $t(1)$ as the first term, find the next four terms for each sequence. For each sequence, write an explanation of what you did to get the next term and write an equation for $t(n)$.

b.   Would your terms be different if the sequences were geometric? Find the next four terms for each sequence if they are geometric. For each sequence, write an explanation of what you did to get the next term and write an equation for $t(n)$.

c.   Create a totally different type of sequence for each pair of values shown above, based on your own equation. Write your equation clearly (using words or algebra) so that someone else will be able to find the next three terms that you want.

5-120.   For the function $g(x) = x^3 + x^2 - 6x$, find the value of each expression below.

a. $g(1)$ b. $g(-1)$ c. $g(-2)$ d. $g(10)$

e.   Find at least one value of x for which $g(x) = 0$.

f.   If $f(x) = x^2 - x + 3$, find $g(x) - f(x)$.

5-121.   Write equations to solve each of the following problems.

a.   When the Gleo Retro (a trendy commuter car) is brand new, it costs $23,500. Each year it loses 15% of its value. What will the car be worth when it is 15 years old?

b.   Each year the population of Algeland increases by 12%. The population is currently 14,365,112. What will the population be 20 years from now?

5-122.   An arithmetic sequence has $t(8) = 1056$ and $t(13) = 116$. Write an equation for the sequence. What is $t(5)$?

5-123.   Describe the domain of each function or sequence below.

a.   The function $f(x) = 3x - 5$.   b.   The sequence $t(n) = 3n - 5$.

c.   The function $f(x) = \frac{5}{x}$.   d.   The sequence $t(n) = \frac{5}{n}$.

Chapter 5 Closure What have I learned?

Reflection and Synthesis

The activities below offer you a chance to reflect about what you have learned during this chapter. As you work, look for concepts that you feel very comfortable with, ideas that you would like to learn more about, and topics you need more help with. Look for connections between ideas as well as connections with material you learned previously.

①   TEAM BRAINSTORM

What have you studied in this chapter? What ideas were important in what you learned? With your team, brainstorm a list. Be as detailed as you can. To help get you started, a list of Learning Log entries and Math Notes boxes are below.

What topics, ideas, and words that you learned *before* this chapter are connected to the new ideas in this chapter? Again, be as detailed as you can.

How long can you make your list? Challenge yourselves. Be prepared to share your team's ideas with the class.

Learning Log Entries
- Lesson 5.1.1 – Exponential Functions, Part 1
- Lesson 5.3.2 – Multipliers
- Lesson 5.3.3 – Sequence vs. Functions

Math Notes
- Lesson 5.1.1 – The Elimination Method
- Lesson 5.1.2 – Continuous and Discrete Graphs
- Lesson 5.3.2 – Types of Sequences

②   MAKING CONNECTIONS

Below is a list of the vocabulary used in this chapter. Make sure that you are familiar with all of these words and know what they mean. Refer to the glossary or index for any words that you do not yet understand.

arithmetic sequence	sequence generator	common ratio
linear function	exponential function	first term
geometric sequence	$t(0)$	initial value
multiplier	y-intercept	domain
sequence	term	common difference
recursive sequence	term number	

Make a concept map showing all of the connections you can find among the key words and ideas listed above. To show a connection between two words, draw a line between them and explain the connection, as shown in the model below. A word can be connected to any other word as long as you can justify the connection. For each key word or idea, provide an example or sketch that shows the idea.

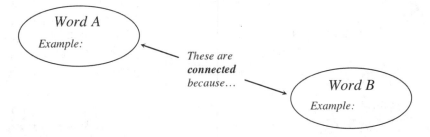

Your teacher may provide you with vocabulary cards to help you get started. If you use the cards to plan your concept map, be sure either to re-draw your concept map on your paper or to glue the vocabulary cards to a poster with all of the connections explained for others to see and understand.

While you are making your map, your team may think of related words or ideas that are not listed here. Be sure to include these ideas on your concept map.

Four members of a study team were analyzing the sequence 3, 7, 11, ... They found the equation for the sequence to be $t(n) = 4n - 1$, and they were trying to figure out if 200 could be a term of their sequence.

They made the following statements. Which students justified their statements? Are the justifications convincing? Explain why or why not.

Shinna: "I think it's not, because all the terms in the sequence are odd and 200 is an even number."

Aldo: "I think it is, because the equation $200 = 4n - 1$ has a solution."

James: "It can't be, because the solution to $200 = 4n - 1$ is $n = 50.25$, which is not a whole number. There can't be a 50.25th term!"

Leslie: "I think 199 and 203 are terms of the sequence, but not 200."

Now create your own sequence. Then figure out what the 110th term of your sequence would be and whether the number 419 is a term in your sequence. Use multiple representations to justify your answers thoroughly.

Alternatively your portfolio entry could showcase your early understanding of an exponential function by explaining everything you know about the function $f(x) = 2^x - 3$. Provide one or two representative example problems.

Obtain the Chapter 5 Closure Resource Page: Sequence vs. Function Graphic Organizer from your teacher. Use this page to compare and contrast sequences and functions in their multiple representations. How are they similar? How are they different?

④ **WHAT HAVE I LEARNED?**

Most of the problems in this section represent typical problems found in this chapter. They serve as a gauge for you. You can use them to determine which types of problems you can do well and which types of problems require further study and practice. Even if your teacher does not assign this section, it is a good idea to try these problems and find out for yourself what you know and what you need to work on.

Solve each problem as completely as you can. The table at the end of the closure section has answers to these problems. It also tells you where you can find additional help and practice with problems like these.

CL 5-124.   Determine if the following sequences are arithmetic, geometric, or neither:

a. $-7, -3, 1, 5, 9, \ldots$ b. $-64, -16, -4, -1, \ldots$

c. $1, 0, 1, 4, 9, \ldots$ d. $0, 2, 4, \ldots$

CL 5-125.   Find an equation to represent each table as a sequence.

a.

n	$t(n)$
1	4
2	1
3	-2
4	

b.

n	$t(n)$
1	6
2	7.2
3	8.64
4	

CL 5-126.   Solve the following systems algebraically.

a. $x + 2y = 17$
      $x - y = 2$

b. $4x + 5y = 11$
      $2x + 6y = 16$

c. $4x - 3y = -10$
      $x = \frac{1}{4}y - 1$

d. $2x + y = -2x + 5$
      $3x + 2y = 2x + 3y$

CL 5-127. Solve each equation after first rewriting it in a simpler equivalent form.

a. $3(2x-1)+12 = 4x-3$

b. $\frac{3x}{7}+\frac{2}{7}=2$

c. $\frac{x-3}{x}=\frac{3}{5}$

d. $4x(x-2)=(2x+1)(2x-3)$

CL 5-128. Simplify each expression.

a. $(-3x)^2$

b. $(3x)^{-2}$

c. $\frac{2(3x)^2}{3x^3}$

d. $\frac{2(3x)^2}{(3x)^{-2}}$

CL 5-129. Create multiple representations of each line described below.

a. A line with slope 4 and y-intercept -6.

b. A line with slope $\frac{3}{2}$ that passes through the point $(5,7)$.

CL 5-130. Create an explicit equation for each recursively-defined sequence below.

a. $a_1 = 17$, $a_{n+1} = a_n - 7$

b. $t(1) = 3$, $t(n+1) = 5 \cdot t(n)$

CL 5-131. Use a graph to describe the domain and range of each function or sequence below.

a. The function $f(x) = (x-2)^2$.

b. The sequence $t(n) = 3n - 5$.

CL 5-132. When a family with two adults and three children bought tickets for an amusement park, they paid a total of $56.50. The next family in line, with four children and one adult, paid $49.50. Find the adult and child ticket prices by writing and solving a system of equations.

CL 5-133. Check your answers using the table at the end of this section. Which problems do you feel confident about? Which problems were hard? Have you worked on problems like these in previous math classes? Use the table to make a list of topics you need to learn more about, and a list of topics you just need to practice more.

Answers and Support for Closure Activity #4
What Have I Learned?

Note: MN = Math Note, LL = Learning Log

Problem	Solutions		Need Help?	More Practice
CL 5-124.	a. arithmetic c. neither	b. geometric d. arithmetic	Section 5.2 MN: 5.3.2	Problems 5-41, 5-43, 5-49, 5-86, and 5-119
CL 5-125.	a. $t(n) = -3n + 7$ b. $t(n) = 5(1.2)^n$ or $t(n) = 6(1.2)^{n-1}$		Lessons 5.2.2 and 5.3.2	Problems 5-37, 5-63, 5-67, 5-85, 5-101, and 5-108
CL 5-126.	a. $(7, 5)$ c. $(-\frac{1}{4}, 3)$	b. $(-1, 3)$ d. $(1, 1)$	Sections 4.2 and 4.3 MN: 4.2.2 and 4.2.3 LL: 4.2.5	Problems CL 4-118, 5-7, 5-22, 5-23, 5-36, 5-53, 5-69, and 5-105
CL 5-127.	a. -6 c. 7.5	b. 4 d. $\frac{3}{4}$	Lesson 3.2.1 Checkpoints 2 and 4	Problems CL 2-107, CL 3-107, CL 4-118, 5-15, and 5-107
CL 5-128.	a. $9x^2$ c. $\frac{6}{x}$	b. $\frac{1}{9x^2}$ d. $162x^4$	Section 3.1 Checkpoint 5A	Problems 5-9, 5-10, 5-13, 5-24, 5-55, and 5-104

Problem	Solutions		Need Help?	More Practice
CL 5-129.	a. $y = 4x - 6$		Lessons 2.1.4 and 2.3.1	Problems CL 2-101,
			Checkpoint 5B	CL 2-103, 5-16, and 5-90
			LL: 2.3.1	

CL 5-129. a. $y = 4x - 6$

x	y
-3	-18
-2	-14
-1	-10
0	-6
1	-2
2	2
3	6

b. $y = \frac{3}{2}x - \frac{1}{2}$

x	y
-3	-5
-2	-3.5
-1	-2
0	-0.5
1	1
2	2.5
3	4

Problem	Solutions	Need Help?	More Practice
CL 5-130.	a. $t(n) = 24 - 7n$ b. $t(n) = \frac{3}{5}(5)^n$	Lesson 5.2.3 MN: 5.3.2	Problems 5-71, 5-77, 5-106, and 5-108
CL 5-131.	a. Domain: all real numbers Range: $y \geq 0$ b. Domain: all positive integers; Range: all numbers of the form $3n - 5$	Lessons 1.2.5 and 5.3.3 LL: 5.3.3	Problems CL 2-108(c), 5-25, and 5-123
CL 5-132.	$2a + 3c = 56.5$, $a + 4c = 49.5$ adults cost $15.50, children cost $8.50	Chapter 4 MN: 4.2.3 LL: 4.2.5	Problems CL 4-123, 5-70, and 5-80

244

Appendix

In this appendix, you will use tools called "algebra tiles" to represent expressions and equations physically and visually. You will lay a strong foundation for simplifying expressions and solving equations that you will need and build upon repeatedly throughout the course.

Guiding Question

Mathematically proficient students make sense of problems and persevere in solving them.

As you work through this chapter, ask yourself:

How can algebra tiles help me make sense of and solve problems with variables, expressions, and equations?

Appendix Outline

This appendix introduces algebra tiles to help you develop the symbolic-manipulation skills of writing and simplifying algebraic expressions. A special focus will be placed on the meaning of "minus" and how to make "zero." You will also solve for a variable if you know that two expressions are equal.

A.1.1 What is a variable?

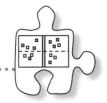

∙∙

Exploring Variables and Combining Like Terms

When you worked on problems in Chapter 1, you may recall the dimensions of the hot tub were unknown, the length of time for one of your team members to sign her/his name was unknown, and the output of a function machine was unknown. In many of the problems, some quantity was unknown.

In Algebra and in future mathematics courses, you will continue to work with unknown quantities that can be represented using **variables**. Today you will be introduced to tools called "algebra tiles" that will help you and your team members answer some important questions about algebra, such as "What is a variable?" and "How can we use it?"

A-1.   Your teacher will give you and your team a set of
        algebra tiles to use during this algebra course. As you
        explore the tiles, discuss the following questions with
        your team. Be prepared to share your responses with
        the class. Templates for the tiles are also available at
        www.cpm.org/students/resources.htm.

- How many different shapes can you find? What are the names of all of the different shapes?

- How are the shapes different? How are they the same?

- How are the different kinds of shapes related? Which fit together and which do not?

A-2.   Draw a picture of each size of tile on your paper. Then complete the activities
        below.

a.   The algebra tiles will be referred to by their areas. Since the smallest
      square has sides 1 unit long, its area is 1 square unit. The name for this
      tile, then, is "one." It can also be called a "unit tile." Can you use the unit
      tile to find the lengths of the sides of the other algebra tiles? Why or why
      not?

b.   Name the other tiles using their areas. Be sure to use what you know
      about the area of a rectangle and the area of a square.

A-3.   JUMBLED PILES

Your teacher will show you a jumbled pile of algebra tiles and will challenge
you to name all of them. What is the best description for the collection of tiles?
Is your description the best possible?

A-4.   Build each collection of tiles represented below. Then name the collection
using a simpler algebraic expression, if possible. If it is not possible to simplify
the expression, explain why not.

a. $3x + 5 + x^2 + y + 3x^2 + 2$ b. $2x^2 + 1 + xy + x^2 + 2xy + 5$

c. $2 + x^2 + 3x + y^2 + 4y + xy$ d. $3y + 2 + 2xy + 4x + y^2 + 4y + 1$

A-5.   In your Learning Log, using your own words, explain what
a variable is. Then sketch a diagram of each type of
algebra tile, recording each dimension and an area label.
Explain when tiles can and cannot be combined, and
include examples to support your statements. Title this
entry "Variables" and include today's date.

METHODS AND MEANINGS

Non-Commensurate

Two measurements are called **non-commensurate** if no
combination of one measurement can equal a combination of the
other. For example, your algebra tiles are called non-commensurate
because no combination of unit squares will ever be exactly equal to a
combination of x-tiles (although at times they may appear close in
comparison). In the same way, in the example below, no combination of
x-tiles will ever be exactly equal to a combination of y-tiles.

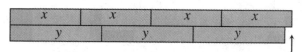

No matter what number of each size tile,
these two piles will never exactly match.

A-6. Suppose you put one of your *x*-tiles and two unit tiles with another pile of three *x*-tiles and five unit tiles. What is in this new pile? Write it as a sum.

A-7. Suppose one person in your team has two x^2-tiles, three *x*-tiles, and one unit tile on his desk and another person has one x^2-tile, five *x*-tiles, and eight unit tiles on her desk. You decide to put all of the tiles together on one desk. What could you call this new group of tiles? Write it as a sum.

A-8. Copy the following figures onto your paper. Then find the area and perimeter of each shape, assuming that all corners are right angles. Be sure to show all of your work.

a.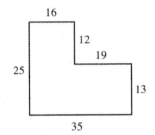

b.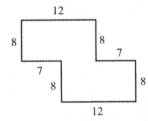

A-9. Consider the rectangle at right.

a. Find the perimeter of the large outer rectangle shown at right.

b. Notice that the areas of two of the parts have been labeled inside the rectangle. Find the total area. Remember to show all work leading to your solution.

A-10. The word "evaluate" has many different meanings. In algebra, when you are asked to **evaluate** an expression for a specified value of the variable(s), you are being asked to find the value of the expression. You do this by replacing a variable with a number and calculating the result. For example, if you are asked to evaluate the expression $4x - 2$ when $x = -7$, you would put -7 in place of the variable and then calculate: $4 \cdot (-7) - 2 = -30$.

Evaluate the expressions below for the given values of x and y.

a. $\frac{6}{x} + 9$ if $x = 3$

b. $8x - 3 + y$ if $x = 2$ and $y = 1$

c. $2xy$ if $x = 5$ and $y = -3$

d. $2x^2 - y$ if $x = 3$ and $y = 8$

A-11. Simplify each expression.

a. $-\frac{1}{2} + \frac{3}{4}$

b. $-\frac{1}{3} - \frac{1}{6}$

c. $-\frac{2}{3} \cdot 12$

d. $-4 \div -\frac{1}{2}$

A.1.2 What is the perimeter?

Simplifying Expressions by Combining Like Terms

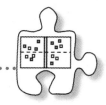

While Lesson A.1.1 focused on the *area* of an algebra tile, today's lesson will focus on the *perimeter*. What is perimeter? How can you find it? By the end of this lesson, you will be able to find the perimeters of complex shapes that are formed with multiple tiles.

You will learn various ways to find perimeter, recognizing that there are different ways to "see" perimeter. When you are finding the perimeter of a complex shape, discovering a convenient shortcut can help you find the perimeter more quickly. As you work through this lesson's activities, be sure to share any insight into finding perimeter with your teammates and with the whole class.

While working today, ask yourself and your teammates these focus questions:

How did you see it?

How can you write it?

Is your expression as simplified as possible?

A-12. Your teacher will provide a set of algebra tiles for you and your team to use today. After you receive the tiles, find one tile of each shape. Then, for each shape, review its name (area). Next, find the *perimeter* of each tile. Decide with your team how to write a simplified expression that represents each perimeter. Be prepared to share the perimeters you find with the class.

A-13. In parts (a) through (d) below, you will find shapes formed by algebra tiles. Complete the following activities for each shape:

- Use tiles to build the shape.

- Sketch and label the shape on your paper and write an expression that represents the perimeter.

- Simplify the perimeter expression as much as possible.

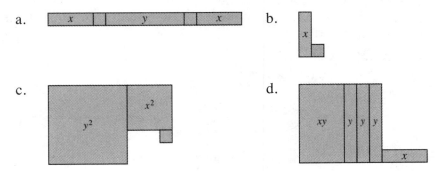

A-14. Calculate the perimeter of each shape in problem A-13 if the length of each *x*-tile is 3 units and the length of each *y*-tile is 8 units. Show all work.

A-15. **EXTENSION**

If the perimeter of the shape at right is 32 units, what are possible values for *x* and *y*? Is there more than one possible solution for each variable? If so, find another solution. If not, explain how you know there is only one solution.

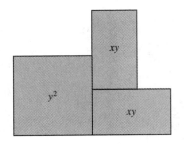

A-16. In your Learning Log, create your own shape using three different-shaped algebra tiles. Draw the shape and show how to write a simplified expression for its perimeter. Title this entry "Finding Perimeter and Combining Like Terms" and include today's date.

METHODS AND MEANINGS

Expressions and Terms

A mathematical **expression** is a combination of numbers, variables, and operation symbols. Addition and subtraction separate expressions into parts called **terms**. For example, $4x^2 - 3x + 6$ is an expression. It has three terms: $4x^2$, $3x$, and 6.

A more complex expression is $2x + 3(5 - 2x) + 8$, which has three terms: $2x$, $3(5 - 2x)$, and 8. However, the term $3(5 - 2x)$ also has an expression inside the parentheses: $5 - 2x$. 5 and $2x$ are terms of this inside expression.

A-17. Simplify each algebraic expression below, if possible. If it is not possible to simplify the expression, explain why not.

a. $3y + 2y + y^2 + 5 + y$

b. $3y^2 + 2xy + 1 + 3x + y + 2x^2$

c. $3xy + 5x + 2 + 3y + x + 4$

d. $4m + 2mn + m^2 + m + 3m^2$

A-18. Remember that one meaning of the word "evaluate" is to replace a variable with a number and to calculate the result. For example, evaluating the expression x^2 when $x = -2$ gives the solution $(-2)^2 = 4$.

Evaluate the expressions below for the given values.

a. $-4d + 3$ if $d = -1$

b. $k - m$ if $k = 4$ and $m = -10$

c. $\frac{t}{w}$ if $t = 6$ and $w = -3$

d. $x^2 + y^2$ if $x = 7$ and $y = 5$

Core Connections Algebra

A-19.   The diagram at right is the floor plan of Randy's
apartment. Use the diagram to answer the
following questions, assuming all measurements
are in feet.

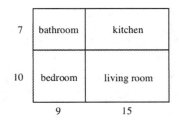

a.   What are the dimensions (length and
width) of Randy's living room?

b.   Randy's friends are coming to visit him soon.
He plans to keep them out of his bedroom. Find the area of each of the
other three rooms he will have to clean.

c.   What is the total area of the rooms he will have to clean?

A-20.   Examine the graph at right. Then complete
parts (a) and (b) below.

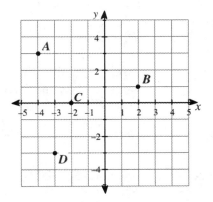

a.   In (x, y) form, name the coordinates of
points $A, B, C,$ and D.

b.   On graph paper, draw a set of axes like
the ones shown at right. Then plot
points $E(5, 2)$, $F(-3, -1)$, $G(0, -4)$, and
$H(2, -3)$.

A-21.   If algebra tiles have the dimensions shown at right,
what would you call the tile collection below? (What
is the total area of all of the pieces?) Write the
expression algebraically, using x, x^2, y, y^2, and xy.

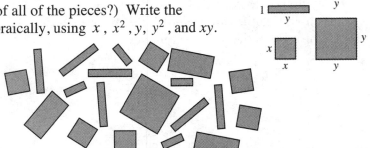

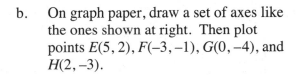

A-22.   Without using a calculator, compute the value of each expression below.

a. $-14 + (-31)$

b. $-(-8) - (-2)$

c. $\frac{-16}{-8}$

d. $-11 \cdot 24$

e. $\frac{1}{2} - \frac{3}{4}$

f. $46 \div (-23)$

A.1.3 What does "minus" mean?

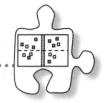

Writing Algebraic Expressions

In this section, you will look at algebraic expressions and see how they can be interpreted using an Expression Mat. To achieve this goal, you first need to understand the different meanings of the "minus" symbol, which is found in expressions such as $5 - 2$, $-x$, and $-(-3)$.

A-23.   LEARNING LOG

What does " – " mean? With your team, find as many ways as you can to describe this symbol and discuss how the descriptions differ from each another. Share your ideas with the class and record the different uses in your Learning Log. Title this entry "Meanings of Minus" and include today's date.

A-24.   USING AN EXPRESSION MAT

Your introduction to algebra tiles in Lessons A.1.1 and A.1.2 involved only positive values. Today you will look at how you can use algebra tiles to represent "minus." Below are several tiles with their associated values. The shaded tiles are positive, and the un-shaded tiles are negative; the diagram at right will appear throughout the text as a reminder.

 $= 5$ $= -3$ $= 3x$ $= -2y$

"Minus" can also be represented with a tool called an **Expression Mat**, shown at right. An Expression Mat is an organizing tool that is used to represent expressions. An Expression Mat has a positive region at the top and a negative (or "opposite") region at the bottom.

Problem continues on next page. →

Core Connections Algebra

A-24.   *Problem continued from previous page.*

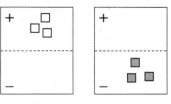

Value: –3   Value: –3

The value –3 can be shown in multiple ways, two of which are shown on the Expression Mats at right. Notice that the diagram on the left side uses negative tiles in the "+" region, while the diagram on the right side uses positive tiles in the "–" region.

Use your new knowledge of representing "minus" with an Expression Mat to build the expressions described below.

a.   Build two different representations of $-2x$ using an Expression Mat.

b.   Now build two different representations of $3x - (-4)$. How many different ways can you build $3x - (-4)$?

A-25.   During your discussion of problem A-24, did you see all of the different ways to represent "minus"? Discuss how you could use an Expression Mat to represent the different meanings discussed in class.

A-26.   **BUILDING EXPRESSIONS**

Use an Expression Mat to create each of the following expressions with algebra tiles. Find at least two different representations of each expression. Sketch each representation on your paper and be prepared to share your different representations with the class.

a. $-3x + 4$ b. $-(y - 2)$ c. $-y - 3$ d. $5x - (3 - 2x)$

A-27.   In problem A-26, you represented algebraic expressions with algebra tiles. In this problem, you will need to reverse your thinking to write an expression from a diagram of algebra tiles.

Working with a partner, write algebraic expressions for each representation below. Start by building each problem with your algebra tiles.

a.   b. 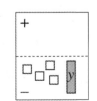   c. 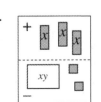   d.

A-28.   Patti, Emilie, and Carla are debating the answer to part (d) of problem A-27. Patti wrote $2 - 1 + 2x - 3$. Carla thinks that the answer is $2x + 2 - 4$. Emilie is convinced that the answer is $2x - 2$. Discuss with your team how each person might have arrived at her answer. Who do you think is correct? When you decide, write an explanation on your paper and justify your answer.

A-29.   Reflect about what you have learned from today's lesson as you answer the following question in your Learning Log. Title this entry "Representing Expressions on an Expression Mat" and include today's date.

Using an Expression Mat, find two different ways to represent $x - 1 - (2x - 3)$. Sketch the two different representations and write a few sentences to describe the differences in the ways you built each representation.

METHODS AND **M**EANINGS

MATH NOTES

Order of Operations

Mathematicians have agreed on an **order of operations** for simplifying expressions.

Original expression:

$$(10 - 3 \cdot 2) \cdot 2^2 - \frac{13 - 3^2}{2} + 6$$

Circle expressions that are grouped within parentheses or by a fraction bar:

$$\boxed{(10 - 3 \cdot 2)} \cdot 2^2 - \frac{\boxed{13 - 3^2}}{2} + 6$$

Simplify *within* circled terms using the order of operations:

- Evaluate exponents.

$$\boxed{(10 - 3 \cdot 2)} \cdot 2^2 - \frac{\boxed{13 - 3 \cdot 3}}{2} + 6$$

- Multiply and divide from left to right.

$$\boxed{(10 - 6)} \cdot 2^2 - \frac{\boxed{13 - 9}}{2} + 6$$

- Combine terms by adding and subtracting from left to right.

$$(4) \cdot 2^2 - \frac{4}{2} + 6$$

Circle the remaining terms:

$$\boxed{4 \cdot 2^2} - \boxed{\frac{4}{2}} + \boxed{6}$$

Simplify *within* circled terms using the order of operations as above.

$$\boxed{4 \cdot 2 \cdot 2} - \boxed{\frac{4}{2}} + 6$$

$$16 - 2 + 6$$

$$20$$

A-30. Copy and simplify the following expressions by combining like terms. Using or drawing sketches of algebra tiles may be helpful.

a. $2x + 3x + 3 + 4x^2 + 10 + x$

b. $4x + 4y^2 + y^2 + 9 + 10 + x + 3x$

c. $2x^2 + 30 + 3x^2 + 4x^2 + 14 + x$

d. $20 + 5xy + 4y^2 + 10 + y^2 + xy$

A-31. Plot the points $A(5, 3)$, $B(-4, 3)$, $C(-4, -6)$, and $D(5, -6)$ on a set of axes. Use a ruler to connect them in order, including D back to A, to form a **quadrilateral** (a shape with four sides).

    a. What kind of quadrilateral was formed?

    b. How long is each side of the quadrilateral?

    c. What is the area of the quadrilateral?

    d. What is the perimeter of the quadrilateral?

A-32. Write an equation to solve the following problem. Write your answer with a complete sentence.

Susan is buying three different colors of tiles for her kitchen floor. She is buying 107 red tiles, and three times as many navy-blue tiles as beige tiles. If Susan buys 435 tiles altogether, how many tiles of each color does she buy?

Let b = the number of beige tiles. Your equation should start with "435 =" and use b as the only variable.

A-33. Without using a calculator, compute the value of each expression below.

    a. $-3 + 6$ b. $(-2)(-9)$

    c. $-4 - 9 - 11$ d. $-12 - 18$ e. $\frac{3}{4}(-8)$

    f. $(-2)(-2)(2)$ g. $7 + (-19)$ h. $-15 \div 15$

A-34. Solve each proportion.

    a. $\frac{6}{8} = \frac{30}{m}$ b. $\frac{3}{5} = \frac{x}{9}$ c. $\frac{20}{30} = \frac{y}{9}$ d. $\frac{x}{3} = 9$

A.1.4 What makes zero?

Using Zero to Simplify Algebraic Expressions

Today you will continue your work with rewriting algebraic expressions. As you work with your team, ask yourself and your teammates these focus questions:

How did you see it?

How can you write it?

Is your expression as simplified as possible?

A-35.   LIKELY STORY!

Imagine the following situations:

- Ramona babysits her neighbor's baby and stuffs the $15 she earns into her purse. When she gets home, the $15 is nowhere to be found. It must have fallen out of her purse.

- The Burton Pumas football team completes a pass and gains 12 yards. But on the very next play, the quarterback holds onto the ball too long and gets sacked, losing 12 yards.

- You are at the beach. You dig a hole in the sand and place the sand you remove in a pile next to your hole. Someone comes along and pushes the pile back into the hole.

What do these situations have in common? Can you represent each of them using math symbols and numbers? How?

A-36.   How can you represent zero with tiles on an Expression Mat? With your team, try to find at least two different ways to do this (and more if you can). Be ready to share your ideas with the class.

A-37.   Gretchen used seven algebra tiles to build the expression shown at right.

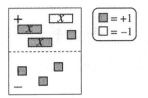

a.   Build this collection of tiles on your own Expression Mat and write its value.

b.   Represent this same value three different ways, each time using a *different number* of tiles. Be ready to share your representations with the class.

A-38.   Build each expression below so that your representation does not match those of your teammates. Once your team is convinced that together you have found four different, valid representations, sketch your representation on your paper and be ready to share your answer with the class.

a. $-3x + 5 + y$ b. $-(-2y + 1)$ c. $2x - (x - 4)$

A-39.   Write the algebraic expression shown on each Expression Mat below. Build the model and then simplify the expression by removing as many tiles as you can *without changing the value of the expression*. Finally, write the simplified algebraic expression.

a.   b.

A-40.   Simplify each of the following expressions by building it on your Expression Mat and removing zeros. Your teacher will give you instructions about how to represent your work on your paper.

a. $3x - (2x + 4)$ b. $7 - (4y - 3) + 2y - 4$

A-41.   In your Learning Log, describe the different ways you can represent zero using your Expression Mat. Include an example and be sure to draw the tiles. Title this entry "Using Zeros to Simplify" and include today's date.

Core Connections Algebra

METHODS AND MEANINGS

Evaluating Expressions and Equations

The word **evaluate** indicates that the value of an expression should be calculated when a variable is replaced by a numerical value.

For example, when you evaluate the expression $x^2 + 4x - 3$ for $x = 5$, the result is:

$$(5)^2 + 4(5) - 3$$
$$25 + 20 - 3$$
$$42$$

When you evaluate the equation $y = 3x^2 - 5x + 2$ for $x = 4$, the result is:

$$y = 3(4)^2 - 5(4) + 2$$
$$y = 3(16) - 5(4) + 2$$
$$y = 48 - 20 + 2$$
$$y = 30$$

In each case remember to follow the Order of Operations.

A-42. Bob, Kris, Janelle, and Pat are in a study team. Bob, Kris, and Janelle have algebra tiles on their desks. Bob has two x^2-tiles, four x-tiles, and seven unit tiles; Kris has one x^2-tile and five unit tiles; and Janelle has ten x-tiles and three unit tiles. Pat's desk is empty. The team decides to put all of the tiles from the three desks onto Pat's desk. Write an algebraic expression for the new collection of tiles on Pat's desk.

A-43. Can zero be represented by any number of tiles? Using only the unit tiles (only the 1 and –1 tiles), determine if you can represent zero on an Expression Mat with the number of tiles below. If you can, draw an Expression Mat demonstrating that it is possible. If it is not possible, explain why not.

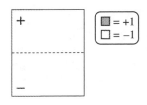

a. 2 tiles   b. 6 tiles   c. 3 tiles

Appendix: Representing Expressions   261

A-44.   Read the Math Notes box for this lesson. Then evaluate each equation below.

    a.   For $y = 2 + 3x$ when $x = 4$, what does y equal?

    b.   For $a = 4 - 5c$ when $c = -\frac{1}{2}$, what does a equal?

    c.   For $n = 3d^2 - 1$ when $d = -5$, what does n equal?

    d.   For $v = -4(r - 2)$ when $r = -1$, what does v equal?

    e.   For $3 + k = t$ when $t = 14$, what does k equal?

A-45.   Write and simplify the algebraic expression shown in each Expression Mat below.

    a.    b.   c.

A-46.   Write an expression that represents the perimeter of the shape built with algebra tiles at right.

A-47.   Copy and complete each of the Diamond Problems below. The pattern used in the Diamond Problems is shown at right.

    a.   b.   c.   d.

A.1.5 How can I simplify the expression?

Using Algebra Tiles to Simplify Algebraic Expressions

Which is greater: 58 or 62? That question might seem easy to answer, because the numbers are ready to be compared. However, if you are asked which is greater, $2x + 8 - x - 3$ or $6 + x + 1$, the answer is not so obvious! In this lesson, you and your teammates will investigate how to compare two algebraic expressions and decide which one is greater.

A-48.   For each expression below, use an Expression Mat to build the expression. Then find a different way to represent the same expression using tiles.

   a. $7x - 3$ b. $-(-2x + 6) + 3x$

A-49.   COMPARING EXPRESSIONS

Two expressions can be represented at the same time using an **Expression Comparison Mat**. The Expression Comparison Mat puts two Expression Mats side-by-side so you can compare them and see which is greater. For example, in the picture at right, the expression on the left represents –3, while the expression on the right represents –2. Since $-2 > -3$, the expression on the right is greater.

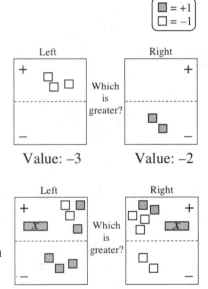

Build the Expression Comparison Mat shown at right. Write an expression representing each side of the Expression Mat.

   a.   Can you simplify each of the expressions so that fewer tiles are used? Develop a method to simplify both sides of the Expression Comparison Mats. Why does it work? Be prepared to justify your method to the class.

   b.   Which side of the Expression Comparison Mat do you think is greater (has the largest value)? Agree on an answer as a team. Make sure each person in your team is ready to justify your conclusion to the class.

A-50. As Karl simplified some algebraic expressions, he recorded his work on the diagrams below.

- Explain in writing what he did to each Expression Comparison Mat on the left to get the Expression Comparison Mat on the right.

- If necessary, simplify further to determine which Expression Mat is greater. How can you tell if your final answer is correct?

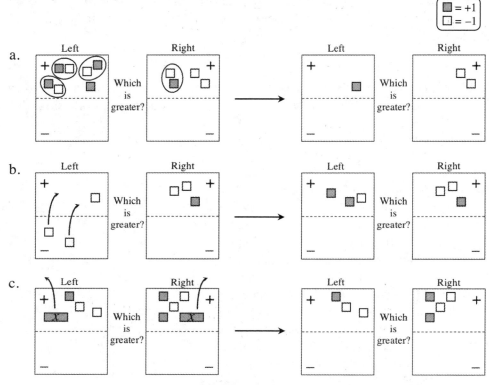

A-51. Use Karl's "legal" simplification moves to determine which side of each Expression Comparison Mat below is greater. Record each of your "legal" moves on the Lesson A.1.5A Resource Page by drawing on it the way Karl did in problem A-50. After each expression is simplified, state which side is greater (has the largest value). Be prepared to share your process and reasoning with the class.

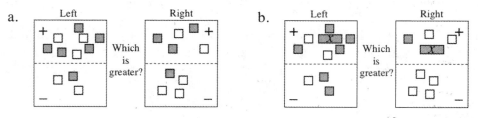

A-52.   In your Learning Log, explain each of the types of "legal" moves that you can use to simplify and compare expressions. For each type of "legal" move, sketch an example. Title this entry "Legal Moves for Simplifying and Comparing Expressions" and include today's date.

METHODS AND MEANINGS

Combining Like Terms

Combining tiles that have the same area to write a simpler expression is called **combining like terms**. See the example shown at right.

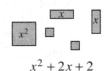

$x^2 + 2x + 2$

When you are not working with actual tiles, it can help to picture the tiles in your mind. You can use these images to combine the terms that are the same in expressions and equations. Here are two examples:

Example 1: $2x^2 + xy + y^2 + x + 3 + x^2 + 3xy + 2 \implies 3x^2 + 4xy + y^2 + x + 5$

Example 2: $3x^2 - 2x + 7 - 5x^2 + 3x - 2 \implies -2x^2 + x + 5$

Remember that addition and subtraction separate expressions into **terms**.

A-53.   Simplify the following expressions by combining like terms, if possible.

a. $x + x - 3 + 4x^2 + 2x - x$

b. $8x^2 + 3x - 13x^2 + 10x^2 - 25x - x$

c. $4x + 3y$

d. $20 + 3xy - 3 + 4y^2 + 10 - 2y^2$

A-54.   Copy and complete each of the Diamond Problems below. The pattern used in the Diamond Problems is shown at right.

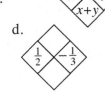

a.

b.

c.

d.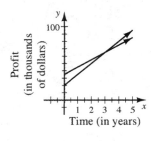

A-55.   The two lines at right represent the growing profits of Companies A and B.

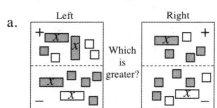

a.   Sketch this graph on your paper. If Company A started out with more profit than Company B, determine which line represents A and which represents B. Label the lines appropriately.

b.   In how many years will both companies have the same profit?

c.   Approximately what will that profit be?

d.   Which company's profits are growing more quickly? How can you tell?

A-56.   Use legal simplification moves to determine which side of the Expressions Comparison Mat is greater.

a.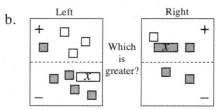

b.

A-57.   Evaluate each expression to find y.

a. $y = 2 + 4.3x$ when $x = -6$

b. $y = (x - 3)^2$ when $x = 9$

c. $y = x - 2$ when $x = 3.5$

d. $y = 5x - 4$ when $x = -2$

A-58.   Sam read 75 pages of a new mystery novel in 2 hours. If the book contains 350 pages and he always reads at the same rate, how long will it take him to the read the entire novel?

A.1.6 Which is greater?

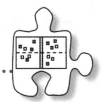

Using Algebra Tiles to Compare Expressions

Can you always tell if one algebraic expression is greater than another? In this lesson, you will compare the values of two expressions, practicing the different simplification strategies you have learned in this appendix so far.

A-59.   WHICH IS GREATER?

Write an algebraic expression for each side of the Expression Comparison Mats given below. Use the "legal" simplification moves you worked with in Lesson A.1.5 to determine which expression on the Expression Comparison Mat is greater.

a.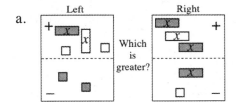

b.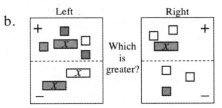

c.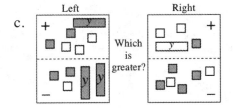

d.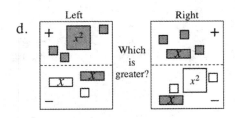

e.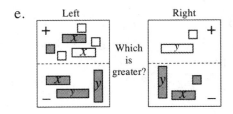

f.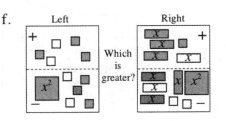

A-60. Using algebra tiles, build the expressions shown on the Expression Comparison Mat below.

    a.   Simplify the expressions using the "legal" moves that you developed in Lesson A.1.5.

    b.   Can you tell which expression is greater? Explain your answer in a few sentences on your paper. Be prepared to share your conclusion with the class.

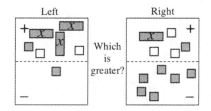

METHODS AND **M**EANINGS

Simplifying an Expression

MATH NOTES

    In addition to combing like terms, the following two ways to simplify an expression are common.

- Flip tiles and move them from the negative region to the positive region (that is, find the opposite). For example, the two unit tiles in the "−" region can be flipped and placed in the "+" region.

- Remove an equal number of opposite tiles that are in the same region. For example, the positive and negative tile to the right can be removed.

A-61. Find a simplified algebraic expression for each
Expression Mat below.

a.

b.

c.

A-62. Cairo wants to create a graph representing the heights and bases of all
rectangles that have an area of 36 square units. He started by drawing the
rectangles A, B, C, and D below. Examine the dimensions (length and width)
of each rectangle.

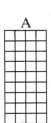

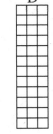

a. Copy the graph at right onto graph paper.
Then match the letter of each rectangle
above with a point on the graph. Which
point is not matched?

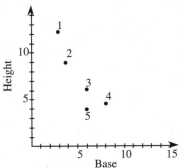

b. What are the base, height, and area for the
unmatched point?

c. Why should the unmatched point not be on Cairo's graph?

d. Find the dimensions of three more rectangles that have areas of 36 square
units. At least one of your examples should have dimensions that are not
integers. Place a new point on the graph for each new rectangle you find.

e. Connect all of the points representing an area of 36 square units. Describe
the resulting graph.

A-63.   Without using a calculator, compute the value of each expression below.

   a. $7 - 2 \cdot (-5)$ b. $6 + 3(7 - 3 \cdot 2)^2$

   c. $5 \cdot (-3)^2$ d. $35 \div (16 - 3^2) \cdot 2$

   e. $-3 \cdot 4 + 5 \cdot (-2)$ f. $7 - 6(10 - 4 \cdot 2) \div 4$

A-64.   One of Teddy's jobs at home is to pump gas for his family's sedan and truck. When he fills the truck up with 12 gallons of gas, he notices that it costs him $39.48.

   a.   How much does one gallon of gas cost? Explain how you found your answer.

   b.   How much will it cost him to fill up the sedan if it needs 15 gallons of gas? Show your work.

   c.   When Teddy filled up the tank on his moped, it cost $13.16. How much gas did his moped need? Explain how you know.

A-65.   Draw a circle on your paper and lightly shade in three-fourths of the circle.

   a.   Divide the entire circle into eight equal parts. How many parts are shaded?

   b.   Using fractions, write and solve a related division problem.

A-66.   If $f(x) = 2x + 3$, evaluate each expression below.

   a. $f(-5)$ b. $f(-\tfrac{1}{2})$ c. $f(4)$ d. $f(-2)$

A.1.7 How can I write it?

Simplifying and Recording Work

Today you will continue to compare expressions as you strengthen your simplification strategies. At the same time, you will work with your class to find ways to record your work so that another student can follow your strategies.

A-67.   Use algebra tiles to build the expressions below on an Expression Comparison Mat. Use "legal" simplification moves to determine which expression is greater, if possible. If it is not possible to tell which expression is greater, explain why.

a.   Which is greater: $3x - (2 - x) + 1$ or $-5 + 4x + 4$?

b.   Which is greater: $2x^2 - 2x + 6 - (-3x)$ or $-(3 - 2x^2) + 5 + 2x$?

c.   Which is greater: $-1 + 6y - 2 + 4x - 2y$ or $x + 5y - (-2 + y) + 3x - 6$?

A-68.   RECORDING YOUR WORK

Although using algebra tiles can make some situations easier because you can "see" and "touch" the math, it can be difficult to remember what you did to solve a problem unless you take good notes.

Use the simplification strategies you have learned to determine which expression on the Expression Comparison Mat at right is greater. Record each step as instructed by your teacher. Also record the simplified expression that remains after each move. This will be a written record of how you solved this problem. Discuss with your team what the best way is to record your moves.

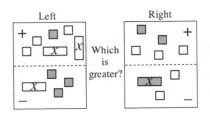

A-69. While Athena was comparing the expressions shown at right, she was called out of the classroom. When her teammates needed help, they looked at her paper and saw the work shown below. Unfortunately, she had forgotten to explain her simplification steps.

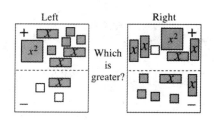

Can you help them figure out what Athena did to get each new set of expressions?

Left Expression	Right Expression	Explanation
$3x + 4 - x - (-2) + x^2$	$-1 + x^2 + 4x - (4 + 2x)$	Original expressions
$3x + 4 - x - (-2)$	$-1 + 4x - (4 + 2x)$	
$3x + 4 - x + 2$	$-1 + 4x - 4 - 2x$	
$2x + 6$	$2x - 5$	
6	-5	
Because $6 > -5$, the left side is greater.		

A-70. For each pair of expressions below, determine which is greater. Carefully record your steps as you go. If you cannot tell which expression is greater, write, "Not enough information." Make sure that you record the result after each type of simplification. For example, if you flip all of the tiles from the "–" region to the "+" region, record the resulting expression and use words or symbols to indicate what you did. Be ready to share your work with the class.

a.
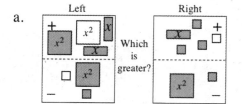

b.
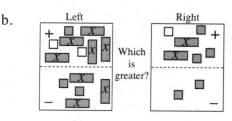

c. Which is greater: $5 - (2y - 4) - 2$ or $-y - (1 + y) + 4$?

d. Which is greater: $3xy + 9 - 4x - 7 + x$ or $-2x + 3xy - (x - 2)$?

A-71.   Solve this problem by writing an equation. Write your answer with a complete sentence. Let x = the number of adults. Your equation should start with "1220 =" and use x as the only variable.

The number of students attending the fall play was 150 more than the number of adults attending. A total of 1220 people attended the play. How many students attended the play?

A-72.   Sylvia simplified the expressions on the Expression Comparison Mat shown at right. Some of her work is shown. Are all of her moves "legal"? Explain.

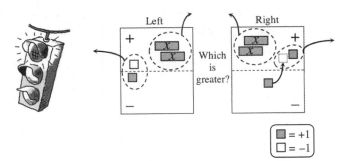

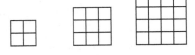

A-73.   Examine the tile pattern at right.

a.   On graph paper, draw Figures 4 and 5.

Figure 1   Figure 2   Figure 3

b.   What would Figure 10 look like? How many tiles would it have on each side? What about Figure 100?

c.   Cami has a different tile pattern. She decided to represent the number of tiles in her pattern in a table, as shown below. Can you use the table to predict how many tiles would be in Figure 5 of her tile pattern? How many tiles would Figure 8 have? Explain how you know.

Figure Number	1	2	3	4
Number of Tiles	5	9	13	17

A-74.   Examine the shape made with algebra tiles at right.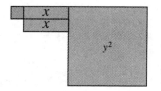

a.   Write an expression that represents the
perimeter of the shape. Then evaluate your
expression for $x = 6$ and $y = 10$ units.

b.   Write an expression that represents the area of the shape.
What is the area if $x = 6$ and $y = 10$ units?

A-75.   CALCULATOR CHECK

Use your scientific calculator to compute the value of
each expression in the left-hand column below. Match
each result to an answer in the right-hand column.

a. $-3 + 16 - (-5)$ 1. -16

b. $(3 - 5)(6 + 2)$ 2. 327

c. $17(-23) + 2$ 3. 0.5

d. $5 - (3 - 17)(-2 + 25)$ 4. 18

e. $(-4)(-2.25)(-10)$ 5. -90

f. $-1.5 - 2.25 - (-4.5)$ 6. 0.75

g. $\frac{4-5}{-2}$ 7. -389

A-76.   Alicia used 4 gallons of gasoline to travel 90 miles. At the same rate, how far
can she travel on a full tank that holds 18 gallons?

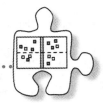

A.1.8 What if both sides are equal?

Using Algebra Tiles to Solve for x

Can you always tell whether one algebraic expression is greater than another? In this section, you will continue to practice the different simplification strategies you have learned so far to compare two expressions and see which one is greater. However, sometimes you do not have enough information about the expressions. When both sides of an equation are equal, you can learn even more about x. As you work today, focus on these questions:

How can you simplify?

How can you get x alone?

Is there more than one way to simplify?

Is there always a solution?

A-77. WHICH IS GREATER?

Build each expression represented below with the tiles provided by your teacher. Use "legal" simplification moves to determine which expression is greater, if possible. If it is not possible to determine which expression is greater, explain why it is impossible. Be sure to record your work on your paper.

a.

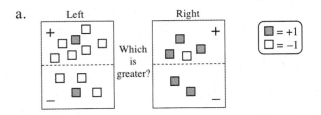

b. Which is greater: $x+1-(1-2x)$ or $3+x-1-(x-4)$?

A-78.   WHAT IF BOTH SIDES ARE EQUAL?

If the number 5 is compared to the number 7, then it is clear that 7 is greater. However, what if you compare x with 7? In this case, x could be smaller, larger, *or equal to* 7.

Examine the Expression Comparison Mat below.

a.   If the left expression is smaller than the right expression, what does that tell you about the value of x?

b.   If the left expression is greater than the right expression, what does that tell you about the value of x?

c.   What if the left expression is equal to the right expression? What does x have to be for the two expressions to be equal?

A-79.   SOLVING FOR X

Later in this course, you will learn more about situations like parts (a) and (b) in the preceding problem, called "inequalities." For now, to learn more about x, assume that the left expression and the right expression are equal. The two expressions will be brought together on one mat to create an **Equation Mat**, as shown in the figure below. The double line down the center of an Equation Mat represents the word "equals." It is a wall that separates the left side of an equation from the right side.

a.   Obtain the "Equation Mat" resource page from your teacher. Using algebra tiles, build the equation represented by the Equation Mat at right. Simplify as much as possible and then solve for x. Be sure to record your work.

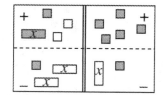

b.   Using algebra tiles, build the equation $2x - 5 = -1 + 5x + 2$ by placing $2x - 5$ on the left side and $-1 + 5x + 2$ on the right side. Then use your simplification skills to simplify this equation as much as possible so that x is alone on one side of the equation. Use the fact that both sides are equal to solve for x. Record your work.

276

A-80.   Now apply this new solving skill by building, simplifying, and solving each
         equation below for x. Record your work.

   a. $3x - 7 = 2$ b. $1 + 2x - x = x - 5 + x$

   c. $3 - 2x = 2x - 5$ d. $3 + 2x - (x + 1) = 3x - 6$

   e. $-(x + 3 - x) = 2x - 7$ f. $-4 + 2x + 2 = x + 1 + x$

A-81.   Verify your solutions to parts (b) through (d) of problem A-80 are correct by
         "showing the check." That is, substitute your answer into the original equation
         to show that you have a true statement.

METHODS AND MEANINGS

Using an Equation Mat

MATH NOTES

An **Equation Mat**
can help you
visually represent an
equation with algebra tiles.

The double line represents the
"equals" sign (=).

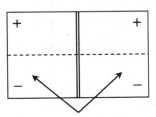

For each side of the equation, there
is a positive and a negative region.

For example, the equation
$2x - 1 - (-x + 3) = 6 - 2x$ can be
represented by the Equation Mat at
right. (Note that there are other
possible ways to represent this equation
correctly on the Equation Mat.)

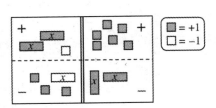

A-82.   **WHICH IS GREATER?**

For each Expression Comparison Mat below, simplify and determine which side is greater.

a.
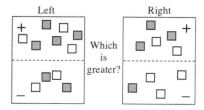

b.
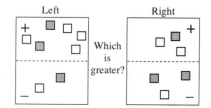

A-83.   Solve this problem by writing an equation using only one variable. Then write your answer with a complete sentence.

Mairé is thinking of two numbers. The first number is 14 less than the second number. When she adds them, she gets 40. Help her younger sister, Enya, figure out the numbers.

A-84.   Simplify each expression below as much as possible.

a. $3y - y + 5x + 3 - 7x$

b. $-1 - (-5x) - 2x + 2x^2 + 7$

c. $6x + 2 - 1 - 4x - 3 - 2x + 2$

d. $\frac{2}{3}x - 3y + \frac{1}{3}x + 2y$

A-85.   Plot the points $(0, 0)$, $(3, 2)$, and $(6, 4)$ on graph paper. Then draw a line through the points. Name the coordinates of three more points on the same line.

A-86.   Mr. Dexter's teams earned the following scores on a quiz: 15, 20, 19, 20, 16, 20, 14, 18, and 17.

a.   What is the mean (average score)?

b.   What is the median (middle score)?

A-87.   Simplify each expression.

a. $-\frac{2}{3} + \frac{4}{5}$

b. $2 - \frac{3}{8}$

c. $-\frac{3}{5} \cdot 10$

d. $\frac{2}{3} \div -2$

A.1.9 What is *x*?

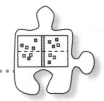

Today you will explore more equations on the Equation Mat and will examine all of the tools you have developed so far to solve for *x*. While you are working on these problems, be prepared to answer the following questions:

How can you simplify?

Can you get the variable alone?

Is there more than one way to simplify?

Is there always a solution?

A-88.   On your paper, write the equation represented in each diagram below. For each equation, simplify as much as possible and then solve for *x* or *y*. Be sure to record your work on your paper.

$$\square = +1$$
$$\square = -1$$

a.

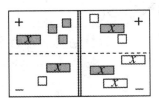

b.

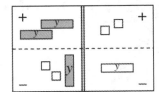

A-89.   **IS THERE A SOLUTION?**

While solving homework last night, Richie came across three homework questions that he thinks have no solution. Build each equation below and determine if it has a solution for *x*. If it has a solution, find it. If it does not have a solution, explain why not.

$$\square = +1$$
$$\square = -1$$

a.

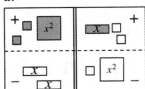

b.

c.

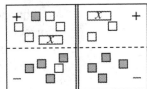

A-90.   Continue to develop your equation-solving strategies by solving each equation
below (if possible). Remember to build each equation, simplify as much as
possible, and solve for x or y. There are often multiple ways to solve equations,
so remember to justify that each step is "legal." If you cannot solve for x,
explain why not. Be sure to record your work.

  a. $-x + 2 = 4$ b. $4x - 2 + x = 2x + 8 + 3x$

  c. $4y - 9 + y = 6$ d. $9 - (2 - 3y) = 6 + 2y - (5 + y)$

A-91.   In your Learning Log, make a list of all the legal algebra
tile moves. Then for each one, write its corresponding
algebraic explanation. Title this entry "Using Algebra
Tiles to Solve Equations" and include today's date.

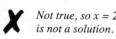

METHODS AND MEANINGS

Checking a Solution

To check a solution to an equation, substitute the solution into the
equation and verify that it makes the two sides of the equation equal.

For example, to verify that $x = 10$ is a solution to the equation
$3(x - 5) = 15$, substitute 10 into the equation for x and then verify that
the two sides of the equation are equal.

As shown at right, $x = 10$ is a solution
to the equation $3(x - 5) = 15$.

$$3(10 - 5) \overset{?}{=} 15$$
$$3(5) \overset{?}{=} 15$$
$$15 = 15 \quad \checkmark \quad \textit{Correct!}$$

What happens if your answer is
incorrect? To investigate this, test
any solution that is not correct. For
example, try substituting $x = 2$ into
the same equation. The result shows
that $x = 2$ is not a solution to this
equation.

$$3(2 - 5) \overset{?}{=} 15$$
$$3(-3) \overset{?}{=} 15$$
$$-9 \neq 15 \quad \boldsymbol{\times} \quad \textit{Not true, so } x = 2$$
$$\textit{is not a solution.}$$

Review & Preview

A-92.   Translate the Equation Mat at right into an equation. Remember that the double line represents "equals."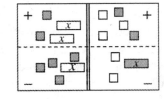

A-93.   Ling wants to save $87 for tickets to a rock concert. If she has $23 now and will save $4 per week, how long will it take her to get enough money to buy the tickets?

A-94.   On graph paper, plot the points $(0, 0)$, $(-2, 1)$, and $(2, -1)$. Then draw a line through them. Name the coordinates of three more points on the same line that have integer coordinates.

A-95.   Solve each equation and then show the check to prove that your answer is correct.

   a. $2 - 4x = 8 - x$ b. $x + 4 - 3x = 4 - (x - 1)$

A-96.   Use legal simplification moves to determine which side of the Expression Comparison Mat is greater.

   a. 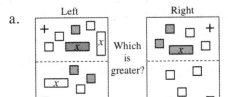   b.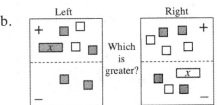

A-97.   Evaluate the expressions below for the given values.

   a. $6m + 2n^2$ for $m = 7$ and $n = 3$ b. $\frac{5x}{3} - 2$ for $x = -18$

   c. $(6x)^2 - \frac{x}{5}$ for $x = 10$ d. $(k - 3)(k + 2)$ for $k = 1$

Appendix Closure   What have I learned?

Reflection and Synthesis

The activities below offer you a chance to reflect about what you have learned during this chapter. As you work, look for concepts that you feel very comfortable with, ideas that you would like to learn more about, and topics you need more help with. Look for connections between ideas as well as connections with material you learned previously.

①   TEAM BRAINSTORM

What have you studied in this chapter? What ideas were important in what you learned? With your team, brainstorm a list. Be as detailed as you can. To help get you started, a list of Learning Log entries and Math Notes boxes are below.

What topics, ideas, and words that you learned *before* this chapter are connected to the new ideas in this chapter? Again, be as detailed as you can.

How long can you make your list? Challenge yourselves. Be prepared to share your team's ideas with the class.

Learning Log Entries
- Lesson A.1.1 – Variables
- Lesson A.1.2 – Finding Perimeter and Combining Like Terms
- Lesson A.1.3 – Meanings of Minus
- Lesson A.1.3 – Representing expressions on an Expression Mat
- Lesson A.1.4 – Using Zeros to Simplify
- Lesson A.1.5 – Legal Moves for Simplifying and Comparing Expressions
- Lesson A.1.9 – Solutions of an Equation

Math Notes
- Lesson A.1.1 – Non-Commensurate
- Lesson A.1.2 – Expression and Terms
- Lesson A.1.3 – Order of Operations
- Lesson A.1.4 – Evaluating Expressions and Equations
- Lesson A.1.5 – Combining Like Terms
- Lesson A.1.6 – Simplifying an Expression
- Lesson A.1.8 – Using an Equation Mat
- Lesson A.1.9 – Checking a Solution

②   MAKING CONNECTIONS

Below is a list of the vocabulary used in this chapter. Make sure that you are familiar with all of these words and know what they mean. Refer to the glossary or index for any words that you do not yet understand.

combining like terms	algebra tiles	area
equal	Equation Mat	equation
variable	evaluate	expression
zero	Expression Mat	greater
minus	negative	opposite
order of operations	simplify	solution
solve	term	

Make a concept map showing all of the connections you can find among the key words and ideas listed above. To show a connection between two words, draw a line between them and explain the connection, as shown in the model below. A word can be connected to any other word as long as you can justify the connection. For each key word or idea, provide an example or sketch that shows the idea.

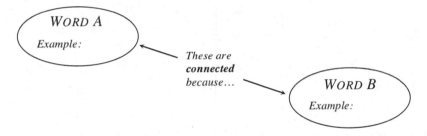

Your teacher may provide you with vocabulary cards to help you get started. If you use the cards to plan your concept map, be sure either to re-draw your concept map on your paper or to glue the vocabulary cards to a poster with all of the connections explained for others to see and understand.

While you are making your map, your team may think of related words or ideas that are not listed here. Be sure to include these ideas on your concept map.

While simplifying the expressions shown in the
Expression Comparison Mat below, the four
members of a study team made the following
statements. Which students justified their
statements? And were the justifications
convincing? Explain why or why not.

Rosalita: "I think we can take the
positive unit tile and
negative unit tile away
from the left side because
they make zero."

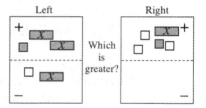

Anthony: "I think we can take an x-tile
away from both sides."

Barry: "I don't think we can tell which side is greater because there
are more x-tiles on the left side than on the right."

Deshawn: "I think we can remove a positive and negative unit tile from
the "+" region on the right side because they are opposites, so
they make zero."

Your teammate needs help understanding why $-(-2x-3)=2x+3$. She thinks
that $-(-2x-3)=2x-3$. Justify why $-(-2x-3)=2x+3$ so that she is
convinced.

Obtain the Appendix Closure Resource Page: Simplifying/Solving Graphic
Organizer from your teacher. Choose an equation that showcases what you
have learned about solving an equation. Use the Resource Page to solve that
equation. Make sure to show your tile diagram, the algebraic representation,
and the step-by-step justification (legal tile moves). Then algebraically check
your answer.

④　　　　　　WHAT HAVE I LEARNED?

Most of the problems in this section represent typical problems found in this chapter. They serve as a gauge for you. You can use them to determine which types of problems you can do well and which types of problems require further study and practice. Even if your teacher does not assign this section, it is a good idea to try these problems and find out for yourself what you know and what you still need to work on.

Solve each problem as completely as you can. The table at the end of the closure section has answers to these problems. It also tells you where you can find additional help and practice with problems like these.

CL A-98.　Examine the Expression Mat at right.

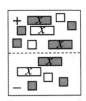

a.　Copy the Expression Mat onto your paper.

b.　Write an expression for the tiles as they appear.

c.　On your drawing, circle all of the zeros that you can find to simplify the expression.

d.　Write the completely simplified expression.

CL A-99.　Zeke ran 4 miles in 45 minutes. If he keeps up the same pace, how long will it take him to run 10 miles? Explain your method or reasoning.

CL A-100.　Write expressions for each side of the Expression Comparison Mat. Use "legal" moves to simplify and determine which is greater.

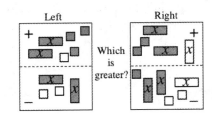

CL A-101.   Solve the following problem by writing an equation using only one variable. Write your answer with a complete sentence.

Ralph and Alphonse are shooting marbles. Ralph has five more marbles than Alphonse, and they have a total of 73 marbles. How many marbles does each of them have?

CL A-102.   Simplify each expression with or without algebra tiles. Record your steps.

a. $3 + 7x - (2 + 9x)$

b. $6 - (3x - 4) + 7x - 11$

CL A-103.   Copy the pattern below onto graph paper. Draw Figures 1 and 5 on your paper.

a.   How many tiles are in each figure?

b.   How is the pattern changing?

c.   How many tiles would Figure 6 have?

Figure 2   Figure 3   Figure 4

CL A-104.   Find the area and perimeter of the figure at right.

CL A-105.   Evaluate $6x - (3y + 7) - xy$ when $x = 5$ and $y = 3$.

CL A-106.   Simplify the expression below by combining like terms:

$$3x^2 + 10 - y^2 + 4x - 8x^2 - 5y - 8 + y^2 + 3$$

CL A-107.   Solve this equation to find x and then show the check:

$$2 - (3x - 4) = 2x - 9$$

CL A-108.   Check your answers using the table at the end of the closure section. Which problems do you feel confident about? Which problems were hard? Use the table to make a list of topics you need help on and a list of topics you need to practice more.

Answers and Support for Closure Activity #4
What Have I Learned?

Note: MN = Math Note, LL = Learning Log

Problem	Solution	Need Help?	More Practice
CL A-98.	b. $2x - x + 3 - 2 - (x - x + 2 - 1)$ c. One possible answer: d. x	Lessons A.1.3 and A.1.4 MN: A.1.5 LL: A.1.3 and A.1.4	Problems A-27, A-30, A-37, A-39, A-40, A-43, A-45, and A-61
CL A-99.	112.5 minutes	Explanations and practice of topics from previous courses are available in the *Core Connections, Courses 1-3 Parent Guide with Extra Practice*, available free at www.cpm.org.	Problems A-58, A-64, and A-76
CL A-100.	Left: $-1 + 2x + 3 - (2x - 2) = 4$ Right: $2x + 2 - x - (2x - x - 2 + 1) = 3$ The left expression is greater than the right expression.	Lesson A.1.6 MN: A.1.6 LL: A.1.5	Problems A-61, A-72, A-77, and A-82
CL A-101.	Let x = Alphonse's number of marbles, $x + (x + 5) = 73$ Ralph has 39 marbles, and Alphonse has 34 marbles.	Explanations and practice of topics from previous courses are available in the *Core Connections, Courses 1-3 Parent Guide with Extra Practice*, available free at www.cpm.org.	Problems A-32, A-71, A-83, and A-93

Problem	Solution	Need Help?	More Practice
CL A-102.	a. $-2x+1$ b. $4x-1$	Lesson A.1.7	Problem A-84
CL A-103.	a. 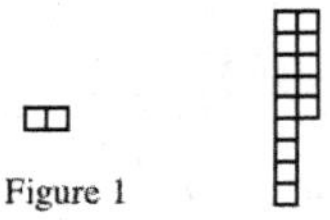 Figure 1 Figure 5 b. Each figure has three more tiles than the one before it. c. Figure 6 would have 17 tiles.	Lesson 1.1.2	Problems CL 1-85 and A-73
CL A-104.	Perimeter $= 6x+10$ Area $= 2x^2 + 7x + 6$	Lesson A.1.1 and A.1.2	Problems A-21, A-46, and A-74
CL A-105.	$6 \cdot 5 - (3 \cdot 3 + 7) - 5 \cdot 3 = -1$	MN: A.1.3 and A.1.4	Problems A-10, A-18, A-44, A-57, and A-97
CL A-106.	$-5x^2 + 4x - 5y + 5$	Lessons A.1.1, A.1.3, A.1.2, and A.1.4 MN: A.1.5 LL: A.1.2, A.1.3, and A.1.4	Problems A-4, A-17, A-30, A-53, and A-84
CL A-107.	$x = 3$	Lessons A.1.8 and A.1.9 MN: A.1.9 LL: A.1.9	Problems A-80, A-90, and A-95

Core Connections Algebra
Checkpoint Materials

Notes to Students (and their Teachers)

Students master different skills at different speeds. No two students learn exactly the same way at the same time. At some point you will be expected to perform certain skills accurately. Most of the Checkpoint problems incorporate skills that you should have developed in previous courses. If you have not mastered these skills yet it does not mean that you will not be successful in this class. However, you may need to do some work outside of class to get caught up on them.

Starting in Chapter 1 and finishing in Chapter 11, there are 15 problems designed as Checkpoint problems. Each one is marked with an icon like the one above and numbered according to the chapter that it is in. After you do each of the Checkpoint problems, check your answers by referring to this section. If your answers are incorrect, you may need some extra practice to develop that skill. The practice sets are keyed to each of the Checkpoint problems in the textbook. Each has the topic clearly labeled, followed by the answers to the corresponding Checkpoint problem and then some completed examples. Next, the complete solution to the Checkpoint problem from the text is given, and there are more problems for you to practice with answers included.

Remember, looking is not the same as doing! You will never become good at any sport by just watching it, and in the same way, reading through the worked examples and understanding the steps is not the same as being able to do the problems yourself. How many of the extra practice problems do you need to try? That is really up to you. Remember that your goal is to be able to do similar problems on your own confidently and accurately. This is your responsibility. You should not expect your teacher to spend time in class going over the solutions to the Checkpoint problem sets. If you are not confident after reading the examples and trying the problems, you should get help outside of class time or talk to your teacher about working with a tutor.

Another source for help with the Checkpoint problems and other topics in *Core Connections Algebra* is the *Parent Guide with Extra Practice*. This resource is available for download free of charge at www.cpm.org.

Checkpoint Topics, Volume 1

1. Solving Linear Equations, Part 1 (Integer Coefficients)
2. Evaluating Expressions and the Order of Operations
3. Operations with Rational Numbers
4. Solving Linear Equations, Part 2 (Fractional Coefficients)
5A. Laws of Exponents and Scientific Notation
5B. Writing the Equation of a Line

Checkpoint 1

Problem 1-49

Solving Linear Equations, Part 1 (Integer Coefficients)

Answers to problem 1-49: a: $x = -2$, b: $x = 1\frac{1}{2}$, c: $x = 0$, d: no solution

Equations in one variable may be solved in a variety of ways. Commonly, the first step is to simplify by combining like terms. Next isolate the variable on one side and the constants on the other. Finally, divide to find the value of the variable. Note: When the process of solving an equation ends with different numbers on each side of the equal sign (for example, $2 = 4$), there is *no solution* to the problem. When the result is the same expression or number on each side of the equation (for example, $x + 3 = x + 3$) it means that *all real numbers* are solutions.

Example: Solve $4x + 4x - 3 = 6x + 9$

Solution:

$$
\begin{array}{ll}
4x + 4x - 3 = 6x + 9 & \text{problem} \\
8x - 3 = 6x + 9 & \text{simplify} \\
2x = 12 & \text{add 3, subtract } 6x \text{ on each side} \\
x = 6 & \text{divide}
\end{array}
$$

Check:
$$
\begin{array}{c}
4(6) + 4(6) - 3 = 6(6) + 9 \\
24 + 24 - 3 = 36 + 9 \\
48 - 3 = 45 \\
45 = 45 \checkmark
\end{array}
$$

Now we can go back and solve the original problems.

a.
$$
\begin{array}{c}
3x + 7 = -x - 1 \\
4x = -8 \\
x = -2
\end{array}
$$

b.
$$
\begin{array}{c}
1 - 2x + 5 = 4x - 3 \\
-2x + 6 = 4x - 3 \\
9 = 6x \\
1\frac{1}{2} = x
\end{array}
$$

c.
$$
\begin{array}{c}
4x - 2 + x = -2 + 2x \\
5x - 2 = 2x - 2 \\
3x = 0 \\
x = 0
\end{array}
$$

d.
$$
\begin{array}{c}
3x - 4 + 1 = -2x - 5 + 5x \\
3x - 3 = 3x - 5 \\
-3 = -5 \\
-3 \neq -5 \Rightarrow \text{no solution}
\end{array}
$$

Here are some more to try. Solve each equation.

1. $2x - 3 = -x + 3$ 2. $3x + 2 + x = x + 5$

3. $6 - x - 3 = 4x - 8$ 4. $4x - 2 - 2x = x - 5$

5. $-x - 3 = 2x - 6$ 6. $-x + 2 = x - 5 - 3x$

7. $1 + 3x - x = x - 4 + 2x$ 8. $5x - 3 + 2x = x + 7 + 6x$

9. $4y - 8 - 2y = 4$ 10. $-x + 3 = 6$

11. $3y + 7 - y = 5 + 2y + 2$ 12. $4y + 7 = 2y + 7$

13. $-x - 3 = 2x - 6$ 14. $10 = x + 5 + x$

15. $-4 + 3x - 1 = 2x + 1 + 2x$ 16. $2x - 7 = -x - 1$

Answers

1. $x = 2$ 2. $x = 1$

3. $x = 2\frac{1}{5}$ 4. $x = -3$

5. $x = 1$ 6. $x = -7$

7. $x = 5$ 8. no solution

9. $y = 6$ 10. $x = -3$

11. all real numbers   12. $y = 0$

13. $x = 1$ 14. $x = 2\frac{1}{2}$

15 $x = -6$ 16. $x = 2$

Checkpoint 2

Problem 2-92

Evaluating Expressions and the Order of Operations

Answers to problem 2-92: a: –8, b: 1, c: –2, d: 17, e: –45, f: 125

In general, simplify an expression by using the Order of Operations:

- Evaluate each exponential (for example, $5^2 = 5 \cdot 5 = 25$).
- Multiply and divide each term from left to right.
- Combine like terms by adding and subtracting from left to right.

But simplify *the expressions in parentheses* or any other expressions of grouped numbers first. Numbers above or below a "fraction bar" are considered grouped. A good way to remember is to circle the terms like in the following example. Remember that terms are separated by + and – signs.

Example 1: Evaluate $2x^2 - 3x + 2$ for $x = -5$

Solution: $2(-5)^2 - 3(-5) + 2$
$2(25) - 3(-5) + 2$
$50 - (-15) + 2$
$50 + 15 + 2 = 67$

Example 2: Evaluate $5\left(\frac{x+2y}{x-y}\right)$ for $x = -3, y = 2$

Solution: $5\left(\frac{-3+2 \cdot 2}{-3-2}\right)$
$5\left(\frac{-3+4}{-3-2}\right)$
$5\left(\frac{1}{-5}\right) = -1$

Now we can go back and solve the original problems.

a. $2x + 3y + z$
$2(-2) + 3(-3) + 5$
$-4 + -9 + 5 = -8$

b. $x - y$
$(-2) - (-3)$
$-2 + 3 = 1$

c. $2\left(\frac{x+y}{z}\right)$
$2\left(\frac{-2+-3}{5}\right)$
$2\left(\frac{-5}{5}\right) = 2(-1) = -2$

d. $3x^2 - 2x + 1$
$3(-2)^2 - 2(-2) + 1$
$3(4) - 2(-2) + 1$
$12 - (-4) + 1 = 17$

e. $3y(x + x^2 - y)$
$3(-3)(-2 + (-2)^2 - (-3))$
$3(-3)\left(-2 + 4 - (-3)\right)$
$3(-3)(5) = -45$

f. $\frac{-z^2(1-2x)}{y-x}$
$\frac{-(5)^2(1-2(-2))}{(-3)-(-2)}$
$\frac{-25(1-(-4))}{(-3)-(-2)} = \frac{-25(5)}{-1} = 125$

Here are some more to try. Evaluate each expression for $x = 4$, $y = -2$, $z = -3$.

1. $2x - 3$

2. $z^2 + 5$

3. $3z - 2y$

4. $xy - 4z$

5. $y - 2 + x$

6. $z - 8 - y$

7. $x^2 + 10x - 20$

8. $2\left(\frac{2+x}{y+1}\right)$

9. $y^2 - 3y + 7$

10. $2yz - x^2$

11. $-\frac{x}{3y}$

12. $(y + z) \cdot \frac{1}{4} x$

13. $2z(y + x^2 - x)$

14. $\frac{10+y}{3y(x+1)}$

15. $2\left(\frac{x+y}{y}\right)$

16. $(2x + y^2)(3 + z)$

17. $y - 5 + 3z^2$

18. $x^2 + 12z - 4y$

19. $\frac{2y^2 x}{x+2}$

20. $x(3 + zy) - 2x^2$

21. $z^2 + 8zy - y^2$

22. $x^3 - 4y$

23. $6z - y^2 + \frac{x+2}{z}$

24. $\frac{-y^2(xz-5y)}{3x-4y}$

Answers

1. 5

2. 14

3. −5

4. 4

5. 0

6. −9

7. 36

8. −12

9. 17

10. −4

11. $\frac{2}{3}$

12. −5

13. −60

14. $-\frac{4}{15}$

15. −2

16. 0

17. 20

18. −12

19. $5\frac{1}{3}$

20. 4

21. 53

22. 72

23. −24

24. $\frac{2}{5}$

Checkpoint 3

Problem 3-110

Operations with Rational Numbers

Answers to problem 3-110: a: $-\frac{19}{24}$, b: $4\frac{5}{6}$, c: $1\frac{2}{5}$, d: $-2\frac{2}{3}$, e: $-3\frac{7}{12}$, f: $2\frac{2}{7}$

Use the same processes with rational numbers (positive and negative fractions) as are done with integers (positive and negative whole numbers).

Example 1: Compute $\frac{1}{3}+\left(-\frac{9}{20}\right)$

Solution: When adding a positive number with a negative number, subtract the values and the number further from zero determines the sign.

$$\frac{1}{3}+-\frac{9}{20} = \frac{1}{3}\cdot\frac{20}{20} + -\frac{9}{20}\cdot\frac{3}{3} = \frac{20}{60} + -\frac{27}{60} = -\frac{7}{60}$$

Example 2: Compute $-1\frac{1}{4}-\left(-3\frac{9}{10}\right)$

Solution: Change any subtraction problem to "addition of the opposite" and then follow the addition process.

$$-1\frac{1}{4}-\left(-3\frac{9}{10}\right)\Rightarrow-1\frac{1}{4}+3\frac{9}{10}=-1\frac{5}{20}+3\frac{18}{20}=2\frac{13}{20}$$

Example 3: Compute $-1\frac{1}{4}\div 7\frac{1}{2}$

Solution: With multiplication or division, if the signs are the same, then the answer is positive. If the signs are different, then the answer is negative.

$$-1\frac{1}{4}\div 7\frac{1}{2}=-\frac{5}{4}\div\frac{15}{2}=-\frac{5}{4}\cdot\frac{2}{15}=-\frac{\cancel{5}\cdot\cancel{2}}{\cancel{2}\cdot 2\cdot 3\cdot\cancel{5}}=-\frac{1}{6}$$

Now we can go back and solve the original problems.

a. Both numbers are negative so add the values and the sign is negative.

$$-\frac{2}{3}+-\frac{1}{8}=-\frac{2}{3}\cdot\frac{8}{8}+-\frac{1}{8}\cdot\frac{3}{3}=-\frac{16}{24}+-\frac{3}{24}=-\frac{19}{24}$$

b. Change the subtraction to addition of the opposite.

$$3\frac{1}{2}-\left(-1\frac{1}{3}\right)=3\frac{1}{2}+1\frac{1}{3}=3+\frac{1}{2}\cdot\frac{3}{3}+1+\frac{1}{3}\cdot\frac{2}{2}=3+\frac{3}{6}+1+\frac{2}{6}=4\frac{5}{6}$$

c. The signs are the same so the product is positive. Multiply as usual.

$$-4\frac{1}{5}\cdot-\frac{1}{3}=-\frac{21}{5}\cdot-\frac{1}{3}=\frac{7\cdot\cancel{3}\cdot 1}{5\cdot\cancel{3}}=\frac{7}{5}=1\frac{2}{5}$$

d. The signs are different so the quotient is negative. Divide as usual.

$$-\frac{2}{3}\div\frac{1}{4}=-\frac{2}{3}\cdot\frac{4}{1}=-\frac{2\cdot 4}{3\cdot 1}=-\frac{8}{3}=-2\frac{2}{3}$$

Solutions continue on next page. →

Solutions continued from previous page.

e. When adding a positive number with a negative number, subtract the values and the number further from zero determines the sign.

$$1\tfrac{3}{4}+-5\tfrac{1}{3}=\tfrac{7}{4}+-\tfrac{16}{3}=\tfrac{7}{4}\cdot\tfrac{3}{3}+-\tfrac{16}{3}\cdot\tfrac{4}{4}=\tfrac{21}{12}+-\tfrac{64}{12}=-\tfrac{43}{12}=-3\tfrac{7}{12}$$

f. The signs are the same so the quotient is positive. Divide as usual.

$$-2\tfrac{2}{3}\div-1\tfrac{1}{6}=-\tfrac{8}{3}\div-\tfrac{7}{6}=-\tfrac{8}{3}\cdot-\tfrac{6}{7}=\tfrac{8\cdot\cancel{6}\,2}{\cancel{3}\cdot7}=\tfrac{16}{7}=2\tfrac{2}{7}$$

Here are some more to try. Compute each of the following problems with rational numbers.

1. $-\tfrac{2}{5}+\tfrac{1}{2}$

2. $\tfrac{3}{4}-\left(-\tfrac{5}{12}\right)$

3. $-\tfrac{5}{7}+\tfrac{4}{5}$

4. $-1\tfrac{6}{7}+\left(-\tfrac{3}{4}\right)$

5. $\left(3\tfrac{1}{3}\right)\cdot\left(-\tfrac{2}{5}\right)$

6. $-2\tfrac{1}{4}\cdot\tfrac{2}{3}$

7. $-2\tfrac{7}{12}\div-\tfrac{1}{6}$

8. $3\tfrac{1}{2}+\left(-4\tfrac{3}{8}\right)$

9. $-1\tfrac{1}{4}-\left(-3\tfrac{1}{6}\right)$

10. $\left(2\tfrac{5}{9}\right)\cdot\left(-\tfrac{3}{7}\right)$

11. $-4\tfrac{3}{4}-\left(-\tfrac{5}{7}\right)$

12. $\tfrac{2}{3}\div-1\tfrac{4}{9}$

13. $-\tfrac{5}{9}\cdot1\tfrac{2}{3}$

14. $-\tfrac{3}{5}\div-1\tfrac{1}{10}$

15. $-5\tfrac{1}{2}\div-\tfrac{3}{4}$

16. $10\tfrac{5}{8}+\left(-2\tfrac{1}{2}\right)$

17. $5\tfrac{1}{5}+\left(-2\tfrac{2}{15}\right)$

18. $12\tfrac{3}{4}-\left(-1\tfrac{5}{8}\right)$

19. $-2\tfrac{7}{9}\cdot3\tfrac{1}{7}$

20. $-1\tfrac{1}{5}\div-\tfrac{1}{10}$

21. $5\tfrac{1}{12}-\left(-2\tfrac{6}{7}\right)$

22. $-6\tfrac{1}{7}\cdot-\tfrac{4}{5}$

23. $-1\tfrac{1}{8}\div2\tfrac{3}{4}$

24. $-2\tfrac{3}{5}-3\tfrac{1}{10}$

Answers

1. $\tfrac{1}{10}$

2. $1\tfrac{1}{6}$

3. $\tfrac{3}{35}$

4. $-2\tfrac{17}{28}$

5. $-1\tfrac{1}{3}$

6. $-1\tfrac{1}{2}$

7. $15\tfrac{1}{2}$

8. $-\tfrac{7}{8}$

9. $1\tfrac{11}{12}$

10. $-1\tfrac{2}{21}$

11. $-4\tfrac{1}{28}$

12. $-\tfrac{6}{13}$

13. $-\tfrac{25}{27}$

14. $\tfrac{6}{11}$

15. $7\tfrac{1}{3}$

16. $8\tfrac{1}{8}$

17. $3\tfrac{1}{15}$

18. $14\tfrac{3}{8}$

19. $-8\tfrac{46}{63}$

20. 12

21. $7\tfrac{79}{84}$

22. $4\tfrac{32}{35}$

23. $-\tfrac{9}{22}$

24. $-5\tfrac{7}{10}$

Checkpoint 4
Problem 4-86
Solving Linear Equations, Part 2 (Fractional Coefficients)

Answers to problem 4-86: a: –12, b: –24, c: $x = \frac{16}{5}$

Equations in one variable with fractional coefficients may be solved in a variety of ways. Commonly, the first step is to multiply all the terms by a common denominator to remove the fractions. Then solve in the usual way. Combine like terms. Isolate the variable on one side and the constants on the other. Finally, divide to find the value of the variable.

Example 1: Solve $\frac{1}{2}x + x - 3 = \frac{1}{3}x + 4$

Solution:

$\frac{1}{2}x + x - 3 = \frac{1}{3}x + 4$	problem
$6(\frac{1}{2}x + x - 3) = 6(\frac{1}{3}x + 4)$	multiply by the common denominator
$3x + 6x - 18 = 2x + 24$	simplify
$9x - 18 = 2x + 24$	simplify
$7x = 42$	add 18, subtract $2x$ from each side
$x = 6$	divide

Example 2: Solve for y: $\frac{y}{2} + \frac{y}{3} - 3 = y$

Solution:

$\frac{y}{2} + \frac{y}{3} - 3 = y$	problem
$6(\frac{y}{2}) + 6(\frac{y}{3}) + 6(-3) = 6(y)$	multiply by the common denominator
$3y + 2y - 18 = 6y$	simplify
$-18 = y$	subtract $5y$ from each side

Now we can go back and solve the original problems.

a.
$$\frac{1}{6}m - 3 = -5$$
$$6(\frac{1}{6}m - 3) = 6(-5)$$
$$m - 18 = -30$$
$$m = -12$$

b.
$$\frac{2}{3}x - 3 = \frac{1}{2}x - 7$$
$$(6)\frac{2}{3}x - (6)\cdot 3 = (6)\frac{1}{2}x - (6)\cdot 7$$
$$4x - 18 = 3x - 42$$
$$x = -24$$

c.
$$x + \frac{x}{2} - 4 = \frac{x}{4}$$
$$4(x + \frac{x}{2} - 4) = 4(\frac{x}{4})$$
$$4x + 2x - 16 = x$$
$$5x = 16$$
$$x = \frac{16}{5}$$

Here are some more to try. Solve each equation.

1. $\frac{2}{3}x - 7 = \frac{1}{3}x + 3$

2. $\frac{5}{4}x - 7 = x - 5$

3. $\frac{1}{3}y = \frac{1}{4}y + 7$

4. $\frac{2}{3}x + 7 = -\frac{1}{5}x + 3$

5. $\frac{x}{2} + \frac{x}{3} = 1$

6. $\frac{2x}{3} + \frac{x}{4} = 3$

7. $x + 7 + \frac{1}{3}x = \frac{3}{2}x - 2$

8. $\frac{1}{4}x + \frac{2}{3} - x = \frac{3}{5}x - \frac{1}{2}$

9. $\frac{1}{3}y + 7 + \frac{1}{6}y = \frac{1}{2}y - 1$

10. $\frac{x}{5} + \frac{2x}{3} + x = 2$

11. $3x - \frac{x}{4} + 9 = 1 - \frac{x}{2} + 8$

12. $\frac{1}{3}y - 2 + \frac{1}{2}y = 1 + y - \frac{y}{6} - 3$

Answers

1. $x = 30$

2. $x = 8$

3. $y = 84$

4. $x = -\frac{60}{13}$

5. $x = \frac{6}{5}$

6. $x = \frac{36}{11}$

7. $x = 54$

8. $x = \frac{70}{81}$

9. no solution

10. $x = \frac{15}{14}$

11. $x = 0$

12. all real numbers

Checkpoint 5A

Problem 5-55

Laws of Exponents and Scientific Notation

Answers to problem 5-55: a: 4^7, b: 1, c: $x^{-2} = \frac{1}{x^2}$, d: $\frac{y^6}{x^3}$, e: 1.28×10^4, f: 8×10^{-3}

The laws of exponents summarize several rules for simplifying expressions that have exponents. The rules are true for any base if $x \neq 0$.

$$x^a \cdot x^b = x^{(a+b)}$$
$$(x^a)^b = x^{ab}$$
$$\frac{x^a}{x^b} = x^{(a-b)}$$

$$x^0 = 1$$
$$x^{-a} = \frac{1}{x^a}$$

Scientific notation is a way of writing a number as a product of two factors separated by a multiplication sign. The first factor must be less than 10 and greater than or equal to 1. The second factor has a base of 10 and an integer exponent.

Example 1: Simplify $4^2 \cdot 4^{-4}$

Solution: In a multiplication problem, if the bases are the same, add the exponents and keep the base. If the answer ends with a negative exponent, take the reciprocal and change the exponent to positive.

$$4^2 \cdot 4^{-4} = 4^{-2} = \frac{1}{4^2} = \frac{1}{16}$$

Example 2: Simplify $\frac{(x^2)^3 \cdot y^4}{x^{-2} \cdot y}$

Solution: Separate the fraction into two fractions with bases x and y. With an exponent on an exponent, multiply the exponents. Next, to divide expressions with exponents and the same base, subtract the exponents.

$$\frac{(x^2)^3 \cdot y^4}{x^{-2} \cdot y} = \frac{(x^2)^3}{x^{-2}} \cdot \frac{y^4}{y} = \frac{x^6}{x^{-2}} \cdot \frac{y^4}{y^1} = x^8 \cdot y^3 = x^8 y^3$$

Example 3: Multiply and give the answer in scientific notation. $(8 \times 10^4) \cdot (4.5 \times 10^{-2})$

Solution: Separate the number parts and the exponent parts. Multiply the number parts normally and the exponent part by adding the exponents. If this answer is not in scientific notation, change it appropriately.

$$(8 \times 10^4) \cdot (4.5 \times 10^{-2}) = (8 \times 4.5) \cdot (10^4 \times 10^{-2}) = 36 \times 10^2 = (3.6 \times 10^1) \times 10^2 = 3.6 \times 10^3$$

Now we can go back and solve the original problems.

a. $4^2 \cdot 4^5 = 4^{(2+5)} = 4^7$

b. $(5^0)^3 = 5^{0 \cdot 3} = 5^0 = 1$

c. $x^{-5} \cdot x^3 = x^{(-5+3)} = x^{-2} = \frac{1}{x^2}$

d. $(x^{-1} \cdot y^2)^3 = (\frac{1}{x} \cdot y^2)^3 = (\frac{y^2}{x})^3 = \frac{y^6}{x^3}$

e. $(8 \times 10^5) \cdot (1.6 \times 10^{-2}) = 12.8 \times 10^3 = (1.28 \times 10^1) \times 10^3 = 1.28 \times 10^4$

f. $\frac{4 \times 10^3}{5 \times 10^5} = \frac{4}{5} \times 10^{(3-5)} = 0.8 \times 10^{-2} = (8 \times 10^{-1}) \times 10^{-2} = 8 \times 10^{-3}$

Here are some more to try. Simplify each expression. For problems 19 through 24 write the final answer using scientific notation.

1. $5^4 \cdot 5^{-1}$

2. $3^3 \cdot 3^3 \cdot 3^6$

3. $x^2 \cdot (x^4)^{-2}$

4. $y^{-2} \cdot \frac{1}{y^2} \cdot y^3$

5. $3^3 \cdot 3^5 \cdot \left(\frac{1}{3}\right)^2$

6. $(3^3 \cdot 4^{-6})^2 \cdot 6^7$

7. $x^{-3} \cdot x^0$

8. $x^1 \cdot \frac{x}{x^3} \cdot \frac{y^{-2}}{y}$

9. $\frac{7^4 \cdot 9^2}{9^3 \cdot 7^2}$

10. $\frac{14^3}{14^{-2}} \cdot 14^0$

11. $\left(\frac{x^2 \cdot y^4}{x^3 \cdot y^4}\right)^0$

12. $\frac{(y^2)^3}{y^6} \cdot y^4$

13. $\left(\frac{5^2}{5^4}\right)^{-1}$

14. $(7^2 \cdot 7^3)^4$

15. $\frac{y^3 \cdot y^2 \cdot y^{-3}}{y^{-4} \cdot y^3}$

16. $\left(\frac{1}{x^4}\right)^{-2} \cdot x \cdot x^0$

17. $\left(\frac{2^4}{7^{-3}}\right)\left(\frac{7^{-2}}{2^5}\right)^{-1}$

18. $\frac{9^3 \cdot 9^{-5}}{9^0}$

19. $(4.25 \times 10^3) \cdot (2 \times 10^5)$

20. $(1.2 \times 10^4) \cdot (7.1 \times 10^{-2})$

21. $(6.9 \times 10^7) \cdot (3 \times 10^2)$

22. $(5.63 \times 10^{-6}) \cdot (4 \times 10^{-7})$

23. $(6 \times 10^{-3})^2$

24. $2.7 \times 10^4 \div 3.2 \times 10^{-2}$

Answers

1. 5^3

2. 3^{12}

3. $x^{-6} = \frac{1}{x^6}$

4. $y^{-1} = \frac{1}{y}$

5. 3^6

6. $3^{13} \cdot 2^{-17}$

7. $x^{-3} = \frac{1}{x^3}$

8. $x^{-1} \cdot y^{-3} = \frac{1}{xy^3}$

9. $\frac{7^2}{9}$

10. 14^5

11. 1

12. y^4

13. 5^2

14. 7^{20}

15. y^3

16. x^9

17. $2^9 \cdot 7^5$

18. 9^{-2}

19. 8.5×10^8

20. 8.52×10^2

21. 2.07×10^{10}

22. 2.252×10^{-12}

23. 3.6×10^{-5}

24. 8.4375×10^5

Checkpoint 5B

Problem 5-90

Writing the Equation of a Line

Answers to problem 5-90: a: $y = 2x - 3$, b: $y = -3x - 1$, c: $y = \frac{2}{3}x - 2$, d: $y \approx \frac{5}{2}x + 9$

Except for a vertical line, any line may be written in the form $y = mx + b$ where "b" represents the y-intercept of the line and "m" represents the slope. (Vertical lines are always of the form $x = k$.) The slope is a ratio indicating the steepness and direction of the line. The slope is calculated by $m = \frac{\text{vertical change}}{\text{horizontal change}} = \frac{\Delta y}{\Delta x}$.

Example 1: Write the equation of the line with slope $-\frac{1}{2}$ and passing through the point $(6, 3)$.

Solution: Write the general equation of a line. $\qquad y = mx + b$

Substitute the values we know for m, x, and y. $\qquad 3 = -\frac{1}{2}(6) + b$

$\qquad\qquad\qquad\qquad\qquad\qquad\qquad\qquad\qquad 3 = -3 + b$

Solve for b. $\qquad\qquad\qquad\qquad\qquad\qquad\qquad 6 = b$

Write the complete equation. $\qquad\qquad\qquad y = -\frac{1}{2}x + 6$

Example 2: Write the equation of the line passing through the points $(8, 3)$ and $(4, 6)$.

Solution: Draw a generic slope triangle. $\qquad (4, 6) \quad \overset{4}{\diagdown} \quad$

$\qquad\qquad\qquad\qquad\qquad\qquad\qquad\qquad\qquad -3 \quad \frac{\Delta y}{\Delta x} = \frac{-3}{4}$,

Calculate the slope using the given two points. $\qquad (8, 3) \quad m = -\frac{3}{4}$

Write the general equation of a line. $\qquad\qquad\qquad y = mx + b$

Substitute m and one of the points for x and y, in this case $(8, 3)$. $\qquad\qquad\qquad 3 = -\frac{3}{4}(8) + b$

$\qquad\qquad\qquad\qquad\qquad\qquad\qquad\qquad\qquad 3 = -6 + b$

Solve for b. $\qquad\qquad\qquad\qquad\qquad\qquad\qquad 9 = b$

Write the complete equation. $\qquad\qquad\qquad y = -\frac{3}{4}x + 9$

Now we can go back and solve the original problems.

a. $y = mx + b$

$17 = 2 \cdot 10 + b$

$17 = 20 + b$

$-3 = b$

$y = 2x - 3$

b. $y = mx + b$

$m = -3;\ (x, y) = (-2, 5)$

$5 = -3(-2) + b$

$5 = 6 + b$

$-1 = b$

$y = -3x - 1$

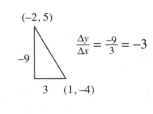

$(-2, 5)$

-9

$3 \quad (1, -4)$

$\frac{\Delta y}{\Delta x} = \frac{-9}{3} = -3$

c. Looking at the table, the entry $(0, -2)$ tells that $b = -2$. For every increase of 2 in the y-value, the x-value increases by 3. This means the slope is $\frac{2}{3}$. If $m = \frac{2}{3}$ and $b = -2$ then the equation is $y = \frac{2}{3}x - 2$.

d. Looking at the graph, the y-intercept (b) is about 9. Estimating another point on the graph $(2, 14)$ and drawing a slope triangle gives $m = \frac{\Delta y}{\Delta x} = \frac{5}{2}$. Using $y = mx + b$, the equation is $y \approx \frac{5}{2}x + 9$.

Here are some more to try. Use the given information to find an equation of the line.

1. slope $= 5$, through $(3, 13)$

2. through $(1, 1), (0, 4)$

3. slope $= -\frac{5}{3}$, through $(3, -1)$

4. through $(1, 3), (-5, -15)$

5. slope $= -4$, through $(-2, 9)$

6. through $(2, -1), (3, -3)$

7. slope $= -2$, through $(-4, -2)$

8. through $(1, -4), (-2, 5)$

9. slope $= \frac{1}{3}$, through $(6, 9)$

10. through $(-4, 1), (5, -2)$

11. slope $= -\frac{1}{4}$, through $(-2, 6)$

12. through $(-3, -2), (5, -2)$

13. undefined slope through $(5, 2)$

14. through $(3, 6), (3, -1)$

15.

x	-2	-1	0	1	2
y	-3	-1	1	3	5

16.

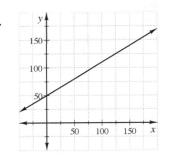

17.

x	-4	-2	0	2	4
y	1	2	3	4	5

19.

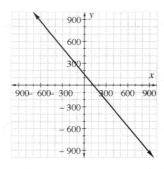

18.

x	5	3	0	1	2
y	17	11	2	5	8

20.

x	-5	1	0	3	-2
y	7		2		4

22.

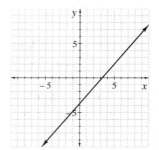

21.

x	-1	4	2	-4	-2
y	7		-2		10

Answers

1. $y = 5x - 2$
2. $y = -3x + 4$
3. $y = -\frac{5}{3}x + 4$
4. $y = 3x$
5. $y = -4x + 1$
6. $y = -2x + 3$
7. $y = -2x - 10$
8. $y = -3x - 1$
9. $y = \frac{1}{3}x + 7$
10. $y = -\frac{1}{3}x - \frac{1}{3}$
11. $y = -\frac{1}{4}x + 5\frac{1}{2}$
12. $y = -2$
13. $x = 5$
14. $x = 3$
15. $y = 2x + 1$
16. $y \approx \frac{3}{5}x + 50$
17. $y = \frac{1}{2}x + 3$
18. $y = 3x + 2$
19. $y \approx -\frac{7}{6}x + 150$
20. $y = -x + 2$
21. $y = -3x + 4$
22. $y \approx \frac{6}{5}x - 4$

Glossary

absolute value   The absolute value of a number is the distance of the number from zero. Since the absolute value represents a distance, without regard to direction, it is always non-negative. Thus the absolute value of a negative number is its opposite, while the absolute value of a non-negative number is just the number itself. The absolute value of x is usually written "$|x|$". For example, $|-5| = 5$ and $|22| = 22$. (p. 5)

additive identity   The number 0 is called the additive identity because adding 0 to any number does not change the number. (p. 117)

Additive Identity Property   The Additive Identity Property states that adding zero to any expression leaves the expression unchanged. That is, $a + 0 = a$. For example, $-2xy^2 + 0 = -2xy^2$. (p. 117)

additive inverse   The additive inverse of a number is the number we can add to that number to get the additive identity, 0. So, for the number 5, the additive inverse is -5; for the number -13, the additive inverse is 13. For any number x, the additive inverse is $-x$. (p. 117)

Additive Inverse Property   The Additive Inverse Property states that for every number a there is a number $-a$ such that $a + (-a) = 0$. For example, the number 5 has an additive inverse of -5; $5 + (-5) = 0$. The additive inverse of a number is often called its opposite. For example, 5 and -5 are opposites. (p. 117)

Additive Property of Equality   The Additive Property of Equality states that equality is maintained if the same amount is added to both sides of an equation. That is, if $a = b$, then $a + c = b + c$. For example, if $y = 3x$, then $y + 1.5 = 3x + 1.5$.

algebra   A branch of mathematics that uses variables to generalize the rules of numbers and numerical operations.

algebra tiles   An algebra tile is a manipulative whose area represents a constant or variable quantity. The algebra tiles used in this course consist of large squares with dimensions x-by-x and y-by-y; rectangles with dimensions x-by-1, y-by-1, and x-by-y; and small squares with dimensions 1-by-1. These tiles are named by their areas: x^2, y^2, x, y, xy, and 1, respectively. The smallest squares are called "unit tiles." In this text, shaded tiles will represent positive quantities while unshaded tiles will represent negative quantities. (p. 106)

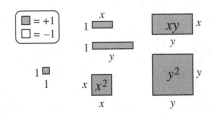

annual   Occurring once every year.

appreciation   An increase in value. (p. 348)

area   For this course, area is the number of square units needed to fill up a region on a flat surface. In later courses, the idea will be extended to cones, spheres, and more complex surfaces.

$$3 \begin{array}{|c|c|c|c|c|}\hline & & & & \\\hline & & & & \\\hline & & & & \\\hline\end{array}$$

5

Area = 15 square units

area model   See *generic rectangle*. (p. 109)

arithmetic sequence   In an arithmetic sequence the difference between sequential terms is constant. Each term of an arithmetic sequence can be generated by adding the common difference to the previous term. For example in the sequence, 4, 7, 10, 13, ..., the common difference is 3. (p. 232)

association   A relationship between two (or more) variables. An association between numerical variables can be displayed on a scatterplot, and described by its form, direction, strength, and outliers. Possible association between two categorical variables can be studied in a relative frequency table. Also see *scatterplot*. (p. 155)

Associative Property of Addition   The Associative Property of Addition states that if a sum contains terms that are grouped, the sum can be grouped differently with no effect on the total. That is, $a + (b + c) = (a + b) + c$. For example, $3 + (4 + 5) = (3 + 4) + 5$. (p. 117)

Associative Property of Multiplication   The Associative Property of Multiplication states that if a product contains terms that are grouped, the product can be grouped differently with no effect on the result. That is, $a(bc) = (ab)c$. For example, $2 \cdot (3 \cdot 4) = (2 \cdot 3) \cdot 4$. (p. 117)

asymptote   A line that a graph of a curve approaches as closely as you wish. An asymptote is often represented by a dashed line on a graph. For example, the graph at right has an asymptote at $y = -3$. (p. 312)

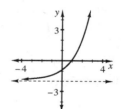

average   See *mean*.

axes   In a coordinate plane, two number lines that meet at right angles at the origin $(0, 0)$. The x-axis runs horizontally and the y-axis runs vertically. See the example at right.

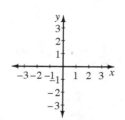

b   When the equation of a line is expressed in $y = mx + b$ form, the constant b gives the y-intercept of the line. For example, the y-intercept of the line $y = -\frac{1}{3}x + 7$ is 7. (p. 69)

bar graph A bar graph is a set of rectangular bars that have height proportional to the number of data elements in each category. Usually the bars are separated from each other. It is a way of displaying one-variable data that can be put into categories (like what color you prefer, your gender, or the state you were born in). Also see *histogram*.

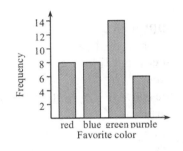

base When working with an exponential expression in the form b^a, b is called the base. For example, 2 is the base in 2^5. (5 is the exponent, and 32 is the value.) Also see *exponent*. (p. 100)

best-fit line See *line of best fit*.

bin width An interval, or the width of a bar, on a histogram.

binomial An expression that is the sum or difference of exactly two terms, each of which is a monomial. For example, $-2x + 3y^2$ is a binomial. (p. 467)

boundary line or curve (1) A line or curve on a two-dimensional graph that divides the graph into two regions. A boundary line or curve is used when graphing inequalities with two variables. For example, the inequality $y < \frac{2}{3}x + 2$ is graphed at right. The dashed boundary line has equation $y = \frac{2}{3}x + 2$. A boundary line is also sometimes called a "dividing line." (2) The line that determines the upper or lower limit on the values that a prediction is likely to be. Also see *upper boundary line* and *lower boundary line*. (p. 544)

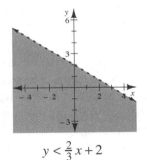

$$y < \frac{2}{3}x + 2$$

boundary point The endpoint of a ray or segment on a number line where an inequality is true. For strict inequalities (that is, inequalities involving < or >), the point is not part of the solution. We find boundary points by solving the equality associated with our inequality. For example, the solution to the equation $2x + 5 = 11$ is $x = 3$, so the inequality $2x + 5 \geq 11$ has a boundary point at 3. The solution to that inequality is illustrated on the number line at right. A boundary point is also sometimes called a "dividing point." (p. 544)

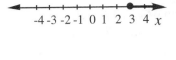

boxplot A graphic way of displaying the five number summary of a distribution of data: minimum, first quartile, median, third quartile, and maximum. A **modified boxplot** displays outliers separately from the boxplot. Also see *five number summary*. (p. 633, 640)

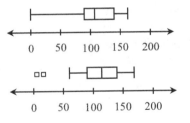

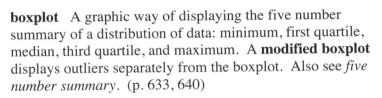

categorical data Data that can be put into categories (like what color you prefer, your gender, or the state you were born in), as opposed to numerical data that can be placed on a number line. (p. 469)

center (of a data distribution) A number that represents the middle of a data set, or that represents a "typical" value of the set. Two ways to measure the center of a data set are the mean and the median. When dealing with measures of center, it is often useful to consider the distribution of the data. For symmetric distributions with no outliers, the mean or median can represent the middle, or "typical" value, of the data well. However, in the presence of outliers or non-symmetrical data distributions, the median may be a better measure. Also see *mean* and *median*. (p. 541)

circle graph A way of displaying data that can be put into categories (like what color you prefer, your gender, or the state you were born in). A circle graph shows the proportion each category is of the whole.

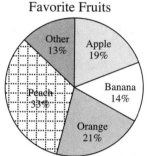

Favorite Fruits

closed sets A set of numbers is said to be closed under an operation if the result of applying the operation to any two numbers in the set produces a number in the set. For example, the whole numbers are a closed set under addition, because if you add any two whole numbers the result is always a whole number. However, the whole numbers are not closed under division: if you divide any two whole numbers you do not always get a whole number. (p. 112, 134)

closure properties A closure properties states that a particular set of numbers is a closed set under a specific operation. For example, the closure property of rational numbers states that the product or sum of two rational numbers is a rational number. For example, $\frac{1}{2}$ and $\frac{3}{4}$ are both rational numbers; $\frac{1}{2}+\frac{3}{4}$ is $\frac{5}{4}$; and $\frac{5}{4}$ is a rational number. Also, 2.2 and 0.75 are both rational numbers; $2.2 \cdot 0.75$ is 1.65; and 1.65 is a rational number. (p. 112, 134)

coefficient (numerical) A number multiplying a variable or product of variables. For example, -7 is the coefficient of $-7xy^2$. (p. 113)

coincide Two graphs coincide if they have all their points in common. For example, the graphs of $y = 2x + 4$ and $3y = 6x + 12$ coincide; both graphs are lines with a slope of 2 and a y-intercept of 4. When the graphs of two equations coincide, those equations share all the same solutions and have an infinite number of intersection points. (p. 175)

combination histogram and boxplot A way to visually represent a distribution of data. The boxplot is drawn with the same x-axis as the histogram.

Core Connections Algebra

combining like terms Combining two or more like terms simplifies an expression by summing constants and summing those variable terms in which the same variables are raised to the same power. For example, combining like terms in the expression $3x + 7 + 5x - 3 + 2x^2 + 3y^2$ gives $8x + 4 + 2x^2 + 3y^2$. When working with algebra tiles, combining like terms involves putting together tiles with the same dimensions. (p. 583)

common difference The difference between consecutive terms of an arithmetic sequence or the *generator* of the sequence. When the common difference is positive the sequence increases; when it is negative the sequence decreases. In the sequence $3, 7, 11, ..., 43$, the common difference is 4. (p. 351)

common factor A common factor is a factor that is the same for two or more terms. For example, x^2 is a common factor of $3x^2$ and $-5x^2y$. (p. 371)

common ratio Common ratio is another name for the multiplier or *generator* of a geometric sequence. It is the number to multiply one term by to get the next one. In the sequence: $96, 48, 24, ...$ the common ratio is $\frac{1}{2}$. (p. 232, 351)

Commutative Property of Addition The Commutative Property of Addition states that if two terms are added, the order can be reversed with no effect on the total. That is, $a + b = b + a$. For example, $7 + 12 = 12 + 7$. (p. 117)

Commutative Property of Multiplication The Commutative Property of Multiplication states that if two expressions are multiplied, the order can be reversed with no effect on the result. That is, $ab = ba$. For example, $5 \cdot 8 = 8 \cdot 5$. (p. 117)

complete graph A complete graph is one that includes everything that is important about the graph (such as intercepts and other key points, asymptotes, or limitations on the domain or range), and that makes the rest of the graph predictable based on what is shown.

completing the square In this course, we use completing the square to convert a quadratic equation in standard form into perfect square form. To complete the square, we add (or subtract) a constant to (or from) both sides of the equation so that the quadratic expression can be factored into a perfect square. For example, when given the quadratic equation $x^2 - 6x + 4 = 0$, we can complete the square by adding 5 to both sides. The resulting equation, $x^2 - 6x + 9 = 5$, has a left-hand side we can factor, resulting in the perfect square form quadratic equation $(x - 3)^2 = 5$. (p. 403)

complex numbers Numbers written in the form $a + bi$ where a and b are real numbers. Each complex number has a real part, a, and an imaginary part, bi. Note that real numbers are also complex numbers with $b = 0$, and imaginary numbers are complex numbers where $a = 0$. (p. 499)

compound interest Interest that is paid on both the principal and the previously accrued interest. (p. 320)

consecutive integers   Integers that are in order without skipping any of them. For example, 8, 9, and 10 are consecutive numbers. (p. 185)

constant of proportionality (*k*)   In a proportional relationship, equations are of the form $y = kx$, where k is the constant of proportionality.

constant term   A number that is not multiplied by a variable. In the expression $2x + 3(5 - 2x) + 8$, the number 8 is a constant term. The number 3 is not a constant term, because it is multiplied by a variable inside the parentheses. (p. 113)

constraint   A limitation or restriction placed on a function or situation, either by the context of the situation or by the nature of the function. (p. 445)

continuous   For this course, when the points on a graph are connected and it makes sense to connect them, we say the graph is continuous. Such a graph will have no holes or breaks in it. This term will be more completely defined in a later course. (p. 204)

coordinate(s)   The number corresponding to a point on the number line or an ordered pair (x, y) that corresponds to a point in a two-dimensional coordinate system. In an ordered pair, the x-coordinate appears first and the y-coordinate appears second. For example, the point $(3, 5)$ has an x-coordinate of 3. (p. 589)

coordinate plane   A flat surface defined by two number lines meeting at right angles at their zero points. A coordinate plane is also sometimes called a "Cartesian Plane."

coordinate system   A system of graphing ordered pairs of numbers on a coordinate plane. An ordered pair represents a point, with the first number giving the horizontal position relative to the x-axis and the second number giving the vertical position relative to the y-axis. For example, the diagram at right shows the point $(3, 5)$ graphed on a coordinate plane.

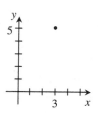

correlation coefficient, *r*   A measure of how much or how little data is scattered around the least squares regression line. It is a measure of the strength of an association that has already been determined to be linear. The correlation coefficient takes on values between -1 and 1. The closer to 1 or -1 the correlation coefficient is, the less scattered the data is around the LSRL. (p. 289)

counterexample   An example showing that a statement has at least one exception; that is, a situation in which the statement is false. For example, the number 4 is a counterexample to the hypothesis that all even numbers are greater than 7. (p. 107)

counting numbers   See *natural numbers*. (p. 499)

Core Connections Algebra

cubic A cubic polynomial is a polynomial of the form $y = ax^3 + bx^2 + cx + d$. "Cube" refers to the third (3) power.

cube root In the equation $a = b^3$, the value b that is multiplied by itself three times to give the value a. For example, the cube root of 8 is 2 because $8 = 2 \cdot 2 \cdot 2 = 2^3$. This is written $\sqrt[3]{8} = 2$. (p. 20)

data distribution See *distribution*. (p. 542)

delta (Δ) A symbol that means "change in." (p. 61)

dependent variable When one quantity depends for its value on one or more others, it is called the dependent variable. For example, we might relate the speed of a car to the amount of force you apply to the gas pedal. Here, the speed of the car is the dependent variable; it depends on how hard you push the pedal. The dependent variable appears as the output value in an $x \rightarrow y$ table, and is usually placed relative to the vertical axis of a graph. We often use the letter y and the vertical y-axis for the dependent variable. When working with functions or relations, the dependent variable represents the output value. In Statistics, the dependent variable is often called the response variable. Also see *independent variable*. (p. 253)

depreciation A decrease in value possibly because of normal wear and tear, age, decay, decrease in price. (p. 348)

description of a function A complete description of a function includes: a description of the shape of the graph, where it increasing and/or decreases, all the intercepts, domain and range, description of special points, and description of lines of symmetry.

difference of squares A polynomial that can be factored as the product of the sum and difference of two terms. The general pattern is $x^2 - y^2 = (x + y)(x - y)$. Most of the differences of squares found in this course are of the form $a^2 x^2 - b^2 = (ax + b)(ax - b)$, where a and b are nonzero real numbers. For example, the difference of squares $4x^2 - 9$ can be factored as $(2x + 3)(2x - 3)$. (p. 383)

dimensions The dimensions of a flat region or space tell how far it extends in each direction. For example, the dimensions of a rectangle might be 16 cm wide by 7 cm high.

direct proportion (or direct variation) Two quantities, x and y, are directly proportional (vary directly) if they have the relationship $y = kx$, where k is the constant of proportionality. Also see *inverse proportion*. (p. 11)

direction (of an association) If one variable in a relationship increases as the other variable increases, the direction is said to be a positive association. If one variable decreases as the other variable increases, there is said to be a negative association. If there is no apparent pattern in the scatterplot, then the variables have no association. When describing a linear association, you can use the slope, and its numerical interpretation in context, to describe the direction of the association. (p. 155)

discrete graph A graph that consists entirely of separated points is called a discrete graph. For example, the graph shown at right is discrete. Also see *continuous*. (p. 204)

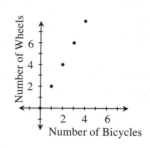

discriminant For quadratic equations in standard form $ax^2 + bx + c = 0$, the discriminant is $b^2 - 4ac$. If the discriminant is positive, the equation has two roots; if the discriminant is zero, the equation has one root; if the discriminant is negative, the equation has no real-number roots. For example, the discriminant of the quadratic equation $2x^2 - 4x - 5$ is $(-4)^2 - 4(2)(-5) = 56$, which indicates that that equation has two roots (solutions). (p. 629)

distribution The statistical distribution of a variable is a description (usually a list, table, or graph) of the number of times each possible outcome occurs. A distribution of data is often summarized with its center, shape, spread, and outliers, and can be displayed with a combination histogram and boxplot. (p. 640)

Distributive Property We use the Distributive Property to write a product of expressions as a sum of terms. The Distributive Property states that for any numbers or expressions a, b, and c, $a(b + c) = ab + ac$. For example, $2(x + 4) = 2 \cdot x + 2 \cdot 4 = 2x + 8$. We can demonstrate this with algebra tiles or in a generic rectangle. (p. 120)

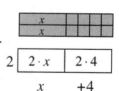

dividing line See *boundary line*.

dividing point See *boundary point*.

domain The set of all input values for a relation or function. For example, the domain of the function graphed at right is $x \geq -3$. For variables, the domain is the set of numbers the variable may represent. Also see *input*. (p. 35)

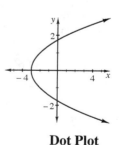

Dot Plot

dot plot A way of displaying one-variable data that has an order and can be placed on a number line. Dot plots are generally used when the data is discrete (separate and distinct) and numerous pieces of data are of equal value.

double-peaked See *shape (of a data display)*. (p. 640)

Elimination Method A method for solving a system of equations. The key step in using the Elimination Method is to add or subtract both sides of two equations to eliminate one of the variables. For example, the two equations in the system at right can be added together to get the simplified result $7x = 14$. We can solve this equation to find x, then substitute the x-value back into either of the original equations to find the value of y. (p. 198)

$$5x + 2y = 10$$
$$2x - 2y = 4$$

endpoint Either of the two points that mark the ends of a line segment. Also see *line segment*.

equal Two quantities are equal when they have the same value. For example, when $x = 4$, the expression $x + 8$ is equal to the expression $3x$ because their values are the same.

Equal Values Method A method for solving a system of equations. To use the equal values method, take two expressions that are each equal to the same variable and set those expressions equal to each other. For example, in the system of equations at right, $-2x + 5$ and $x - 1$ each equal y. So we write $-2x + 5 = x - 1$, then solve that equation to find x. Once we have x, we substitute that value back into either of the original equations to find the value of y. (p. 151)

$$y = -2x + 5$$
$$y = x - 1$$

equation A mathematical sentence in which two expressions appear on either side of an "equals" sign (=), stating that the two expressions are equivalent. For example, the equation $7x + 4.2 = -8$ states that the expression $7x + 4.2$ has the value -8. In this course, an equation is often used to represent a rule relating two quantities. For example, a rule for finding the area y of a tile pattern with figure number x might be written $y = 4x - 3$.

Equation Mat An organizing tool used to visually represent two equal expressions using algebra tiles. For example, the Equation Mat at right represents the equation $2x - 1 - (-x + 3) = 6 - 2x$. (p. 106)

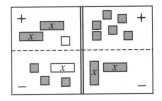

equivalent Two expressions are equivalent if they have the same value. For example, $2 + 3$ is equivalent to $1 + 4$. Two equations are equivalent if they have all the same solutions. For example, $y = 3x$ is equivalent to $2y = 6x$. Equivalent equations have the same graph. (p. 479)

evaluate To evaluate an expression, substitute the value(s) given for the variable(s) and perform the operations according to the order of operations. For example, evaluating $2x + y - 10$ when $x = 4$ and $y = 3$ gives the value 1. (p. 597)

event One or more results of an experiment. (p. 469)

explicit equation (for a sequence) An equation for a term in a sequence that determines the value of any term $t(n)$ directly from n, without necessarily knowing any other terms in the sequence. Also see *recursive equation*. (p. 220)

exponent   In an expression of the form b^a, a is called the exponent. For example, in the expression 2^5, 5 is called the exponent. (2 is the base, and 32 is the value.) The exponent indicates how many times to use the base as a multiplier. For example, in 2^5, 2 is used 5 times: $2^5 = 2 \cdot 2 \cdot 2 \cdot 2 \cdot 2 = 32$. For exponents of zero, the rule is: for any number $x \neq 0$, $x^0 = 1$. For negative exponents, the rule is: for any number $x \neq 0$, $x^{-n} = \frac{1}{x^n}$, and $\frac{1}{x^{-n}} = x^n$. Also see *laws of exponents*. (p. 100)

exponential function   An exponential function in this course has an equation of the form $y = ab^x + c$, where a is the initial value, b is positive and is the multiplier, and $y = c$ is the equation of the horizontal asymptote. An example of an exponential function is graphed at right. (p. 11)

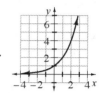

expression   An expression is a combination of individual terms separated by plus or minus signs. Numerical expressions combine numbers and operation symbols; algebraic (variable) expressions include variables. For example, $4 + (5 - 3)$ is a numerical expression. In an algebraic expression, if each of the following terms, $6xy^2$, 24, and $\frac{y-3}{4+x}$, are combined, the result may be $6xy^2 + 24 - \frac{y-3}{4+x}$. An expression does not have an "equals" sign. (p. 113)

Expression Comparison Mat   An Expression Comparison Mat puts two Expression Mats side-by-side so they can be compared to see which represents the greater value. For example, in the Expression Comparison Mat at right, Mat A represents –3, while Mat B represents –2. Since –2 > –3 Mat B is greater. (p. 263)

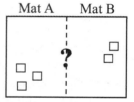

Expression Mat   An organizing tool used to visually represent an expression with algebra tiles. (p. 254)

extrapolate   A prediction made outside the range of the observed data. Often extrapolations are not very reliable predictions. (p. 351)

factor   (1) In arithmetic: When two or more integers are multiplied, each of the integers is a factor of the product. For example, 4 is a factor of 24, because $4 \cdot 6 = 24$. (2) In algebra: When two or more algebraic expressions are multiplied together, each of the expressions is a factor of the product. For example, x^2 is a factor of $-17x^2y^3$, because $(x^2)(-17y^3) = -17x^2y^3$. (3) To factor an expression is to write it as a product. For example, the factored form of $x^2 - 3x - 18$ is $(x-6)(x+3)$. (p. 647, 479)

factored completely   A polynomial is factored completely if none of the resulting factors can be factored further using integer coefficients. For example, $-2(x+3)(x-1)$ is the completely factored form of $-2x^2 - 4x + 6$. (p. 478)

factored form   A quadratic equation in the form $a(x+b)(x+c) = 0$, where a is nonzero, is said to be in factored form. For example, $-7(x+2)(x-1.5) = 0$ is a quadratic equation in factored form. (p. 467)

family of functions A group of functions that have at least one common characteristic, usually the shape and the form of the equation. For example the quadratic family of functions have graphs that are parabolas, and equations of the form $y = ax^2 + bx + c$. Examples of other families are linear functions, exponential functions, and absolute value functions. (p. 11)

Fibonacci Sequence The sequence of numbers $1, 1, 2, 3, 5, 8, 13, \ldots$. Each term of the Fibonacci sequence (after the first two terms) is the sum of the two preceding terms. (p. 221)

Figure 0 The figure that comes before Figure 1 in a tile pattern. When representing a tile pattern with a graph, the y-intercept of the graph is the number of tiles in Figure 0. When representing a tile pattern with an equation in $y = mx + b$ form, b gives the number of tiles in Figure 0. (p. 45)

first quartile (Q1) The median of the lower half of a set of data which has been written in numerical order. (p. 633)

five number summary A way of summarizing the center and spread of a one-variable distribution of data. The five number summary includes the minimum, first quartile, median, third quartile, and maximum of the set of data. For more on finding quartiles, see the Math Notes box in Lesson 11.2.1. Also see *boxplot*. (p. 633)

form (of an association) The form of an association can be linear or non-linear. The form can contain clusters of data. A residual plot can help determine if a particular form is appropriate for modeling the relationship. (p. 155)

fraction The quotient of two quantities in the form $\frac{a}{b}$ where b is not equal to 0. (p. 597)

Fraction Busters "Fraction busting" is a method of simplifying equations involving fractions that uses the Multiplicative Property of Equality to rearrange the equation so that no fractions remain. To use this method, multiply both sides of an equation by the common denominator of all the fractions in the equation. The result will be an equivalent equation with no fractions. For example, when given the equation $\frac{x}{7} + 2 = \frac{x}{3}$, we can multiply both sides by the "fraction buster" 21. The resulting equation, $3x + 42 = 7x$, is equivalent to the original but contains no fractions. (p. 581)

fractional exponents Raising a number to a fractional exponent indicates a power as well as a root. $x^{a/b} = \sqrt[b]{x^a} = (\sqrt[b]{x})^a$. (p. 444)

frequency The number of times that something occurs within an interval or data set.

function A relationship in which for each input value there is one and only one output value. For example, the relationship $f(x) = x + 4$ is a function; for each input value (x) there is exactly one output value. In terms of ordered pairs (x, y), no two ordered pairs of a function have the same first member (x). See also *description of a function* and *function notation*. (p. 28)

function notation When a rule expressing a function is written using function notation, the function is given a name, most commonly "f," "g," or "h." The notation $f(x)$ represents the output of a function, named f, when x is the input. It is pronounced "f of x." For example, $g(2)$, pronounced "g of 2", represents the output of the function g when $x = 2$. If $g(x) = x^2 + 3$, then $g(2) = 7$. (p. 25)

generator The generator of a sequence tells what you do to each term to get the next term. Note that this is different from the function for the nth term of the sequence. The generator only tells you how to find the following term, when you already know one term. In an arithmetic sequence the generator is the common difference; in a geometric sequence it is the multiplier or common ratio. (p. 232)

generic rectangle A type of diagram used to visualize multiplying expressions without algebra tiles. Each expression to be multiplied forms a side length of the rectangle, and the product is the sum of the areas of the sections of the rectangle. For example, the generic rectangle at right can be used to multiply $(2x + 5)$ by $(x + 3)$. (p. 374)

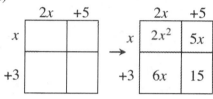

$$(2x + 5)(x + 3) = 2x^2 + 11x + 15$$

area as a product   area as a sum

geometric sequence A geometric sequence is a sequence that is generated by a multiplier. This means that each term of a geometric sequence can be found by multiplying the previous term by a constant. For example: $5, 15, 45\ldots$ is the beginning of a geometric sequence with generator (common ratio) 3. In general a geometric sequence can be represented $a, ar, ar^2, \ldots + ar^{n-1}$. (p. 232)

graph A graph represents numerical information spatially. The numbers may come from a table, situation (pattern), or rule (equation or inequality). Most of the graphs in this course show points, lines, and/or curves on a two-dimensional coordinate system like the one at right or on a single axis called a number line. Also see *complete graph*.

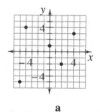

greater than One expression is greater than another if its value is larger. We indicate this relationship with the greater than symbol "$>$". For example, $4 + 5$ is greater than $1 + 1$. We write $4 + 5 > 1 + 1$. (p. 397)

greatest common factor (GCF) (1) For integers, the greatest positive integer that is a common factor of two or more integers. For example, the greatest common factor of 28 and 42 is 14. (2) For two or more algebraic monomials, the product of the greatest common integer factor of the coefficients of the monomials and the variable(s) in each algebraic term with the smallest degree of that variable in every term. For example, the greatest common factor of $12x^3y^2$ and $8xy^4$ is $4xy^2$. (3) For a polynomial, the greatest common monomial factor of its terms. For example, the greatest common factor of $16x^4 + 8x^3 + 12x$ is $4x$. (p. 371)

graphing form A form of the equation of a function or relation that clearly shows key information about the graph. For example: the graphing form for the general equation of a quadratic function (also called vertex form) is $y = a(x - h)^2 + k$. The vertex (h, k), orientation (whether a is positive or negative) and amount of stretch or compression based on $|a| > 1$ or $|a| < 1$ can be appear in the equation.

growth One useful way to analyze a mathematical relationship is to examine how the output value grows as the input value increases. We can see this growth on a graph of a linear relationship by looking at the slope of the graph. (p. 46)

(h, k) In this course h and k are used as parameters in general equations for families of functions $f(x) = af(x - h) + k$ and families of relations to represent the horizontal and vertical shifts of the parent graph. The point (h, k) represents location of a point that corresponds to $(0, 0)$ for parent graphs where $(0, 0)$ is on the graph.

half-life When material decays, the half-life is the time it takes until only half the material remains. (p. 328)

histogram A way of displaying one-variable data that is like a bar graph in that the height of the bars is proportional to the number of elements. However, a histogram is for numerical data. Each bin (bar) of a histogram represents the number of data elements in a range of values, such as the number of people who take from 15 minutes up to, but not including, 30 minutes to get to school. Each bin should the same width and the bins should touch each other. Also see *bar graph*. (p. 540)

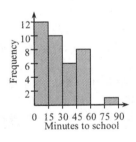

horizontal Parallel to the horizon. The x-axis of a coordinate graph is the horizontal axis. (p. 61)

horizontal lines   Horizontal lines are "flat" and run left to right in the same direction as the x-axis. Horizontal lines have equations of the form $y = b$, where b can be any number. For example, the graph at right shows the horizontal line $y = 3$. The slope of any horizontal line is 0. The x-axis has the equation $y = 0$ because $y = 0$ everywhere on the x-axis. (p. 61)

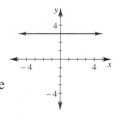

horizontal shift   Used with parent graphs and general equations for functions and relations such as $y = a(x - h)^2 + k$. It is the amount a graph is moved left or right in relation to its parent graph, in this case $y = x^2$. The horizontal shift will be h units to the right if h is positive, to the left if h is negative.

imaginary numbers   The set of numbers that are solutions of equations of the form $x^2 =$ (a negative number) are called imaginary numbers. They are not positive, negative, or zero. The imaginary number i is a solution of the equation $x^2 = -1$, so $i^2 = -1$. In general, imaginary numbers follow the rules of real number arithmetic (e.g. $i + i = 2i$). Multiplying the imaginary number i by every possible real number yields all possible imaginary numbers. (p. 499)

independent variable   When one quantity changes in a way that does not depend on the value of another quantity, the value that changes independently is represented with the independent variable. For example, we might relate the speed of a car to the amount of force you apply to the gas pedal. Here, the amount of force applied may be whatever the driver chooses, so it represents the independent variable. The independent variable appears as the input value in an $x \rightarrow y$ table, and is usually placed relative to the horizontal axis of a graph. We often use the letter x and the horizontal x-axis for the independent variable. When working with functions or relations, the independent variable represents the input value. In Statistics, the independent variable is often called the explanatory variable. Also see *dependent variable*. (p. 253)

inequality   An inequality consists of two expressions on either side of an inequality symbol. For example, the inequality $7x + 4.2 < -8$ states that the expression $7x + 4.2$ has a value less than 8. (p. 446)

inequality symbols   The symbol $\leq$ read from left to right means "less than or equal to." The symbol $\geq$ read from left to right means "greater than or equal to." The symbols $<$ and $>$ mean "less than" and "greater than," respectively. For example, "7<13" means that 7 is less than 13. (p. 397)

initial value   The initial value of a sequence is the first term of the sequence. (p. 217)

input value   The input value is the independent variable in a relation. We substitute the input value into our rule (equation) to determine the output value. For example, if we have a rule for how much your phone bill will be if you talk a certain number of minutes, the number of minutes you talk is the input value. The input value appears first in an $x \to y$ table, and is represented by the variable x. When working with functions, the input value, an element of the domain, is the value put into the function. (p. 3)

integers   The set of numbers $\{ \ldots -3, -2, -1, 0, 1, 2, 3, \ldots \}$. (p. 499)

intercepts   Points where a graph crosses the axes. x-intercepts are points at which the graph crosses the x axis and y-intercepts are points at which the graph crosses the y axis. On the graph at right the x-intercept is $(3, 0)$ and the y-intercept is $(0, 6)$. (p. 504)

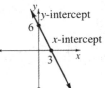

interest   An amount paid which is a percentage of an initial value (principal). For example, a savings account may offer 4% annual interest rate, which means they will pay $4.00 in interest for a principal of $100 kept in the account for one year. (p. 320)

interquartile range (IQR)   A way to measure the spread of data. It is calculated by subtracting the first quartile from the third quartile. (p. 535)

intersection   A point of intersection is a point that the graphs of two or more equations have in common. Graphs may intersect in one, two, several, many or no points. The set of coordinates of a point of intersection are a solution to the equation for each graph. (p. 175)

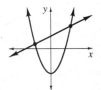

interval   A set of numbers between two given numbers.

inverse function   A function that "undoes" what the original function does. It can also be seen as the x-y interchange of the function. The inverse of a function performs in reverse order the inverse operation for each operation of the function. The graph of an inverse function is a reflection of the original function across the line $y = x$. For example, $y = x^3 + 2$ is equivalent to $x = \sqrt[3]{y - 2}$, its inverse function is written $y = \sqrt[3]{x - 2}$. (p. 529)

inverse operations   Subtraction is the inverse operation for addition and vice versa, division for multiplication, square root for squaring, and more generally taking the nth root for raising to the nth power.

inverse proportion (or inverse variation)   Two quantities, x and y, are inversely proportional (vary inversely) if they have the relationship $y = \frac{k}{x}$, where k is the constant of proportionality. Also see *direct proportion*. (p. 11)

investigating a function   To investigate a function means to make a complete graph of the function and to write down everything you know about the function. Some things to consider are: domain, range, intercepts, asymptotes, inverse, and symmetry. (p. 19)

irrational numbers   The set of numbers that cannot be expressed in the form $\frac{a}{b}$, where a and b are integers and $b \neq 0$. For example, π and $\sqrt{2}$ are irrational numbers. Irrational numbers cannot be written exactly as a decimal. The decimals continue infinitely and never go into a repeating pattern. (p. 499)

lattice points   The points on a coordinate grid where the grid lines intersect. The diagram at right shows two lattice points. The coordinates of lattice points are integers. (p. 52)

laws of exponents   The laws of exponents we study in this course are: (p. 100, 346)

Law	Examples	
$x^m x^n = x^{m+n}$ for all x	$x^3 x^4 = x^{3+4} = x^7$	$2^5 \cdot 2^{-1} = 2^4$
$\frac{x^m}{x^n} = x^{m-n}$ for $x \neq 0$	$x^{10} \div x^4 = x^{10-4} = x^6$	$\frac{5^4}{5^7} = 5^{-3}$
$(x^m)^n = x^{mn}$ for all x	$(x^4)^3 = x^{4 \cdot 3} = x^{12}$	$(10^5)^6 = 10^{30}$
$x^0 = 1$ for $x \neq 0$	$\frac{y^2}{y^2} = y^0 = 1$	$9^0 = 1$
$x^{-1} = \frac{1}{x}$ for $x \neq 0$	$\frac{1}{x^2} = (\frac{1}{x})^2 = (x^{-1})^2 = x^{-2}$	$3^{-1} = \frac{1}{3}$
$x^{m/n} = \sqrt[n]{x^m}$ for $x \geq 0$	$\sqrt{k} = k^{1/2}$	$y^{2/3} = \sqrt[3]{y^2}$

least squares regression line (LSRL)   A unique best-fit line that is found by making the squares of the residuals as small as possible. (p. 271)

"legal" moves   When working with an equation mat or expression comparison mat, there are certain "legal" moves you can make with the algebra tiles that keep the relationship between the two sides of the mat intact. For example, removing an x tile from the positive region of each side of an equation mat is a legal move; it keeps the expressions on each side of the mat equal. The legal moves are those justified by the properties of the real numbers. (p. 106)

less than   (1) One expression is less than another if its value is not as large. We indicate this relationship with the less than symbol "<". For example, $1+1$ is less than $4+5$. We write $1+1 < 4+5$. (2) We sometimes say that one amount is a certain quantity less than another amount. For example, a student movie ticket might cost two dollars *less than* an adult ticket. (p. 397)

"let" statement A "let" statement is written at the beginning of our work to identify the variable that will represent a certain quantity. For example, in solving a problem about grilled cheese sandwiches, we might begin by writing "Let s = the number of sandwiches eaten." It is particularly important to use "let" statements when writing mathematical sentences, so that your readers will know what the variables in the sentences represent. (p. 143)

like terms Two or more terms that contain the same variable(s), with corresponding variables raised to the same power. For example, $5x$ and $2x$ are like terms. Also see *combining like terms*.

line Graphed, a line is made up of an infinite number of points, is one-dimensional, straight, and extends without end in two directions. In two dimensions a line is the graph of an equation of the form $y = mx + b$ or $ax + by = c$.

line segment The portion of a line between two points. A line segment is named using its endpoints. For example, the line segment at right may be named either $\overline{AB}$ or $\overline{BA}$.

line of best fit A line that represents, in general, data on a scatterplot. The line of best fit is a model of numerical two-variable data that helps describe the data. It is also used to make predictions for other data. Also see *least square regression line*. (p. 146)

line of symmetry A line that divides a shape into two pieces that are mirror images of each other. If you fold a shape over its line of symmetry, the shapes on both sides of the line will match perfectly. A shape with a line of symmetry is shown at right. (p. 16)

line of symmetry

linear association See *association*. (p. 155)

linear equation An equation in two variables whose graph is a line. For example, $y = 2.1x - 8$ is a linear equation. The standard form for a linear equation is $ax + by = c$, where a, b, and c are constants and a and b are not both zero. Most linear equations can be written in $y = mx + b$ form, which is more useful for determining the line's slope and y-intercept. (p. 69)

linear inequality An inequality with a boundary line represented by a linear equation. (p. 445)

linear regression A method for finding a best-fit line through a set of points on a scatterplot. Also see *regression* and *least squares regression line*. (p. 271)

looking inside "Looking inside" is a method of solving one-variable equations containing parentheses or an absolute value symbol. To use "looking inside," we first determine what the value of the entire expression inside the parentheses (or absolute value symbol) must be. We then use that fact to solve for the value of the variable. For example, to use "looking inside" to solve the equation $4(x+2) = 36$, we first determine that $x+2$ must equal 9. We then solve the equation $x+2=9$ to find that $x=7$. (p. 488)

lower bound The lowest value that a prediction is likely to be. The lower bound is determined by the lower boundary line. (p. 255)

lower boundary line A line drawn parallel to and below the least squares regression line at a distance equivalent to the largest residual. The lower boundary line determines the lower bound on the values that a prediction is likely to be. (p. 255)

lurking variable A hidden variable that was not part of the statistical study under investigation. Sometimes a lurking variable explains the true cause of an association between two other variables that are linked. (p. 281)

m When the equation of a line is expressed in $y = mx + b$ form, the parameter m gives the slope of the line. For example, the slope of the line $y = -\frac{1}{3}x + 7$ is $-\frac{1}{3}$. (p. 61)

mathematical sentence A mathematical sentence is an equation that uses variables to represent unknown quantities. For example, the mathematical sentence $b + g = 23$ might represent the fact that the total number of boys and girls in the class is 23. It is helpful to define variables using "let" statements before using them in a mathematical sentence. Also see *"let" statement*. (p. 143)

maximum value The largest value in the range of a function or in a data set. For example, the y-coordinate of the vertex of a parabola that opens downward. (p. 535)

mean The arithmetic mean, or average, of several numbers is one way of defining the "center" or "middle" or "typical value" of a set of numbers. The mean represents the center of a set of data well if the distribution of the data is symmetric and has no outliers. To find the mean of a numerical data set, add the values together then divide by the number of values in the set. For example, the mean of the numbers 1, 5, and 6 is $(1 + 5 + 6) \div 3 = 4$.

measure of central tendency Mean and median are measures of central tendency, representing the "center" or "middle" or "typical value" of a set of data. See *center (of a data distribution)*.

mean absolute deviation A way to measure the spread, or the amount of variability, in a set of data. The mean absolute deviation is the average of the distances to the mean, after the distances have been made positive with the absolute value. The standard deviation is a much more commonly used measure of spread than the mean absolute deviation. (p. 546)

median   The middle number of a set of data which has been written in numerical order. If there is no distinct middle, then the mean of the two middle numbers is the median. The median is generally more representative of the "middle" or of a "typical value" than the mean if there are outliers or if the distribution of the data in not symmetric. (p. 535)

minimum value   The smallest value in the range of a function or in a data set. For example, the *y*-coordinate of the vertex of a parabola that opens upward. (p. 535)

model   A mathematical summary (often an equation) of a trend in data, after making assumptions and approximations to simplify a complicated situation. Models allow us to describe data to others, compare data more easily to other data, and allow us to make predictions. For example, mathematical models of weather patterns allow us to predict the weather. No model is perfect, but some models are better at describing trends than other models. Regressions are a type of model. Also see *regression*. (p. 145)

modified boxplot   See *boxplot*. (p. 542)

monomial   An expression with only one term. It can be a number, a variable, or the product of a number and one or more variables. For example, $7, 3x, -4ab$, and $3x^2y$ are each monomials. (p. 369)

multiple representations web   An organizational tool we use to keep track of connections between the four representations of relationships between quantities emphasized in this course. In this course, we emphasize four different ways of representing a numerical relationship: with a graph, table, situation (pattern), or rule (equation or inequality).

multiplicative identity   The number 1 is called the multiplicative identity because multiplying any number by 1 does not change the number. For example, $7(1) = 7$. (p. 117)

Multiplicative Identity Property   The Multiplicative Identity Property states that multiplying any expression by 1 leaves the expression unchanged. That is, $a(1) = a$. For example, $437x \cdot 1 = 437x$. (p. 117)

multiplicative inverse   The multiplicative inverse for a non-zero number is the number we can multiply by to get the multiplicative identity, 1. For example, for the number 5, the multiplicative inverse is $\frac{1}{5}$; for the number $\frac{2}{3}$ the multiplicative inverse is $\frac{3}{2}$. (p. 117)

Multiplicative Inverse Property   The Multiplicative Inverse Property states that for every nonzero number a there is a number $\frac{1}{a}$ such that $a \cdot \frac{1}{a} = 1$. For example, the number 6 has a multiplicative inverse of $\frac{1}{6}$; $6 \cdot \frac{1}{6} = 1$. The multiplicative inverse of a number is usually called its reciprocal. For example, $\frac{1}{6}$ is the reciprocal of 6. For a number in the form $\frac{a}{b}$, where a and b are non-zero, the reciprocal is $\frac{b}{a}$. (p. 117)

Multiplicative Property of Equality   The Multiplicative Property of Equality states that equality is maintained if both sides of an equation are multiplied by the same amount. That is, if $a = b$, then $a \cdot c = b \cdot c$. For example, if $y = 3x$, then $2(y) = 2(3x)$. (p. 117)

multiplier   In a geometric sequence the number multiplied times each term to get the next term is called the multiplier or the common ratio or generator. The multiplier is also the number you can multiply by in order to increase or decrease an amount by a given percentage in one step. For example, to increase a number by 4%, the multiplier is 1.04. We would multiply the number by 1.04. The multiplier for decreasing by 4% is 0.96. (p. 232)

mutually exclusive   Two events are mutually exclusive if they have no outcomes in common. (p. 469)

natural numbers   The natural numbers are the positive integers, { 1, 2, 3, . . . }. They are also called the counting numbers. (p. 499)

negative exponents   Raising a number to a negative exponent is the same as taking the reciprocal of the number. $x^{-a} = \frac{1}{x^a}$ for $x \neq 0$. (p. 346)

negative number   A negative number is a number less than zero. Negative numbers are graphed on the negative side of a number line. (p. 499)

non-commensurate   Two measurements are called non-commensurate if no whole number multiple of one measurement can ever equal a whole number multiple of the other. For example, measures of 1 cm and $\sqrt{2}$ cm are non-commensurate, because no combination of items 1 cm long will ever have exactly the same length as a combination of items $\sqrt{2}$ cm long. (p. 584)

number line   A diagram representing all real numbers as points on a line. All real numbers are assigned to points. The numbers are called the coordinates of the points and the point for which the number 0 is assigned is called the origin. Also see *boundary point*. (p. 433)

number system   The organizational structure used to categorize numbers into complex numbers, imaginary numbers, real numbers, rational numbers, irrational numbers, integers, fractions, whole numbers, negative integers, zero, and natural numbers. (p. 499)

numerical data   Data that can be represented on a number line.

observed value   An actual measurement, as opposed to a prediction made from a model.

one-dimensional   Not having any width or depth. Lines and curves are one-dimensional.

opposite Two numbers are opposites if they are the same distance from zero, but one is positive and one is negative. For example, 5 and –5 are opposites. The opposite of a number is sometimes called its additive inverse, indicating that the sum of a number and its opposite is zero.

Order of Operations The specific order in which certain operations are to be carried out to evaluate or simplify expressions. The order is: parentheses (or other grouping symbols), exponents (powers or roots), multiplication and division (from left to right), and addition and subtraction (from left to right). (p. 593)

ordered pair Two numbers written in order as follows: (x, y). The primary use of ordered pairs in this course is to represent points in an x-y coordinate system. The first coordinate (x) represents the horizontal distance and direction from the origin; the second coordinate (y) represents the vertical distance and direction from the origin. For example, the ordered pair $(3, 5)$ represents the point shown in bold at right.

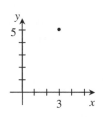

origin The point on a coordinate plane where the x- and y-axes intersect is called the origin. This point has coordinates $(0, 0)$. The point assigned to zero on a number line is also called the origin.

outlier A number in a set of data that is far away from the bulk of the data. (p. 155)

output value The output value is the dependent variable in a relation. When we substitute the input value into our rule (equation), the result is the output value. For example, if we have a rule for how much your phone bill will be if you talk a certain number of minutes, the amount of your phone bill is the output value. The output value appears second in an $x \rightarrow y$ table, and is represented by the variable y. When working with functions, the output value, an element of the range, is the value that results from applying the rule for the function to an input value. (p. 3)

parabola A parabola is a particular kind of mathematical curve. In this course, a parabola is always the graph of a quadratic function $y = ax^2 + bx + c$ where a does not equal 0. The diagram at right shows some examples of parabolas. The highest or lowest point on the graph is called the vertex. (p. 14)

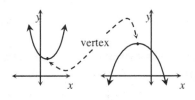

parallel Two or more straight lines on a flat surface that do not intersect (no matter how far they are extended) are parallel. If two lines have the same slope and do not coincide, they are parallel. For example, the graphs of $y = 2x + 3$ and $y = 2x - 2$ are parallel (see diagram at right). When two equations have parallel graphs, the equations have no solutions in common. (p. 175)

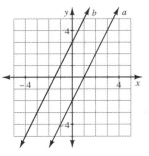

parallel box plots   Two box plots drawn on the same x-axis. Parallel boxplots are used to compare the center and spread of two sets of data.

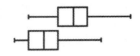

parameter   In a general equations where x and y represent the inputs and outputs of the function, variables such as a, b, c, m, h, and k are often referred to as parameters, and they are often replaced with specific values. For example: in the equation $y = a(x-h)^2 + k$ representing all parabolas that are functions, the a, h, and k are (variable) parameters that give the shape and location, while x and y are the independent and dependent variables. (p. 309)

pattern   A pattern is a set of things in order that change in a regular way. For example, the numbers 1, 4, 7, 10, ... form a pattern, because each number increases by 3. The numbers 1, 4, 9, 16, ... form a pattern, because they are squares of consecutive integers. In this course, we often look at tile patterns, whose figure numbers and areas we represent with a table, a rule (equation), or a graph.

Figure 2   Figure 3   Figure 4

percent   A ratio that compares a number to 100. Percents are often written using the "%" symbol. For example, 0.75 is equal to $\frac{75}{100}$ or 75%. (p. 229)

perfect square form   A quadratic equation in the form $a(x+b)^2 = c$, where a is nonzero, is said to be in perfect square form. For example, $3(x-12)^2 = 19$ is a quadratic equation in perfect square form. (p. 421)

perfect square trinomials   Trinomials of the form $a^2x^2 + 2abx + b^2$, where a and b are nonzero real numbers, are known as perfect square trinomials and factor as $(ax+b)^2$. For example, the perfect square trinomial $9x^2 - 24x + 16$ can be factored as $(3x-4)^2$. (p. 383)

perimeter   The distance around a figure on a flat surface.

Perimeter =
$5 + 8 + 4 + 6 =$ 23 units

piecewise function   A function composed of parts of two or more functions. Each part is usually consists of a function with a restricted (limited) domain. (p. 68)

point   An exact location in space. In two dimensions, an ordered pair specifies a point on a coordinate plane. See *ordered pair*.

Core Connections Algebra

point of intersection   A point of intersection is a point that the graphs of two equations have in common. For example, $(3, 4)$ is a point of intersection of the two graphs shown at right. Two graphs may have one point of intersection, several points of intersection, or no points of intersection. The ordered pair representing a point of intersection gives a solution to the equations of each of the graphs. (p. 167)

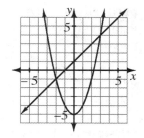

Point-Slope form   The Point-Slope form of the equation of a line is $y - k = m(x - h)$, where (h, k) are the coordinates of a point on the line, and m is the slope of the line. For example, a line with slope –4 passing through the point $(5, 8)$ has the equation $y - 8 = -4(x - 5)$. To find the equation of the line in $y = mx + b$ form, we solve the Point-Slope form equation for y. (p. 172)

polynomial   An expression that is the sum or difference of two or more monomials (terms). For example, $x^8 - 4x^6y + 6x^4y^2$ is a polynomial. (p. 113)

positive number   A positive number is a number greater than zero. Positive numbers are graphed on the positive side of a number line. Zero is neither positive nor negative. (p. 499)

power   A number or variable raised to an exponent in the form x^n. See *exponent*.

power model or power curve   A best-fit curve of the form $y = ax^b$ that represents data on a scatterplot. (p. 296)

predicted value (of an association)   The dependent (y-value) that is predicted for an independent (x-value) by the best-fit model for an association. (p. 253)

prime number   A positive integer with exactly two factors. The only factors of a prime number are 1 and itself. For example, the numbers 2, 3, 17, and 31 are all prime. 31 has no factors other than 1 and 31. (p. 147)

principal   Initial investment or capital. An initial value.

problem-solving strategies   This course incorporates several problem-solving strategies, specifically, making a guess and checking it, using manipulatives (such as algebra tiles), making systematic lists, collecting data, graphing, drawing a diagram, breaking a large problem into smaller subproblems, working backward, and writing and solving equations. For example, a student given the details of a cell-phone pricing plan and asked how many minutes would cost $29.95 might approach the problem by writing an equation and solving it, making a table of times and prices, graphing the relationship, or guessing and checking various numbers of minutes.

product   The result of multiplying. For example, the product of 4 and 5 is 20; the product of $3a$ and $8b^2$ is $24ab^2$. (p. 370)

proportion An equation stating that two ratios (fractions) are equal. For example, the equation below is a proportion. A proportion is a useful type of equation to set up when solving problems involving proportional relationships. (p. 594)

$$\frac{68 \text{ votes for Mr. Mears}}{100 \text{ people surveyed}} = \frac{34 \text{ votes for Mr. Mears}}{50 \text{ people surveyed}}$$

quadrants The coordinate plane is divided by its axes into four quadrants. The quadrants are numbered as shown in the first diagram at right. When graphing data that has no negative values, we sometimes use a graph showing only the first quadrant.

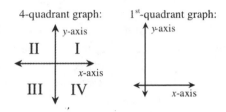

quadratic equation An equation that can be written in the form $ax^2 + bx + c = 0$, where a, b, and c are real numbers and a is nonzero. A quadratic equation written in this form is said to be in standard form. For example, $3x^2 - 4x + 7.5 = 0$ is a quadratic equation. (p. 377)

quadratic expression An expression that can be written in the form $ax^2 + bx + c$, where a, b, and c are real numbers and a is nonzero. For example, $3x^2 - 4x + 7.5$ is a quadratic expression. (p. 369)

Quadratic Formula The Quadratic Formula states that if $ax^2 + bx + c = 0$ and $a \neq 0$, then $x = \frac{-b \pm \sqrt{b^2 - 4ac}}{2a}$. For example, if $5x^2 + 9x + 3 = 0$, then $x = \frac{-9 \pm \sqrt{9^2 - 4(5)(3)}}{2(5)} = \frac{-9 \pm \sqrt{21}}{10}$. (p. 423)

quadrilateral A polygon with four sides. For example, the shape at right is a quadrilateral. (p. 594)

quarterly Occurring four times a year. (p. 322)

quartile Along with the median, the quartiles divide a set of data into four groups of the same size. Also see *boxplot*. (p. 535)

quotient The result of a division problem.

r See *correlation coefficient*.

R^2 See *R-squared*.

radical An expression in the form $\sqrt{a}$, where $\sqrt{a}$ is the positive square root of a. For example, $\sqrt{49} = 7$. Also see *square root*. (p. 431)

radicand The expression under a radical sign. For example, in the expression $3 + 2\sqrt{x-7}$, the radicand is $x - 7$. (p. 431)

range (1) The set of all output values for a function or relation. For example, the range of the function graphed at right is $y > -2$. Also see *domain*. (2) The range of a set of data is a statistic that represents the spread of the data. The range is the difference between the highest and lowest values. (p. 35, 548)

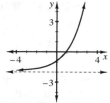

rate A ratio comparing two quantities, often a comparison of time. For example, miles per hour. (p. 66)

ratio A ratio compares two quantities by division. A ratio can be written using a colon, but is more often written as a fraction. For example, we might be interested in the ratio of female students in a particular school to the total number of students in the school. This ratio could be written as 1521:2906 or as the fraction shown at right. (p. 61)

rational numbers Numbers that can be expressed in the form $\frac{a}{b}$, where a and b are integers and $b \neq 0$. For example, 0.75 is a rational number because it can be expressed in the form $\frac{3}{4}$. The decimals of a rational number either terminate or they fall into a repeating pattern that continues infinitely. (p. 499)

ray A ray is part of a line that starts at one point and extends without end in one direction. In the example at right, ray $\overrightarrow{AB}$ is part of $\overleftrightarrow{AB}$ that starts at A and contains all of the points of $\overleftrightarrow{AB}$ that are on the same side of A as point B, including A. Point A is the endpoint of $\overrightarrow{AB}$.

real numbers Irrational numbers together with rational numbers form the set of the real numbers. For example, the following are all real numbers: $2.78, -13267, 0, \frac{3}{7}, \pi, \sqrt{2}$. All real numbers are represented on the number line. (p. 499)

reciprocal The reciprocal of a nonzero number is its multiplicative inverse; that is, the reciprocal of x is $\frac{1}{x}$. For a number in the form $\frac{a}{b}$, where a and b are non-zero, the reciprocal is $\frac{b}{a}$. The product of a number and its reciprocal is 1. For example, the reciprocal of 12 is $\frac{1}{12}$, and $12 \cdot \frac{1}{12} = 1$. Also see *multiplicative inverse*. (p. 117)

recursive equation (for a sequence) An equation for a term in a sequence that requires knowing other terms in the sequence first. For example, the equation for the Fibonacci sequence is recursive because you need to know the previous two terms to find any other term. The equation for the Fibonacci sequence is $t(n) = t(n-2) + t(n-1)$, $t(1) = 1$, $t(2) = 1$. Also see *explicit equation*. (p. 232)

recursive sequence A sequence which can be described by a recursive equation. See *recursive equation*. (p. 232)

reflective symmetry   A type of symmetry where one half of the image is a reflection across a line of the other half of the image. You can fold the image on the line of symmetry and have both halves match exactly. Also see *line of symmetry*. (p. 16)

regression   A method for finding a best-fit line or curve through a set of points on a scatterplot. The most common type of regression is finding the least squares regression line. In this course we also do curved regressions: exponential regressions (fitting $y = a \cdot b^x$) , quadratic regressions (fitting $y = ax^2 + bx + c$) and power regressions (fitting $y = ax^b$). (p. 293)

relative frequency   A ratio or percent. If 60 people are asked, and 15 people prefer "red," the relative frequency of people preferring red is $\frac{15}{60} = 25\%$. (p. 470)

relative frequency table   A two-way table in which the percent of subjects in each combination of categories is displayed. (p. 470)

repeating decimal   A repeating decimal is a decimal that repeats the same sequence of digits forever from some point onward. For example, $4.56073073073\ldots$ is a decimal for which the three digits 073 continue to repeat forever. Repeating decimals are always the decimal expansions of rational numbers. (p. 499)

residual   The distance a prediction is from the actual observed measurement in an association. The residual is the y-value predicted by the best-fit model subtracted from the actual observed y-value. A residual can be graphed with a vertical segment that extends from the observed point to the line or curve made by the best-fit model. It has the same units as the y-axis. (p. 262)

residual plot   A display of the residuals of an association. A residual plot is created in order to analyze the appropriateness of a best-fit model. If a model fits the data well, no apparent pattern will be made by the residuals — the residuals will be randomly scattered. (p. 283)

rewriting   To rewrite an equation or expression is to write an equivalent equation or expression. In this course, "rewriting" also refers to a method of solving one-variable equations. In "rewriting," we use algebraic techniques to write an equation equivalent to the original. This will often involve using the Distributive Property to eliminate parentheses. We then solve the equation using various solution methods, including perhaps rewriting again. For example, to solve the equation $4(x + 2) = 36$ by "rewriting," we use the Distributive Property to rewrite the equation as $4x + 8 = 36$. We then solve this equation to find that $x = 7$. (p. 488)

right angle   An angle that measures 90°. A small square is used to note a right angle, as shown in the example at right.

roots of a quadratic expression   A root or zero of a quadratic expression is a value of x that makes the expression equal to zero. The roots or zeros are the solutions when the

Core Connections Algebra

expression is set equal to zero. The x-intercepts of any quadratic function are roots. (p. 392)

R-squared The correlation coefficient squared, and usually expressed as a percent. R^2 is a measure of the strength of a linear relationship. Its interpretation is that R^2 % of the variability in the dependent variable can be explained by a linear relationship with the independent variable. The rest of the variability is explained by other variables not part of the study. (p. 289)

rule A rule is an equation or inequality that represents the relationship between two numerical quantities. We often use a rule to represent the relationship between quantities in a table, a pattern, a real-world situation, or a graph. For example, the rule $y = 0.4x + 25$ might tell us how to find the total cost y in cents of talking on a pay phone for x minutes.

scatter The variability in data. When the scatter of data forms a pattern, we can often describe and model the data. Random scatter has no discernable pattern. (Note that random scatter does not mean evenly scattered—randomly scattered data often forms clusters and gaps.) See *variability* and *spread*.

scatterplot A way of displaying two-variable numerical data where two measurements are taken for each subject (like height and forearm length, or surface area of cardboard and volume of cereal held in a cereal box). To create a scatterplot, the two values for each subject are written as coordinate pairs and graphed on a pair of coordinate axes (each axis representing a variable). Also see *association*. (p. 253)

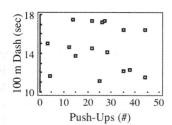

segment See *line segment*.

sequence A function in which the independent variable is a positive integer (sometimes called the "term number"). The dependent variable is the term value. A sequence is usually written as a list of numbers. For example, the arithmetic sequence $5, 8, 11, \ldots$. (p. 210)

set A collection of data or items. (p. 112)

shape (of a data distribution) Statisticians use the following words to describe the overall shape of a data distribution: symmetric, skewed, single-peaked, double-peaked, and uniform. Examples are shown below. (p. 542)

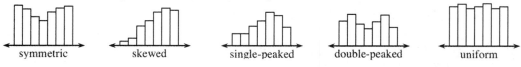

simple interest Interest paid on the principal alone. (p. 320)

simple radical form A number $r\sqrt{s}$ is in simple radical form if no square of an integer divides s and s is not a fraction; that is, there are no perfect square factors (square numbers such as $4, 9, 16$, etc.) under the radical sign and no radicals in the denominator. For example, $5\sqrt{12}$ is not in simple radical form since 4 (the square of 2) divides 12. But $10\sqrt{3}$ is in simple radical form and is equivalent to $5\sqrt{12}$.

simplify To simplify an expression is to write a less complicated expression with the same value. A simplified expression has no parentheses and no like terms. For example, the expression $3-(2x+7)-4x$ can be simplified to $-4-6x$. When working with algebra tiles, a simplified expression uses the fewest possible tiles to represent the original expression. (p. 586)

single-peaked See *shape (of a data display)*. (p. 542)

sketch To sketch the graph of an equation means to show the approximate shape of the graph in the correct location with respect to the axes with key points clearly labeled.

skewed (data display) See *shape (of a data display)*. (p. 542)

slope A ratio that describes how steep (or flat) a line is. Slope can be positive, negative, or even zero, but a straight line has only one slope. Slope is the ratio $\frac{\text{vertical change}}{\text{horizontal change}}$ or $\frac{\text{change in } y \text{ value}}{\text{change in } x \text{ value}}$, sometimes written $\frac{\Delta y}{\Delta x}$. When the equation of a line is written in $y=mx+b$ form, m is the slope of the line. Some texts refer to slope as the ratio of the "rise over the run." A line has positive slope if it slopes upward from left to right on a graph, negative slope if it slopes downward from left to right, zero slope if it is horizontal, and undefined slope if it is vertical. Slope is interpreted in context as the amount of change in the y-variable for an increase of one unit in the x-variable. (p. 61)

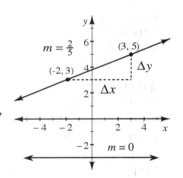

slope triangle A slope triangle is a right triangle drawn on a graph of a line so that the hypotenuse of the triangle is part of the line. The vertical leg length is the change in the y-value (Δy); the horizontal leg length is the change in the x-value (Δx). We use the lengths of the legs in the triangle to calculate the slope ratio $\frac{\Delta y}{\Delta x}$. For example, the diagram at right shows a slope triangle with $\Delta y=2$, $\Delta x=4$. The slope of the line in the example is $\frac{2}{4}$, or $\frac{1}{2}$. (p. 61)

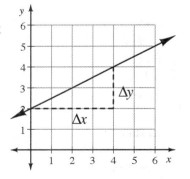

Slope-Intercept form See "$y=mx+b$." (p. 172)

solution   The number or numbers that when substituted into an equation or inequality make the equation or inequality true. For example, $x = 4$ is a solution to the equation $3x - 2 = 10$ because $3x - 2$ equals 10 when $x = 4$. A solution to a two-variable equation is sometimes written as an ordered pair (x, y). For example, $x = 3$ and $y = -2$ is a solution to the equation $y = x - 5$; this solution can be written as $(3, -2)$. (p. 490)

solve   (1) To find all the solutions to an equation or an inequality (or a system of equations or inequalities). For example, solving the equation $x^2 = 9$ gives the solutions $x = 3$ and $x = -3$. (pp. 68, 119, 170)   (2) Solving an equation for a variable gives an equivalent equation that expresses that variable in terms of other variables and constants. For example, solving $2y - 8x = 16$ for y gives $y = 4x + 8$. The equation $y = 4x + 8$ has the same solutions as $2y - 8x = 16$, but $y = 4x + 8$ expresses y in terms of x and some constants. (p. 488)

spread (of a data distribution)   A measure of the amount of variability, or how "spread out" a set of data is. Some ways to measure spread are the range, the mean absolute deviation, the standard deviation, and the interquartile range. For symmetric distributions with no outliers, the standard deviation or the interquartile range can represent the spread of the data well. However, in the presence of outliers or non-symmetrical data distributions, the interquartile range may be a better measure. Also see *variability*. (p. 535)

square root   A number a is a square root of b if $a^2 = b$. For example, the number 9 has two square roots, 3 and –3. A negative number has no real square roots; a positive number has two; and zero has just one square root, namely, itself. Other roots, such as cube root, will be studied in other courses. Also see *radical*. (p. 431)

standard deviation   A way to measure the spread, or the amount of variability, in a set of data. The standard deviation is the square root of the average of the distances to the mean, after the distances have been made positive by squaring. The standard deviation represents the spread of a set of data well if the distribution of the data is symmetric and has no outliers. (p. 548)

Standard form of a linear equation   The Standard form for a linear equation is $ax + by = c$, where a, b, and c are real numbers and a and b are not both zero. For example, the equation $2.5x - 3y = 12$ is in standard form. When you are given the equation of a line in standard form, it is often useful to write an equivalent equation in $y = mx + b$ form to find the line's slope and y-intercept. (p. 172)

standard form of a quadratic   A quadratic expression in the form $ax^2 + bx + c$ is said to be in standard form. For example, the following are all expressions in standard form: $3m^2 + m - 1$, $x^2 - 9$, and $3x^2 + 5x$. (p. 377)

statistic   A numerical fact or calculation that is formed from data. For example, a mean or a correlation coefficient is a statistic. With a capital "S," Statistics is the field of study, which is concerned with summarizing data, and using probability to make predictions from data with natural variability. (p. 533)

step function   A special kind of piecewise function (a function composed of parts of two or more functions). A step function has a graph that is a series of line segments that often looks like a set of steps. (p. 334)

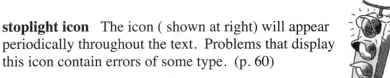

stoplight icon   The icon (shown at right) will appear periodically throughout the text. Problems that display this icon contain errors of some type. (p. 60)

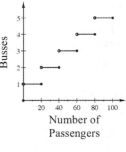

strength (of an association)   A description of how much scatter there is in the data away from the line or curve of best fit. If an association is linear, the correlation coefficient, r, or R-squared can be used to numerically describe and interpret the strength. (p. 155, 289)

subjects   The people or items being measured in a statistical study.

substitution   Replacing one symbol with a number, a variable, or another algebraic expression of the same value. Substitution does not change the value of the overall expression. For example, suppose we are trying to evaluate the expression $13x - 6$ when $x = 4$. Since x has the value 4, we can substitute 4 into the expression wherever x appears, giving us the equivalent expression $13(4) - 6$.

Substitution Method   A method for solving a system of equations by replacing one variable with an expression involving the remaining variable(s). For example, in the system of equations at right the first equation tells you that y is equal to $-3x + 5$. We can substitute $-3x + 5$ in for y in the second equation to get $2(-3x + 5) + 10x = 18$, then solve this equation to find x. Once we have x, we substitute that value back into either of the original equations to find the value of y. (p. 162)

$$y = -3x + 5$$
$$2y + 10x = 18$$

sum   The result of adding two or more numbers. For example, the sum of 4 and 5 is 9. (p. 370)

symmetry   See *line of symmetry*. (p. 16)

system of equations   A system of equations is a set of equations with the same variables. Solving a system of equations means finding one or more solutions that make each of the equations in the system true. A solution to a system of equations gives a point of intersection of the graphs of the equations in the system. There may be zero, one, or several solutions to a system of equations. For example, $(1.5, -3)$ is a solution to the system of equations at right; setting $x = 1.5$, $y = -3$ makes both of the equations true. Also, $(1.5, -3)$ is a point of intersection of the graphs of these two equations. (p. 150)

$$y = 2x - 6$$
$$y = -2x$$

system of inequalities   A system of inequalities is a set of inequalities with the same variables. Solving a system of inequalities means finding one or more regions on the coordinate plane whose points represent solutions to each of the inequalities in the system. There may be zero, one, or several such regions for a system of inequalities. For example, the shaded region at right is a graph of the system of inequalities that appears below it. (p. 450)

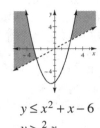

$$y \leq x^2 + x - 6$$
$$y > \tfrac{2}{3}x$$

term   A term is a single number, variable, or the product of numbers and variables. In an expression, terms are separated by addition or subtraction signs. For example, in the expression $1.2x - 45 + 3xy^2$, the terms are $1.2x$, -45, and $3xy^2$. A term is also a component of a sequence. (p. 113, 588)

term number   In a sequence, a number that gives the position of a term in the sequence. A replacement value for the independent variable in a function that determines the sequence. See *sequence*. (p. 212)

terminating decimal   A terminating decimal is a decimal that has only a finite number of non-zero digits, such as 4.067. Terminating decimals are a particular kind of repeating decimal for which the repeating portion is zeros, so the example could be written 4.0670000000… but it is not necessary to write the zeros at the end. (p. 499)

third quartile (Q3)   The median of the upper half of a set of data which has been written in numerical order (p. 535)

tile pattern   See *pattern*.

transformation (of a function)   The conversion of a function to a corresponding function, often by a factor of constant k. Transformations often slide, reflect, stretch, and/or compress graphs of functions. For example, the transformation of $f(x) + k$ moves the graph of the function up or down by an amount k. The transformation $f(-x)$ reflects the graph of the function across the y-axis. (p. 525)

trend line   Another name for a line of best fit. See *line of best fit*.

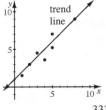

trinomial   A polynomial that is the sum or difference of exactly three terms, each of which is a monomial. For example, $x^2 + 6x + 9$ is a trinomial. (p. 369)

Glossary

two-dimensional Having length and width.

two-way table A way to display categorical two-variable data. The categories of one of the variables is the header of the rows, the other variable is the header of the columns. The entries in the table can be counts (frequencies) or percents (relative frequencies). (p. 470)

undoing In this course, "undoing" refers to a method of solving one-variable equations. In "undoing," we undo the last operation that was applied to an expression by applying its inverse operation. We then solve the resulting equation using various solution methods, including perhaps undoing again. For example, in the equation $4(x + 2) = 36$, the last operation that was applied to the left-hand side was a *multiplication* by 4. So to use "undoing," we *divide* both sides of the equation by 4, giving us $x + 2 = 9$. We then solve the equation $x + 2 = 9$ (perhaps by "undoing" again and subtracting 2 from both sides) to find that $x = 7$. (p. 488)

uniform See *shape (of a data display)*. (p. 542)

unit rate A rate with a denominator of one when simplified. (p. 66)

upper bound The highest value that a prediction is likely to be. The upper bound is determined by the upper boundary line. (p. 255)

upper boundary line A line drawn parallel to and above the least squares regression line at a distance equivalent to the largest residual. The upper boundary line determines the upper bound on the values that a prediction is likely to be. (p. 255)

variability The inconsistency in measured data. Variability comes from two sources. Measurement error is the inconsistency in measurement of the same element repeated times and/or by different people. Element variability is the natural variation of the elements themselves. For example, even though in general people with larger shoe sizes are taller, not all people with the same shoe size have the same height. That is element variability. See *spread*. (p. 535)

variable A symbol used to represent one or more numbers. In this course, letters of the English alphabet are used as variables. For example, in the expression $3x - (8.6xy + z)$, the variables are x, y, and z. (p. 58)

Venn diagram A type of diagram used to classify objects that is usually composed of two or more overlapping circles representing different conditions. An item is placed or represented in the Venn diagram in the appropriate position based on the conditions that the item meets. In the example of the Venn diagram at right, if an object meets one of two conditions, then the object is placed in region A or C but outside region B. If an object meets both conditions, then the object is placed in the intersection (B) of both circles. If an object does not meet either condition, then the object is placed outside of both circles (region D). (p. 469)

vertex (of a parabola) The vertex of a parabola is the highest or lowest point on the parabola (depending on the parabola's orientation). See *parabola*. (p. 15)

vertex form The vertex form for the equation of a quadratic function (also called graphing form) is written $y = a(x - h)^2 + k$.

vertical At right angles to the horizon. On a coordinate graph, the y-axis runs vertically. (p. 61)

vertical lines Vertical lines run up and down in the same direction as the y-axis and are parallel to it. All vertical lines have equations of the form $x = a$, where a can be any number. For example, the graph at right shows the vertical line $x = 2$. The y-axis has the equation $x = 0$ because $x = 0$ everywhere on the y-axis. Vertical lines have undefined slope. (p. 61)

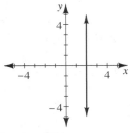

whole numbers The positive integers and zero, $\{0, 1, 2, 3, \ldots\}$. (p. 499)

x-axis The horizontal number line on a coordinate graph. See *axes*.

x-coordinate In an ordered pair, (x, y), that represents a point in the coordinate plane, x is the value of the x-coordinate. That is, the distance from the y-axis that is needed to plot the point.

x-intercept(s) The point(s) where a graph intersects the x-axis. A graph may have several x-intercepts, no x-intercepts, or just one. We sometimes report the x-intercepts of a graph with coordinate pairs, but since the y-coordinate is always zero, we often just give the x-coordinates of x-intercepts. For example, we might say that the x-intercepts of the graph at right are $(0, 0)$ and $(2, 0)$, or we might just say that the x-intercepts are 0 and 2. (p. 73)

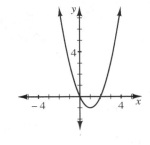

x→y table An x→y table, like the one at right, represents pairs of values of two related quantities. The input value (x) appears first, and the output value (y) appears second. For example, the x→y table at right tells us that the input value 10 is paired with the output value 18 for some rule.

IN (x)	OUT (y)
	8
0	−2
− 4	−10
10	18
−2	
	198
0.5	

y-axis The vertical number line on a coordinate graph. See *axes*.

y-coordinate In an ordered pair, (x, y), that represents a point in the coordinate plane, y is the value of the y-coordinate. That is, the distance from the x-axis that is needed to plot the point.

$y = mx + b$ When two quantities x and y have a linear relationship, that relationship can be represented with an equation in $y = mx + b$ form. The constant m is the slope, and b is the y-intercept of the graph. For example, the graph at right shows the line represented by the equation $y = 2x + 3$, which has a slope of 2 and a y-intercept of 3. This form of a linear equation is also called the slope-intercept form.

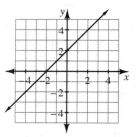

y-intercept(s)   The point(s) where a graph intersects the y-axis. A function has at most one y-intercept; a relation may have several. The y-intercept of a graph is important because it often represents the starting value of a quantity in a real-world situation. For example, on the graph of a tile pattern the y-intercept represents the number of tiles in Figure 0. We sometimes report the y-intercept of a graph with a coordinate pair, but since the x-coordinate is always zero, we often just give the y-coordinate of the y-intercept. For example, we might say that the y-intercept of the graph at right is $(0, 2)$, or we might just say that the y-intercept is 2. When a linear equation is written in $y = mx + b$ form, b tells us the y-intercept of the graph. For example, the equation of the graph at right is $y = x + 2$ and its y-intercept is 2. (p. 69)

zero   A number often used to represent "having none of a quantity." Zero is neither negative nor positive. Zero is the additive identity. (p. 499)

Zero Product Property   The Zero Product Property states that when the product of two or more factors is zero, one of these factors must equal zero. That is, if $a \cdot b = 0$, then either $a = 0$ or $b = 0$ (or both). For example, if $(x + 4)(2x - 3) = 0$, then either $x + 4 = 0$ or $2x - 3 = 0$ (or both). The Zero Product Property can be used to solve factorable quadratic equations. (p. 426)

zeros of a quadratic expression   A root or zero of a quadratic expression is a value of x that makes the expression equal to zero. The roots or zeros are the solutions when the expression is set equal to zero. The x-intercepts of any quadratic function are roots. (p. 419)

Index
Student Version, Volume 1

Many of the pages referenced here contain a definition or an example of the topic listed, often within the body of a Math Notes box. Others contain problems that develop or demonstrate the topic. It may be necessary to read the text on several pages to fully understand the topic. Also, some problems listed here are good examples of the topic and may not offer any explanation. The page numbers below reflect the pages in the Student Version. References to Math Notes boxes are bolded.

Notation
　　function, 25
　　sequence, 216, **232**
Number
　　absolute value, **5**
　　Fibonacci, 213
　　opposite, **117**
　　prime, 147
　　whole, 113

O

Order of Operations
　　Checkpoint 2, 83, 292
　　circle the terms, **257**
Outlier, **155**
Output, 3, 5, *Also see* range.

P

Parabola, 14
　　line of symmetry, 15
　　vertex, 15
Parallel lines, **175**
Percent
　　as a multiplier, 229
　　discount, 230
Perimeter
　　algebra tiles, 102, 251
Piecewise graph, 68
Point
　　coordinates, 253
　　lattice, 52
　　of intersection, **167**
Point-slope
　　linear equation, 76
Point-Slope form, **172**
Polynomial, **113**
Positive
　　association, **155**
　　slope, **61**
Precision, attend to, 135
Prime number, 147
Properties of real numbers, **117**
Proportion, 258
　　direct, **11**
　　inverse, **11**

Q

Quadratic, 14
Quadrilateral, 258
Quantitative reasoning, 134

R

Range, 33, **35**, *Also see* output.
Rate
　　of change, 66, 67
　　unit, 66
Ratio
　　common, **232**
　　rebound, 202, 206
　　slope, 51, **61**
Rational numbers
　　operations with
　　　　Checkpoint 3, 130, 294
Real numbers, properties of, **117**
Reason abstractly and quantitatively, 134
Reasoning
　　critique others, 134
　　repeated, 135
Rebound ratio, 202, 206
reciprocal, **117**
Recorder/Reporter, 4
Recording work, 271
Rectangle, generic, 115, 116, **129**
Recursive
　　equation, 220, **232**
　　sequence, 220, **232**
Reflective symmetry, **16**
Relation
　　function, 28, 29
　　linear, **11**
Repeated reasoning, 135
Representing Data, 9
Resource Manager, 4

S

Save the Earth, 84
Scientific notation
　　Checkpoint 5A, 215, 298
Sequence, 210
　　arithmetic, 212, 215, **232**
　　compared to function, 235
　　Fibonacci, 213, 221
　　first term, 210
　　generator, 210, 227, **232**
　　geometric, 212, 226, 227, **232**
　　graph, **204**, 223
　　growth rate, 223, 224
　　notation, 216, **232**
　　recursive, 220, **232**
　　table, 223
Sequence Families, 211

Common Core State Standards for Mathematics

Algebra I Introduction[1]

The fundamental purpose of the Model Algebra I course is to formalize and extend the mathematics that students learned in the middle grades. This course is comprised of standards selected from the high school **conceptual categories**, which were written to encompass the scope of content and skills to be addressed throughout grades 9–12 rather than through any single course. Therefore, the complete standard is presented in the model course, with clarifying footnotes as needed to limit the scope of the standard and indicate what is appropriate for study in this particular course. For example, the scope of Model Algebra I is limited to linear, quadratic, and exponential expressions and functions as well as some work with absolute value, step, and functions that are piecewise-defined. Therefore, although a standard may include references to logarithms or trigonometry, those functions are not to be included in coursework for Model Algebra I; they will be addressed later in Model Algebra II. Reminders of this limitation are included as footnotes where appropriate in the Model Algebra I standards.

For the high school Model Algebra I course, instructional time should focus on four critical areas: (1) deepen and extend understanding of linear and exponential relationships; (2) contrast linear and exponential relationships with each other and engage in methods for analyzing, solving, and using quadratic functions; (3) extend the laws of exponents to square and cube roots; and (4) apply linear models to data that exhibit a linear trend.

(1) By the end of eighth grade, students have learned to solve linear equations in one variable and have applied graphical and algebraic methods to analyze and solve systems of linear equations in two variables. In Algebra I, students analyze and explain the process of solving an equation and justify the process used in solving a system of equations. Students develop fluency writing, interpreting, and translating among various forms of linear equations and inequalities, and use them to solve problems. They master the solution of linear equations and apply related solution techniques and the laws of exponents to the creation and solution of simple exponential equations.

(2) In earlier grades, students define, evaluate, and compare functions, and use them to model relationships between quantities. In Algebra I, students learn function notation and develop the concepts of domain and range. They focus on linear, quadratic, and exponential functions, including sequences, and also explore absolute value, step, and piecewise-defined functions; they interpret functions given graphically, numerically, symbolically, and verbally; translate between representations; and understand the limitations of various representations. Students build on and extend their understanding

---

[1] Massachusetts Department of Elementary and Secondary Education, *Massachusetts Curriculum Framework for Mathematics*, 2011, p. 108–109.
Common Core State Standards for Mathematics

of integer exponents to consider exponential functions. They compare and contrast linear and exponential functions, distinguishing between additive and multiplicative change. Students explore systems of equations and inequalities, and they find and interpret their solutions. They interpret arithmetic sequences as linear functions and geometric sequences as exponential functions.

(3) Students extend the laws of exponents to rational exponents involving square and cube roots and apply this new understanding of number; they strengthen their ability to see structure in and create quadratic and exponential expressions. They create and solve equations, inequalities, and systems of equations involving quadratic expressions. Students become facile with algebraic manipulation, including rearranging and collecting terms, and factoring, identifying, and canceling common factors in rational expressions. Students consider quadratic functions, comparing the key characteristics of quadratic functions to those of linear and exponential functions. They select from among these functions to model phenomena. Students learn to anticipate the graph of a quadratic function by interpreting various forms of quadratic expressions. In particular, they identify the real solutions of a quadratic equation as the zeros of a related quadratic function. Students expand their experience with functions to include more specialized functions—absolute value, step, and those that are piecewise-defined.

(4) Building upon their prior experiences with data, students explore a more formal means of assessing how a model fits data. Students use regression techniques to describe approximately linear relationships between quantities. They use graphical representations and knowledge of context to make judgments about the appropriateness of linear models. With linear models, they look at residuals to analyze the goodness of fit.

The Standards for Mathematical Practice complement the content standards so that students increasingly engage with the subject matter as they grow in mathematical maturity and expertise throughout the elementary, middle, and high school years.

Algebra I Overview

Number and Quantity

The Real Number System

- Extend the properties of exponents to rational exponents.
- Use properties of rational and irrational numbers.

Quantities

- Reason quantitatively and use units to solve problems.

Algebra

Seeing Structure in Expressions

- Interpret the structure of expressions.
- Write expressions in equivalent forms to solve problems.

Arithmetic with Polynomials and Rational Expressions

- Perform arithmetic operations on polynomials.

Creating Equations

- Create equations that describe numbers or relationships.

Reasoning with Equations and Inequalities

- Understand solving equations as a process of reasoning and explain the reasoning.
- Solve equations and inequalities in one variable.
- Solve systems of equations.
- Represent and solve equations and inequalities graphically.

Functions

Interpreting Functions

- Understand the concept of a function and use function notation.
- Interpret functions that arise in applications in terms of the context.
- Analyze functions using different representations.

Mathematical Practices

1. Make sense of problems and persevere in solving them.
2. Reason abstractly and quantitatively.
3. Construct viable arguments and critique the reasoning of others.
4. Model with mathematics.
5. Use appropriate tools strategically.
6. Attend to precision.
7. Look for and make use of structure.
8. Look for and express regularity in repeated reasoning.

Algebra I Overview

Building Functions

- Build a function that models a relationship between two quantities.
- Build new functions from existing functions.

Linear, Quadratic, and Exponential Models

- Construct and compare linear, quadratic, and exponential models and solve problems.
- Interpret expressions for functions in terms of the situation they model.

Statistics and Probability

Interpreting Categorical and Quantitative Data

- Summarize, represent, and interpret data on a single count or measurement variable.
- Summarize, represent, and interpret data on two categorical and quantitative variables.
- Interpret linear models.

★ Indicates a modeling standard linking mathematics to everyday life, work, and decision-making.
(+) Indicates additional mathematics to prepare students for advanced courses.
* Indicates additional standards required by the State of California.

A   Algebra I

Number and Quantity

The Real Number System   N-RN

Extend the properties of exponents to rational exponents.

1. Explain how the definition of the meaning of rational exponents follows from extending the properties of integer exponents to those values, allowing for a notation for radicals in terms of rational exponents. *For example, we define $5^{1/3}$ to be the cube root of 5 because we want $(5^{1/3})^3 = 5^{(1/3)3}$ to hold, so $(5^{1/3})^3$ must equal 5.*

2. Rewrite expressions involving radicals and rational exponents using the properties of exponents.

Use properties of rational and irrational numbers.

3. Explain why the sum or product of two rational numbers is rational; that the sum of a rational number and an irrational number is irrational; and that the product of a nonzero rational number and an irrational number is irrational.

Quantities   N-Q

Reason quantitatively and use units to solve problems. [Foundation for work with expressions, equations and functions.]

1. Use units as a way to understand problems and to guide the solution of multi-step problems; choose and interpret units consistently in formulas; choose and interpret the scale and the origin in graphs and data displays. ★

2. Define appropriate quantities for the purpose of descriptive modeling. ★

3. Choose a level of accuracy appropriate to limitations on measurement when reporting quantities. ★

Algebra

Seeing Structure in Expressions   A-SSE

Interpret the structure of expressions. [Linear, exponential, quadratic.]

1. Interpret expressions that represent a quantity in terms of its context. ★
    a. Interpret parts of an expression, such as terms, factors, and coefficients. ★
    b. Interpret complicated expressions by viewing one or more of their parts as a single entity. *For example, interpret $P(1 + r)^n$ as the product of P and a factor not depending on P.* ★

2. Use the structure of an expression to identify ways to rewrite it.

Write expressions in equivalent forms to solve problems. [Quadratic and exponential.]

3. Choose and produce an equivalent form of an expression to reveal and explain properties of the quantity represented by the expression. ★
    a. Factor a quadratic expression to reveal the zeros of the function it defines. ★
    b. Complete the square in a quadratic expression to reveal the maximum or minimum value of the function it defines. ★
    c. Use the properties of exponents to transform expressions for exponential functions. *For example, the expression 1.15^t can be rewritten as $(1.15^{1/12})^{12t} \approx 1.012^{12t}$ to reveal the approximate equivalent monthly interest rate if the annual rate is 15%.* ★

Arithmetic with Polynomials and Rational Expressions — A-APR

Perform arithmetic operations on polynomials. [Linear and quadratic.]

1. Understand that polynomials form a system analogous to the integers, namely, they are closed under the operations of addition, subtraction, and multiplication; add, subtract, and multiply polynomials.

Creating Equations — A-CED

Create equations that describe numbers or relationships. [Linear, quadratic, and exponential (integer inputs only); for A.CED.3 linear only.]

1. Create equations and inequalities in one variable including ones with absolute value* and use them to solve problems. *Include equations arising from linear and quadratic functions, and simple rational and exponential functions.* ★
2. Create equations in two or more variables to represent relationships between quantities; graph equations on coordinate axes with labels and scales. ★
3. Represent constraints by equations or inequalities, and by systems of equations and/or inequalities, and interpret solutions as viable or non-viable options in a modeling context. *For example, represent inequalities describing nutritional and cost constraints on combinations of different foods.* ★
4. Rearrange formulas to highlight a quantity of interest, using the same reasoning as in solving equations. *For example, rearrange Ohm's law V = IR to highlight resistance R.* ★

Reasoning with Equations and Inequalities — A-REI

Understand solving equations as a process of reasoning and explain the reasoning. [Master linear; learn as general principle.]

1. Explain each step in solving a simple equation as following from the equality of numbers asserted at the previous step, starting from the assumption that the original equation has a solution. Construct a viable argument to justify a solution method.

Solve equations and inequalities in one variable. [Linear inequalities; literal equations that are linear in the variables being solved for; quadratics with real solutions.]

3. Solve linear equations and inequalities in one variable, including equations with coefficients represented by letters.
3.1 Solve one-variable equations and inequalities involving absolute value, graphing the solutions and interpreting them in context. *
4. Solve quadratic equations in one variable.
   a. Use the method of completing the square to transform any quadratic equation in x into an equation of the form $(x - p)^2 = q$ that has the same solutions. Derive the quadratic formula from this form.
   b. Solve quadratic equations by inspection (e.g., for $x^2 = 49$), taking square roots, completing the square, the quadratic formula, and factoring, as appropriate to the initial form of the equation. Recognize when the quadratic formula gives complex solutions and write them as $a \pm bi$ for real numbers a and b.

Solve systems of equations. [Linear-linear and linear-quadratic.]

5. Prove that, given a system of two equations in two variables, replacing one equation by the sum of that equation and a multiple of the other produces a system with the same solutions.

Algebra I

6. Solve systems of linear equations exactly and approximately (e.g., with graphs), focusing on pairs of linear equations in two variables.
7. Solve a simple system consisting of a linear equation and a quadratic equation in two variables algebraically and graphically.

Represent and solve equations and inequalities graphically. [Linear and exponential; learn as general principle.]

10. Understand that the graph of an equation in two variables is the set of all its solutions plotted in the coordinate plane, often forming a curve (which could be a line).
11. Explain why the *x*-coordinates of the points where the graphs of the equations $y = f(x)$ and $y = g(x)$ intersect are the solutions of the equation $f(x) = g(x)$; find the solutions approximately, e.g., using technology to graph the functions, make tables of values, or find successive approximations. Include cases where $f(x)$ and/or $g(x)$ are linear, polynomial, rational, absolute value, exponential, and logarithmic functions. ★
12. Graph the solutions to a linear inequality in two variables as a half-plane (excluding the boundary in the case of a strict inequality), and graph the solution set to a system of linear inequalities in two variables as the intersection of the corresponding half-planes.

Functions

Interpreting Functions F-IF

Understand the concept of a function and use function notation. [Learn as general principle; focus on linear and exponential and on arithmetic and geometric sequences.]

1. Understand that a function from one set (called the domain) to another set (called the range) assigns to each element of the domain exactly one element of the range. If *f* is a function and *x* is an element of its domain, then $f(x)$ denotes the output of *f* corresponding to the input *x*. The graph of *f* is the graph of the equation $y = f(x)$.
2. Use function notation, evaluate functions for inputs in their domains, and interpret statements that use function notation in terms of a context.
3. Recognize that sequences are functions, sometimes defined recursively, whose domain is a subset of the integers. *For example, the Fibonacci sequence is defined recursively by $f(0) = f(1) = 1$, $f(n + 1) = f(n) + f(n - 1)$ for $n \geq 1$.*

Interpret functions that arise in applications in terms of the context. [Linear, exponential, and quadratic.]

4. For a function that models a relationship between two quantities, interpret key features of graphs and tables in terms of the quantities, and sketch graphs showing key features given a verbal description of the relationship. *Key features include: intercepts; intervals where the function is increasing, decreasing, positive, or negative; relative maximums and minimums; symmetries; end behavior; and periodicity.* ★
5. Relate the domain of a function to its graph and, where applicable, to the quantitative relationship it describes. *For example, if the function h gives the number of person-hours it takes to assemble n engines in a factory, then the positive integers would be an appropriate domain for the function.* ★
6. Calculate and interpret the average rate of change of a function (presented symbolically or as a table) over a specified interval. Estimate the rate of change from a graph. ★

Algebra I

Analyze functions using different representations. [Linear, exponential, quadratic, absolute value, step, piecewise-defined.]

7. Graph functions expressed symbolically and show key features of the graph, by hand in simple cases and using technology for more complicated cases. ★

    a. Graph linear and quadratic functions and show intercepts, maxima, and minima. ★

    b. Graph square root, cube root, and piecewise-defined functions, including step functions and absolute value functions. ★

    e. Graph exponential and logarithmic functions, showing intercepts and end behavior, and trigonometric functions, showing period, midline, and amplitude. ★

8. Write a function defined by an expression in different but equivalent forms to reveal and explain different properties of the function.

    a. Use the process of factoring and completing the square in a quadratic function to show zeros, extreme values, and symmetry of the graph, and interpret these in terms of a context.

    b. Use the properties of exponents to interpret expressions for exponential functions. *For example, identify percent rate of change in functions such as $y = (1.02)^t$, $y = (0.97)^t$, $y = (1.01)^{12t}$, and $y = (1.2)^{t/10}$, and classify them as representing exponential growth or decay.*

9. Compare properties of two functions each represented in a different way (algebraically, graphically, numerically in tables, or by verbal descriptions). *For example, given a graph of one quadratic function and an algebraic expression for another, say which has the larger maximum.*

Building Functions   F-BF

Build a function that models a relationship between two quantities. [For F.BF.1, 2, linear, exponential, and quadratic.]

1. Write a function that describes a relationship between two quantities. ★

    a. Determine an explicit expression, a recursive process, or steps for calculation from a context. ★

    b. Combine standard function types using arithmetic operations. *For example, build a function that models the temperature of a cooling body by adding a constant function to a decaying exponential, and relate these functions to the model.* ★

2. Write arithmetic and geometric sequences both recursively and with an explicit formula, use them to model situations, and translate between the two forms. ★

Build new functions from existing functions. [Linear, exponential, quadratic, and absolute value; for F.BF.4a, linear only.]

3. Identify the effect on the graph of replacing $f(x)$ by $f(x) + k$, $kf(x)$, $f(kx)$, and $f(x + k)$ for specific values of k (both positive and negative); find the value of k given the graphs. Experiment with cases and illustrate an explanation of the effects on the graph using technology. *Include recognizing even and odd functions from their graphs and algebraic expressions for them.*

4. Find inverse functions.

    a. Solve an equation of the form $f(x) = c$ for a simple function f that has an inverse and write an expression for the inverse.

Linear, Quadratic, and Exponential Models   F-LE

Construct and compare linear, quadratic, and exponential models and solve problems.

1. Distinguish between situations that can be modeled with linear functions and with exponential functions. ★

A Algebra I

  a. Prove that linear functions grow by equal differences over equal intervals, and that exponential functions grow by equal factors over equal intervals. ★
  b. Recognize situations in which one quantity changes at a constant rate per unit interval relative to another. ★
  c. Recognize situations in which a quantity grows or decays by a constant percent rate per unit interval relative to another. ★
2. Construct linear and exponential functions, including arithmetic and geometric sequences, given a graph, a description of a relationship, or two input-output pairs (include reading these from a table). ★
3. Observe using graphs and tables that a quantity increasing exponentially eventually exceeds a quantity increasing linearly, quadratically, or (more generally) as a polynomial function. ★

Interpret expressions for functions in terms of the situation they model.
5. Interpret the parameters in a linear or exponential function in terms of a context. ★ [Linear and exponential of form $f(x)=b^x+k$.]
6. Apply quadratic functions to physical problems, such as the motion of an object under the force of gravity. ✱★

Statistics and Probability

Interpreting Categorical and Quantitative Data   S-ID

Summarize, represent, and interpret data on a single count or measurement variable.
1. Represent data with plots on the real number line (dot plots, histograms, and box plots). ★
2. Use statistics appropriate to the shape of the data distribution to compare center (median, mean) and spread (interquartile range, standard deviation) of two or more different data sets. ★
3. Interpret differences in shape, center, and spread in the context of the data sets, accounting for possible effects of extreme data points (outliers). ★

Summarize, represent, and interpret data on two categorical and quantitative variables. [Linear focus, discuss general principle.]
5. Summarize categorical data for two categories in two-way frequency tables. Interpret relative frequencies in the context of the data (including joint, marginal, and conditional relative frequencies). Recognize possible associations and trends in the data. ★
6. Represent data on two quantitative variables on a scatter plot, and describe how the variables are related. ★
  a. Fit a function to the data; use functions fitted to data to solve problems in the context of the data. *Use given functions or choose a function suggested by the context. Emphasize linear, quadratic, and exponential models.* ★
  b. Informally assess the fit of a function by plotting and analyzing residuals. ★
  c. Fit a linear function for a scatter plot that suggests a linear association. ★

Interpret linear models.
7. Interpret the slope (rate of change) and the intercept (constant term) of a linear model in the context of the data. ★
8. Compute (using technology) and interpret the correlation coefficient of a linear fit. ★
9. Distinguish between correlation and causation. ★

THIS BOOK IS THE PROPERTY OF:

Book No._____

ISSUED TO	Year Used	CONDITION	
		ISSUED	RETURNED
_____	_____		
_____	_____		
_____	_____		
_____	_____		
_____	_____		
_____	_____		
_____	_____		
_____	_____		

PUPILS to whom this texbook is issued must not write on any part of it in any way, unless otherwise instructed by the teacher.